MAKING THE MOST OF
INDIGENOUS TREES

Supported by the
National Botanical
Institute

MAKING THE MOST OF

INDIGENOUS TREES

Fanie & Julye-Ann Venter
Main photographer: Pitta Joffe

BRIZA
PUBLICATIONS

Published by
Briza Publications
CK/90/11690/23
P.O. Box 56569
Arcadia, 0007
Pretoria, South Africa

First edition 1996
© Text Fanie & Julye-Ann Venter
© Photographs various photographers
Edited by Emsie du Plessis
Cover design by Ilse van Oudtshoorn
Typesetting by Briza Publications
Reproduction by Unifoto, Cape Town

Printed and bound by Tien Wah Press, Singapore
All rights reserved. No part of this publication
may be reproduced or transmitted in any form or
by any means without the permission of the
copyright holder.

ISBN 1 875093 05 2

CONTENTS

ACKNOWLEDGEMENTS

Bringing a book of this kind to fruition is almost impossible without the assistance, support and advice of a host of people. We have endeavoured to mention all those who have helped us.

Firstly our most sincere thanks to Prof. Brian Huntley, the Chief Director of the National Botanical Institute, for making available the facilities of the Institute. A special word of thanks to Pitta Joffe for sharing her photographic expertise, without which this book would not have materialized. Her enthusiasm and encouragement on the fieldtrips we undertook together are greatly appreciated. Thank you also, Leon Joffe, for your patience and endurance!

This book had its beginnings in a series of articles which appeared in the *Farmer's Weekly*. Mike Fisher, former editor of the magazine, together with the agricultural writer Chris Nel, initiated the idea of bringing the articles together in a book. We are indebted to Chris for his unfailing encouragement and support throughout the project.

The following people are thanked for their assistance with fieldwork for this book: Kobus du Toit of the Department of Agriculture, Northern Province; Willem Gertenbach and Ben Pretorius of the Kruger National Park for permission to photograph in the Park; Andrew Hankey of the Witwatersrand National Botanical Garden; George and Sue Rautenbach of George's Place; and Daan Roux of Letsitele.

We thank Emsie du Plessis for editing the manuscript.

We are most grateful to Marjorie Pawson, who at the last minute, so kindly gave of her time and read through the manuscript, offering advice and corrections.

Our sincere thanks also go to Briza Publications – in particular to Frits and Ilse van Oudtshoorn for their continual support and encouragement.

Last but not least, we are most grateful to the many interested readers of *Farmer's Weekly* who, through their correspondence and love for our indigenous trees, spurred us on to produce this work.

Fanie and Julye-Ann Venter, 1996.

INTRODUCTION

All the trees of the fields shall clap their hands (Isaiah 55 v. 12)

Trees have been part of man's environment since his beginnings. They have many functions and are essential to our existence. Many of us take trees for granted, not always appreciating the vital role they play by bearing fruit, providing nesting sites for birds, shade and shelter for insects, birds and other animals, by rendering material for the manufacture of goods such as paper and furniture, and by supplying the very oxygen we breathe.

Trees are not only functional, but also aesthetically pleasing to the eye. Visualize a landscape devoid of trees!

What is a tree? It can be defined as a woody plant, usually with a single stem, which can grow to a height of 6 m or more.

It has been said that were it not for the ever-increasing human population and the subsequent scramble for more land, there would have been many more trees and vastly greater areas of forest left on earth. Every minute, 24 hectares of rain-forest are being destroyed worldwide – and man is simply not replanting trees fast enough to cancel out this frightening statistic. Also here in South Africa our very rich and varied indigenous tree flora is being rapidly depleted.

The purpose of this book is to introduce the reader, tree lover and unseasoned enthusiast alike to some of our indigenous tree species and in so doing, cultivate in them a love and appreciation for our trees. Furthermore, we hope to encourage the propagation and use of these trees in gardens, farms, parks, game farms and on other private and public land.

The book is also aimed at dispelling some of those 'mythstakes' (myths and mistakes!) firmly established in the minds of some gardeners and farmers, for example the beliefs that indigenous trees grow very slowly, that indigenous plants do not require water or compost and that they need very poor, sandy soil. These 'mythstakes' could be responsible for the wariness with which many people view indigenous trees as garden subjects. However, there certainly is an awakening to the use of our indigenous flora, and growers and nurserymen are now beginning to see its merits. It is our wish that this awakening takes on massive proportions and our indigenous tree species become better known, loved and more widely available.

What role do you play in the conservation of this wealth of tree flora? By propagating and using our indigenous tree species, you can help to ensure their continued existence.

The book has been written with the lay person in mind; botanical terms have been kept to the minimum and were used only where absolutely necessary to ensure correctness. It is to this end that the 137 tree species described in the book are listed alphabetically according to the English common name. To our mind this facilitates access to the text. However, because of the unreliability of a common name, the botanical name is also given, together with the Afrikaans, Zulu and Northern Sotho common names. Tracing and verifying common names in all eleven official languages would be a mammoth task and after careful consideration it was decided to list only these three.

The botanical names were taken from *Plants of southern Africa: names and distribution* (Arnold & De Wet, 1993). A botanical name is made up of two parts, i.e. the genus name followed by the specific epithet. In the case of the botanical name of the sweet thorn, the genus name is *Acacia* and it is followed by the specific name *karroo*, to give *Acacia karroo*. Although these names sometimes seem a mouthful to the lay person, the scientific name prevents the confusion caused by the many and varied common names often given to the same species in different regions and in different languages. A good example is 'tree fuchsia', a common name applied to both *Schotia brachypetala* and *Halleria lucida*. In an attempt to avoid the confusion, a standardized list of common names has been published, the *National list of indigenous trees* (Von Breitenbach, 1986). The English and Afrikaans names have been taken from this work. The *National tree list number* is also listed for each species.

Mention is also made of the family to which a particular species belongs. Genera that have certain important characters in common, belong to the same family. For example, the genera *Acacia* and *Albizia* both belong to the Fabaceae, the pod-bearing family.

Where information is available, mention is made of the medicinal uses and edibility of the various species. Some have been tried and tested by the authors, others not, but no claims are made as to their effectiveness. Indiscriminate use of these medicines could prove fatal and readers are therefore advised to refrain from experimenting.

Finally, it is our wish that this book not only finds its way to the coffee-table collection, but that it also proves to be a most useful tool in the hands of the tree-lover, enthusiast and student.

NOTES ON PROPAGATION

SEED

Propagation by seed is the main method by which plants reproduce in nature. It is also very efficient and widely used in tree propagation. All trees produce seed, except those individuals bearing only male flowers. The process of seed production begins during flowering when pollen is transferred from the male part (or anther) to the female part (or stigma) of the flower – the seed being the end-product of a long physiological process.

In certain plant families it is common to find separate male and female trees. In other words, some individuals (the male trees) have functional stamens with anthers (male parts) in their flowers, while others (the female trees) have functional pistils with stigmas (female parts) in the flowers. An example is the wild plum (*Harpephyllum caffrum*). Only the trees bearing female flowers produce fruit and ultimately seed. It is impossible to distinguish between the male and female trees, except when they are in flower. Therefore, when one selects a wild plum specifically for fruit or seed, it should be in flower so that the flowers can be inspected. Otherwise one should plant three or four – the chances are good that there will be a female tree among them. The surest method of obtaining a female tree is to take a cutting or a truncheon from a female tree. The same applies to a cutting or truncheon from a male tree.

There are various ways of obtaining seed. The Department of Water Affairs and Forestry offers a selection of indigenous tree seed for sale. There are also many private seed companies. Members of the Botanical Society of South Africa are entitled to a certain quota of seed annually. If you choose to collect seed yourself, there are a few points to keep in mind.

Seed harvesting

Firstly, the correct time of harvesting is of utmost importance. If seed is harvested prematurely, it will be immature, thin, shrunken and light because it has not had sufficient time to accumulate food reserves. The result is usually disappointing, the seed being unable to survive a storage period, giving very unsatisfactory germination and weak seedling growth.

It should also be remembered that the seeds of many tree species have a limited life-span – they must therefore be sown as soon as possible after harvesting. The common cabbage tree (*Cussonia spicata*), is a good example. The seeds of most forest tree species have a short shelf-life.

The geographical origin of the seed is another important point to remember when harvesting seed. Seed collected from an Outeniqua yellowwood tree (*Podocarpus falcatus*), growing in the Western Cape and then sown in the Northern Province will not be as ecologically well-adapted as seed collected from trees of the same species growing on the Soutpansberg. If at all possible, it is best to collect seed from trees growing under climatic conditions similar to those of the area where they are to be propagated and grown. These conditions include temperature and rainfall.

Always regard the seed source as important. Seed selected from healthy trees free of disease is likely to produce healthy, disease-free offspring. Very often characters such as branching, growth habit and growth rate are determined by the seed.

If good-quality plants are required, all these factors should be taken into account.

Seeds can be harvested by placing a sheet or canvas under the tree and then shaking the branches, or by picking the seeds by hand. Another possibility is to wait for the seed to ripen and drop, and then gather it from the ground. But one's timing has to be right, because many seeds are soon parasitised by insects or eaten by birds and other animals when left on the ground. A rather labour-intensive method is to cover the fruit on the tree with a stocking or other suitable material and wait for the seed to fall out – a loss for the birds but you will have your seed!

In nature, the seeds of some indigenous tree species first pass through the digestive tract of a bird or other animal where they are exposed to the stomach acids which break down the seeds' chemical inhibitor before the seeds can germinate. In this case one would collect the seed from the animal or birds droppings. Seeds collected in this way have no inhibitor, germinating much more quickly and easily. The cross-berry, (*Grewia occidentalis*), is an example. It was found that seeds collected from the droppings of baboons and monkeys have a much higher germination percentage than those collected from a tree. The mountain hard pear (*Olinia emarginata*), is another example of a tree from which the seed first has to pass through the digestive system of a bird before germination occurs.

Seed storage and longevity

Having harvested the seed, one may not always wish to sow it immediately but rather store it until later. The shelf-life of seed varies from a few weeks to years, depending on the species. In general, seed of tropical and subtropical tree species growing under conditions of high humidity and high temperature is usually short-lived and should be planted soon after harvesting. An example is the forest fever tree (*Anthocleista grandiflora*). Seed of tree species with fleshy fruits is also usually short-lived and does not remain viable for more than a few months. On the other hand, seed with a hard outer covering is inclined to be long-lived. The jackal-berry (*Diospyros mespiliformis*), is a good example. The hard outer covering prevents water from penetrating the seed. As long as the seed coat remains undamaged, the seed can remain viable for up to 10 years. An interesting story is that of the Indian lotus (*Nelumbo nucifera*), seeds of which had been buried for approximately 1 000 years in a Manchurian peat bog; when the impermeable seed coats were cracked, they germinated perfectly.

The seed of the wild plum (*Harpephyllum caffrum*) boiled over a fire to remove the fleshy covering. This fleshy covering also makes a delicious jam!

Humidity level and temperature play an important role in the storage of seed. Generally seed remains viable for longer in a dry climate, whereas seed stored in tropical areas is likely to lose its viability very soon. A lower temperature is likely to lengthen the storage life of seeds.

Seed dormancy

In most cases seed dormancy delays germination. This can be due to a chemical inhibitor within the seed or a physical inhibitor, for example the seed coat. In the case of the sjambok pod (*Cassia abbreviata*), the long pods must be cracked open and the black seed, covered with a sticky green flesh, must be removed and cleaned before sowing. The flesh contains an inhibitor which prevents germination. In nature, seed dormancy ensures that the seed germinates only under favourable environmental conditions. This ensures the survival of the seedling. However, we as gardeners/farmers do not always have the time to wait until the dormancy has been broken and therefore search for ways of breaking it, thus speeding up the germination process.

The hard seed coat of the Transvaal red balloon bush (*Erythrophysa transvaalensis*). This seed must be soaked overnight in boiling water to soften the seed coat and expedite germination.

The hard, impermeable seed coat of certain tree species can be broken down by immersing the seed in boiling water and allowing it to soak overnight. Agitate the seeds now and then. If, after an hour or two, you see visible signs that the seed coat is softening or opening, that is obviously sufficient time. Another method is to immerse the seed in sulphuric or hydrochloric acid at a ratio of about one part seed to two parts acid. Never use a metal or plastic container – only glass, clay pots or wooden containers. The mixture should be agitated or stirred carefully at intervals. Never stir vigorously – this will lead to a rise in temperature and consequent damage to the seed. The length of time for treatment varies from 10 minutes for some species to a few hours for others. The time for the seed of indigenous tree species has not yet been documented and it is a trial-and-error process at present. Wash seeds well in running water for 10 minutes after treatment to remove all traces of the acid. Both the above-mentioned methods break

Seed of Soutpansberg poison rope (*Strophanthus luteolus*). The seed on the right was soaked overnight.

down the outer layer, allowing moisture to enter and thereby accelerating the germination process. Many seeds can be mechanically scarified with a file or sand paper. Care should be taken not to damage the fragile embryo inside. Another method is to crack the outer case physically and remove the vulnerable, soft seed. This has to be done carefully, for any damage to the embryo will make germination impossible. Once exposed, the embryo must be sown immediately, otherwise it will dry out. Seed of the Outeniqua yellowwood has a very hard seed coat. If it is left intact, the seed usually takes up to six months to germinate. However, if the hard seed coat is carefully cracked open and the fragile embryo removed and sown, germination is speeded up to 14 days.

The sowing of seed is discussed in detail under the individual species.

CUTTINGS

Not much work or research has been done on cuttings as a means of propagating our indigenous tree species. This is unfortunate as this method enables one to begin with a plant of reasonable size and it is much quicker than with seed. What is certain is that many indigenous species can be propagated by means of cuttings – but the method has not yet been properly tested. We hope this book will urge the reader to experiment and add to the list of species that can be propagated successfully by means of cuttings.

A rooted cutting of the Kei-apple (*Dovyalis caffra*).

A cutting can be defined as a portion of a leaf, stem or root from a parent plant placed under favourable conditions which encourage it to form roots and shoots, and ultimately a new plant. An advantage of rooted cuttings is that they produce fairly uniform plants. This method eliminates the variation obtained with seedlings and produces a large number of new plants from only a few parent plants. Another advantage is that one has a fair-sized plant right from the start.

Cuttings taken from spring to early summer usually produce the best results. There are exceptions and these are mentioned under the individual species.

Three types of cuttings can be defined according to the type of wood used.

a) Hardwood cuttings (which usually do not have leaves at the time) are taken from the mature hardwood of a tree just before new shoots appear in spring. Individual examples are discussed under individual species.

b) Semi-hardwood cuttings include woody material from evergreen species.

c) Softwood cuttings are taken from the soft new growth of both evergreen and deciduous tree species. The cutting consists of a portion of the stem with two or more leaves at the top. Very often softwood cuttings have proved to root more quickly than both hardwood and semi-hardwood cuttings. Because of their soft, succulent nature, these cuttings require closer attention and more care than the other two types. Desiccation of the cuttings must be prevented.

Obviously the quality and condition of the material used for the cuttings will determine the success. Remember that weak, diseased material used for cuttings will produce weak, diseased plants. Always use healthy material.

It has also been found that the site at which the cuttings is taken will influence the growth habit of the cutting. For example, *Podocarpus falcatus* cuttings taken from lateral branches and shoots produce plants with a lateral growth habit rather than an upright one.

The best time of day to take cuttings is in the early morning when transpiration is at its lowest and the cuttings have the least chance of drying out.

Having cut the various branches, one should sit down and make the cuttings in a cool, shady place. The cuttings should be placed in the planting medium almost immediately and certainly not left lying around in the sun.

Semi-hardwood and hardwood cuttings of a tree should be approximately 150 mm long. The bottom part of the cutting is cut horizontally, just fractionally below a node. The top cut should be made at an angle to allow water to run off its surface. Water collecting on this surface may promote rotting. Another reason for two different cuts is to be able to distinguish between the top and the bottom of the cutting. Sometimes hardwood cuttings are taken when the tree is bare and once the cutting has been made, it is difficult to distinguish between the two

11

ends. It is advisable to strip the cutting of most leaves, leaving only a few at the top. If these are very large, cut them in half to reduce the surface area, thereby reducing loss of water through transpiration. To encourage rooting, the bottom of the cutting is then dipped into a rooting hormone powder or solution – just enough to coat the exposed cut. All that now remains is the medium into which the cuttings must go.

There is a variety of rooting media commercially available that can be used with equal success. The criteria for the choice of medium should include excellent drainage, it must be free of weeds and nematodes, able to support the cuttings, and if the cuttings are to remain in the medium for any length of time it should also provide nutrients.

The following media can be considered:

Seedlings of the Transvaal red balloon bush (*Erythrophysa transvaalensis*) emerging from a covering of coarse river sand. Germination began within days of sowing the presoaked seeds.

a) Sand is a very popular and widely used rooting medium. It must be coarse and clean, and drain freely. Fine sand tends to retain moisture, leading to rotting. A coarse sand mixture requires more frequent watering than other media.

b) Perlite and vermiculite are light, sterile media with very good drainage properties. A combination of the two gives better results than either medium used on its own.

c) Soil is also often used as rooting medium. However, one must ensure that it is a well-aerated sandy loam, not a heavy clay soil which does not drain as well and also tends to lead to rotting of the cuttings. Here again one must insist on a sterilized, weed- and nematode-free medium.

d) Sphagnum moss, although not often used on its own, can be successfully used in combination with one of the above.

The success of the cuttings not only depends on the above-mentioned factors but also on the correct environmental conditions.

A typical cutting-bed with bottom heating cables and automatic misting system.

Cuttings require sufficient but not excessive light. The ideal temperature should never drop below 19°C and should not exceed 28°C. This is achieved by keeping the cuttings in a warm place or by bottom-heat in the cutting bed which can take the form of an electric bottom-heat cable or a series of pipes circulating warm water. This is necessary during the winter months and essential for certain indigenous tree species, e.g. the pepperbark tree (*Warburgia salutaris*).

To limit the rate of transpiration from the cutting, the surrounding atmosphere should be kept as humid as possible. This can be achieved with a fine, intermittent mist spray system. The fine film of water on the leaves reduces transpiration and respiration. The cuttings must be kept moist at all times.

The time before rooting begins, differs from species to species, about three weeks on average. The next step is the hardening-off process. The cutting has rooted and must now be removed gradually from its ideal, protected environment. The transition must be a careful and slow one. As soon as the cuttings have rooted successfully one can begin to reduce the mist spray, lengthening the dry periods. The cuttings will become acclimatised to a drier atmosphere.

The hardening-off section. Rooted cuttings of the black stinkwood (*Ocotea bullata*), transplanted into bags are kept under 60% shade netting for a few weeks until ready to be moved under hail netting.

Having weaned them, one can remove and plant the cuttings into bags. At this stage they are still not ready to be exposed to full sun and should therefore be put under 70% shade netting for a week or two, after which they can be placed under 30% shade netting or hail netting. At this stage they are almost acclimatised to full sun. The next step is to take them out into the open.

TRUNCHEONS

A truncheon is merely a very large cutting and can be defined as a section of a branch of a tree, not less than 50 mm in diameter and 1 m long. Growing indigenous trees from truncheons has proved very successful and it is therefore included here as a worthwhile method of propagation.

One would usually cut off the branch at the point where it meets the main trunk. To prevent an excessive loss of moisture through transpiration, strip the branch/truncheon of most leaves and twigs except some leaves at the top. Truncheons of tree species with a milky latex or thick, fleshy bark should first be allowed to dry and can then be placed straight into the soil in the position where the tree is desired. Examples of such trees include the wild figs (*Ficus* species), coral trees (*Erythrina* species) and the marula (*Sclerocarya birrea* subsp. *africana*). Put a few spadefuls of river sand at the bottom of the hole to prevent fungus growth or rotting and to stimulate root formation. The truncheons should be kept moist.

The advantage of this method is that one starts off with a tree of approximately 1 m or more, well on its way to becoming a lovely, large shade tree. Another bonus is that no special facilities are required – the truncheon can be planted directly *in situ*.

A truncheon of the dwarf coral tree (*Erythrina humeana*). This method allows one to start with a fair-sized plant.

Trees with a thick, fleshy bark, for example marula and African teak (*Pterocarpus angolensis*), respond well when planted by truncheon. Trees that can form roots on the branches or above ground level are usually also very successful candidates from which to take truncheons, for example the various wild fig species. As mentioned before, specific examples are given under the relevant species.

AFRICAN HOLLY

Description An evergreen tree up to 30 m tall with a dense slightly elongated to rounded crown. **Bark** on the young branches smooth and grey, tinged with purple, with raised corky spots (lenticels) but smooth and grey to light brown on the older branches and stems. **Leaves** simple, alternate, shiny dark green, the midrib deeply channelled above and prominent below, side veins looping, the margin smooth but sometimes with distant teeth in the upper third; the leaf stalk is up to 10 mm long and purplish. **Flowers** mostly in clusters in the leaf axils, white to cream-coloured and sweetly scented and sometimes up to 7 mm in diameter, male and female flowers on separate trees. **Fruit** a roundish fleshy berry up to 7 mm in diameter and glossy red when ripe. **Wood** white, hard, fine-grained and moderately heavy.

Afrikaans	Without
Northern Sotho	monamane
Zulu	iPhuphuma
Botanical name	*Ilex mitis*
Family	Holly Family (Aquifoliaceae)
National tree list no.	397

Name derivation *Ilex* = the Latin species name for the holly oak, and *mitis* = unarmed, referring to the leaves without prominent teeth.

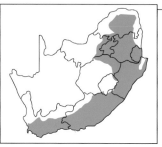

Diagnostic features Evergreen; bark grey and smooth; midrib sunken on upper surface of leaf blade and prominent below; leaf stalk purplish; male and female trees; fruit glossy red when ripe.

Flowering from September to February.
Fruiting from March to May.

Distribution From Ethiopia in the north to the Western Cape in the south.

Habitat Occurs in evergreen woodland and forests but always near water or with its roots in the water. It grows mostly in shade.

Economic value The ripe fruits are popular with fruit-eating birds (Rameron pigeons, cinnamon doves, Knysna and purple-crested louries, black-eyed bulbuls, red-winged and plum-coloured starlings, pied and crested barbets). The wood makes good and durable furniture and is still being used for tables and chairs today. The wood darkens slightly after many years of oiling, taking on a beautiful honey colour.

The African holly makes a good garden subject and can be used to fill in an open space or planted near a pool, fish pond or a birdbath. If planted in groups of up to five, the chances of including a female tree are increased. With its fast growth, dense evergreen crown and light-coloured stem, it can also be used as an accent plant on the lawn or as a street tree. The root system is not aggressive.

Other uses The fruits are edible, with a faint sweetish taste, but can be bitter. Pieces of the bark are chewed as a purgative, having a mild action in most people.

Cultivation It grows easily from fresh seed. Collect fresh seed from the trees and dry in a shady spot. Sow the seeds in flat seedling trays filled with a mixture of river sand and compost (1:1) or in seedling mix available from your local garden centre or nursery. Cover the seed lightly and keep moist. The seeds usually start to germinate 8–20 days after sowing. Germination may be quite erratic. When they reach the two-leaf stage, transplant the seedlings into black nursery bags filled with a sand and compost mix. Seedlings and young plants transplant well. The African holly grows best in a moist spot near water and enjoys being kept well-watered. It is a fast-growing species, up to 900 mm per year. This is one of the few indigenous trees that is really frost-resistant; however, young trees must be protected for the first year or two.

AFRICAN MANGOSTEEN

Description An evergreen tree up to 18 m tall with a dense spreading canopy formed from rigid branches arising at an acute angle, the smaller branches at right angles in whorls of three, all parts of the tree exuding a yellow sap; trees are either male or female. **Bark** on the young branches smooth and glossy but yellowish grey to greyish black, cracking into small blocks on the older branches and stems. **Leaves** simple and usually in whorls of three, hard, leathery and glossy dark green to blueish green, the venation yellowish green and prominent on both surfaces, margin smooth and tightly rolled under and wavy, the leaf stalk 4–8 mm long, the young leaves are a red copper colour. **Flowers** borne in groups of 5–15 on short and knobby side branches on the old stems, flower stalks long and slender, the corolla cream to greenish yellow, sweetly scented and 6–14 mm in diameter, the male flowers resembling small pincushions. **Fruit** a fleshy, roundish to oval berry, orange to red when ripe and up to 35 mm in diameter. **Wood** yellowish white to yellowish brown and heavy (air-dry 850 kg/m³).

Afrikaans	Laeveldse geelmelkhout
Northern Sotho	mokongono
Zulu	umPhimbi
Botanical name	*Garcinia livingstonei*
Family	St. John's Wort Family (Clusiaceae)
National tree list no.	486

Name derivation *Garcinia* = named in honour of Laurent Garcin (1683–1751), a French botanist, and *livingstonei* = named after Dr David Livingstone.

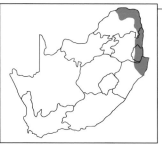

Economic value The roots and bark are eaten by elephant and leaves by giraffe, kudu and bushbuck. Fruits are eaten by kudu, nyala, grey duiker, baboons, vervet monkeys and cattle. The ripe fruits are popular with crested guineafowl, barbets, louries and mousebirds. The wood can be used as general timber but it is susceptible to borer attack. Fruits are produced in profusion and are edible, with a refreshing but slightly sweetish acidic taste. A refreshing drink and a beer can be made from the fruit. It is worthwhile to plant the African mangosteen on any game farm where the conditions are favourable, for it is much utilised by game.

Diagnostic features Evergreen tree with branches and leaves in whorls of three; leaves hard, leathery and dark green with light-coloured venation, young leaves copper-red; male and female trees; male flower resembling a pincushion; fruit an orange to reddish fleshy berry.

Flowering from August to November.
Fruiting from November to February.

Distribution From Somalia in the north to KwaZulu-Natal in the south.

Habitat Grows in riverine fringes to open woodland. Not common in rocky areas, mostly growing on alluvial soils.

Plant trees in an orchard as a long-term project (3–4 years). After four years the first crop of fruit can be harvested, packed and sold on the local market.

Other uses The gum exuding from damaged areas on the stem is edible. Dugout canoes are sometimes made from the trunks by tribes in central Africa. Branches can be cut to a length of 500 mm and the branchlet whorls cleared, except the lower ones that can be cut to a length of 60 mm, making ideal mixers for porridge. Extracts made from the leaves and flowers can be used as an antibiotic. The powdered roots are used as an aphrodisiac.

Cultivation Use only fresh seed. Sow in flat seedling trays filled with river sand. Press seed into the sand until it is flush with the surface, cover with a thin layer of sand and keep moist. The germination percentage is usually 80–100%. Transplant the seedlings when they reach the 2-leaf stage. Seedlings transplant well. This tree grows in full sun or light shade. The growth rate is usually slow, 300–500 mm per year. Grows best in frost-free areas and is drought-resistant.

A protected tree in South Africa.

AFRICAN TEAK

Description A deciduous tree up to 30 m tall. **Bark** on young twigs smooth, grey and covered with hairs but dark grey and rough to fissured on the older branches and stems. **Leaves** compound, with 9–25 sub-opposite pairs of leaflets and a terminal leaflet, the young leaves soft and covered with brown hairs. **Flowers** appearing before the leaves, pea-like, yellow turning orangy yellow, sweetly scented and in branched sprays up to 200 mm long. **Pods** non-splitting and up to 150 mm in diameter, with a broad wing and the centre part covered with hard bristles, fruits remaining on the tree long after the leaves have fallen. **Wood** medium hard, with an off-white sapwood and the heartwood pale honey-brown to reddish brown with purplish brown to dark brown streaks, moderately heavy (air-dry 650 kg/m³).

Afrikaans	Kiaat
Northern Sotho	morôtô
Zulu	umVangazi
Botanical name	*Pterocarpus angolensis*
Family	Pod-bearing Family (Fabaceae)
National tree list no.	236

Name derivation *Pterocarpus* = winged fruit, and *angolensis* = from Angola.

Diagnostic features Tree deciduous; leaves compound, with sub-opposite leaflets and a terminal leaflet; flowers yellow and in branched sprays; fruit a pod with a broad wing and the central part covered with stiff bristles.

Flowering from August to February.
Fruiting from January to June.

Distribution From Zaïre in the north to KwaZulu-Natal in the south.

Habitat Occurs in woodland and wooded grassland. Sometimes as stunted trees in wooded grassland on mountain tops (e.g. Soutpansberg). Regarded as an indicator of well drained soils.

Economic value Ranks as one of the finest furniture woods in the world. Often used for panelling, parquet flooring and for carvings. One of the best woods to use for door and window frames as the linear shrinkage is minimal. The leaves are browsed by elephant and kudu. The pods are eaten by baboons, vervet monkeys and yellow-footed squirrels. Popular with bee farmers as it is a good source of pollen for honeybees. The larvae of the bushveld charaxes (*Charaxes achaemenes achaemenes*) feed on the leaves of this tree. Farmers in suitably warm areas can seriously consider plant-

ing woodlots or small plantations of African teak. Plantations like this have been successfully planted in Mozambique. Up to 20 trees can be grouped in camps where shade is needed during the hot summer months. It is always better to protect young plants from cold winds for the first two years. It makes good bonsai material, reaching an adult shape in three to four years, with leaves much reduced in size. The roots are not aggressive.

Other uses A decoction made from the roots is used for the treatment of malaria and blackwater fever, and an infusion made from roots is taken orally for the treatment of diarrhoea, bilharziasis and abdominal pains. Roots are burnt and the ashes drunk in water to treat asthma and tuberculosis. The bark is boiled and the resulting red fluid is used in treating skin lesions and ringworm. A decoction of the bark is taken orally for piles, and a cold infusion made from bark is taken to relieve stomach disorders, headaches, blood in the urine, earache and ulcers in the mouth. Cataracts and sore eyes are treated by dropping sap on to the eyes. Ripe seeds are burnt and the ashes applied to inflamed areas of the skin and to bleeding gums. The red gummy sap contains 76.7% tannin and a dark red resin.

Cultivation Pods collected in the veld must be opened and the seed taken out. If the seeds are not scarified, only a few, if any, will germinate. Seeds must be left in water for 1–2 days and then planted in flat seedling trays filled with river sand. They should germinate within 20–30 days. Initially, seedling growth is slow but it speeds up later. Transplant seedlings at an early stage for they soon develop a very long taproot. Cuttings made from young coppice shoots should be planted in early spring and can be treated with growth-stimulating hormones before planting. Plant truncheons of 100 mm in diameter or thicker during October in a hole preferably 1 m deep with some river sand placed in the bottom. The sand prevents fungal growth and speeds up root formation. This is not a tree to grow in areas where frost occurs. Under favourable conditions the growth rate is 500–700 mm per year.

The African teak is a protected tree in South Africa.

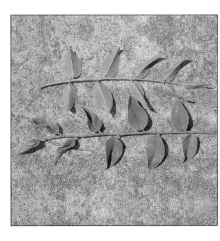

AFRICAN WATTLE

Description A semi-deciduous to deciduous tree up to 15 m tall with a dense rounded to spreading crown. **Bark** smooth and grey on the young branches, twigs covered in reddish brown hairs but brown to grey and rough with lengthwise grooves on the older branches and stems. **Leaves** twice-compound, with 4–9 pairs of pinnae each bearing 10–23 pairs of grey-green leaflets; the growth tip, leaf stalk and rachis covered in dense reddish brown hairs. **Flowers** in erect dense terminal sprays up to 150 mm long in the axils of the leaves, bright yellow, the flower stalk and backs of the sepals covered in reddish brown hairs, the petals bright yellow and crinkled, individual flowers up to 25 mm in diameter. **Fruit** in hanging clusters, a non-splitting, flat, thinly woody pod up to 100 mm long tapering to both ends, grey to greyish brown when dry with one or two bulges showing the location of the seeds. **Wood** with a light brown sapwood and a soft dark brown to blackish heartwood that is heavy (air-dry 912 kg/m³).

Afrikaans	Huilboom
Northern Sotho	mosehla
Zulu	umThobo
Botanical name	*Peltophorum africanum*
Family	Pod-bearing Family (Fabaceae)
National tree list no.	215

Name derivation *Peltophorum* = shield-bearing and refers to the shape of the stigma, and *africanum* = from Africa.

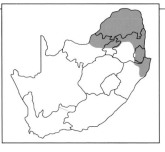

pollen. It produces a good quality timber used for furniture and implement handles. At the turn of the century, the wood of the African wattle was commonly used for *riempie* benches and chairs. The African wattle can be successfully planted along fences to give protection to smaller stock and game during the hot summer months, with the added pleasure of a mass of yellow flowers attracting insects and they, in turn, many insect-eating birds. The larvae of the Van Son's charaxes (*Charaxes vansoni*), Satyr charaxes (*Charaxes ethalion*) and Braine's charaxes (*Charaxes brainei*) feed on the leaves.

Diagnostic features Twigs, growth tip, leaf stalk, rachis, flower stalks and the backs of sepals covered with reddish brown hairs; leaves soft and twice-compound; petals yellow and crinkled at the margins; seed pods tapering to both ends, non-splitting.

Flowering from September to April.
Fruiting from December to May.

Distribution From Zaïre in the north to KwaZulu-Natal in the south.

Habitat Occurs in wooded grassland, woodland and along margins of vleis. Grows mostly on well drained soils.

Economic value The young leaves and especially the pods are relished by cattle and goats. A valuable tree to have in the veld on cattle and game farms, for the leaves and twigs are eaten by elephant, black rhino, giraffe, kudu, impala and grey duiker. A valuable tree for bee-keepers for it is a good source of nectar and

It makes a good shade tree on a lawn and can be successfully planted as a street tree. Popular as a bonsai subject. An adult shape and thick corky bark forms in two to four years, with the leaves much reduced. The root system is not aggressive.

Other uses The powdered decorticated root is applied to wounds to hasten healing. Bark is chewed to relieve colic and an infusion made from the root is taken orally to relieve stomach disorders and to get rid of intestinal parasites. A decoction of the bark and leaves is taken for the same reason. The steam from a hot decoction is used for treating sore eyes and in serious cases it is dropped into the eyes. A decoction made from the powdered stem and root bark is taken for diarrhoea and dysentery and a decoction made from the root is taken by mouth or gargled to treat sores in the throat. Leaves are boiled and the steam is then directed into the mouth to relieve toothache. The wood makes good fuel.

Cultivation Fresh seed (± 1 200 seeds per kilogram) must be placed in hot water and left overnight. Sow the next morning in flat seedling trays or directly into black nursery bags filled with a mixture of river sand and compost (5:1) and keep moist. The seeds take 3–10 days to germinate. Seedlings and young plants transplant well. A fast grower with a growth rate of 1–1.5 m per year. It can withstand frost if protected for the first 2–3 years; it is also resistant to a fair amount of drought.

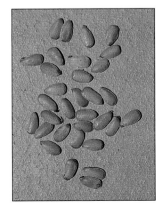

ANA TREE

Description A deciduous tree up to 30 m tall with spreading branches and an erect to roundish crown. **Stems** greenish grey to whitish grey and smooth on young stems but grey and smooth to rough on older branches and stems. Young branches have a characteristic zigzag appearance. Stipules spinescent and paired, straight, whitish and 10–30 mm long. **Leaves** twice-compound, pale grey-green with a conspicuous gland at the base of each pair of pinnae. **Inflorescence** an elongated spike, up to 35–160 x 20 mm, with scented pale cream-coloured flowers. **Fruit** a non-splitting orange to red-brown, curved to twisted pod, 100–350 x 20–50 mm. **Wood** coarse-grained, whitish with a yellowish tinge and prominent annual rings, light (air-dry 540 kg/m³).

Afrikaans	Anaboom
Northern Sotho	mogabo
Zulu	umHlalankwazi
Botanical name	*Faidherbia albida*
Family	Pod-bearing Family (Fabaceae)
National tree list no.	159

Name derivation *albida* = somewhat whitish, referring to the colour of the stems.

10% protein, 50% carbohydrates, 5–14.3% tannin and 2.7% dark yellow fixed oil. The seed can be boiled, the skin removed and eaten. The pods are sometimes dried and ground into a flour which is edible. The larvae of the brown playboy (*Deudorix antalis*) butterfly feed on the young seeds inside the pods.

Plant ana trees in groups of 10–12 scattered in the veld to provide fodder. Try to choose sites without frost and with sandy soil. The growth rate is far slower in heavy soils. It makes an interesting specimen tree if planted in a park. Lines of ana trees can be planted close together along contours in eroded areas to stabilise the soil with their extensive root systems.

Diagnostic features The only 'acacia' with straight spines and elongated inflorescences; young branches with a characteristic zigzag appearance; trees mostly leafless during the summer months; the shape of the pods diagnostic.

Flowering from March to September.
Fruiting from September to December.

Distribution From Israel in the north to KwaZulu-Natal in the south.

Habitat Along rivers, swamps, floodplains and dry river courses.

Economic value A valuable fodder tree for game (elephant, giraffe, kudu, nyala and impala) and domestic animals. The leaves are nutritious and provide fodder during the winter months. A mature tree can bear 0.75–1 metric tons of pods per year. The pods drop from November to January causing a mad scramble by animals to pick them up. The seeds have a high protein content, with the pods high in starch and contain up to

Other uses A decoction of the bark is used for diarrhoea, bleeding, inflamed eyes and as an emetic.

Cultivation Pods can be collected on the ground. Place healthy seed in hot water and leave overnight. Plant the swollen seed the next morning in 150 x 100 mm black plastic bags filled with river sand. Seeds usually germinate within the first 2–5 days. The seedling develops a very long taproot at an early stage. Seedlings of 50–80 mm tall have taproots 500–600 mm long. Therefore it is best to transplant the seedlings directly into the garden or veld when they are ± 50 mm tall. Young trees are susceptible to the white Australian bug. Spray with a systemic insecticide. One of the fastest growing indigenous trees in South Africa, with a growth rate of 1–2 m per year; it can reach 7 m in 3 years under favourable conditions. It can survive up to 5 days of frost per year. Relatively drought-resistant. There should be no difficulty with establishing this valuable tree wherever suitable habitat and conditions exist.

This is a protected tree in South Africa.

APPLE-LEAF

Description A semi-deciduous tree up to 12 m tall with an open rounded crown. **Bark** on the young branches smooth, grey and covered with dense hairs, but grey and flaking on older branches and stems. **Leaves** unevenly compound with 1–3 pairs of opposite leaflets and a larger terminal one, texture hard, glossy above and grey-green beneath, with prominent midribs, the leaf stalk thickset and velvety. **Flowers** in sprays of 120–300 mm long at the tips of the branches, fragrant, with mauve to violet petals (white forms are occasionally encountered) and the calyx covered with grey velvety hairs. Flowers appearing before or together with the new leaves. **Fruit** a flat, non-splitting pendulous pod tapering to both ends and up to 120 x 30 mm, with 1 or 2 light brown, kidney-shaped seeds. **Wood** with the sapwood off-white and the heartwood orange-brown, hard and dense with a straight and fairly close grain and the annual rings prominent and close together, moderately heavy (air-dry 770 kg/m³).

Diagnostic features Bark flaking in old trees; young twigs hairy; leaves hard, unevenly compound with a large terminal leaflet, glossy above, with prominent midribs, flowers mauve to violet, pea-shaped; fruit a non-splitting pod tapering to both ends.

Flowering from September to December.
Fruiting from January to August.

Distribution From Zaïre and Tanzania in the north to KwaZulu-Natal in the south.

Habitat In low-altitude open woodland and on the banks of seasonal streams. Occurs on all types of soil but mostly on sandy or alluvial soils.

Economic value An excellent fodder tree for cattle and game (giraffe, eland, Lichtenstein's hartebeest, kudu, nyala, impala and yellow-spotted rock dassie) and always heavily browsed. At the onset of spring,

Afrikaans	Appelblaar
Northern Sotho	mphata
Zulu	umBhandu
Botanical name	*Lonchocarpus capassa*
Family	Pod-bearing Family (Fabaceae)
National tree list no.	238

Name derivation *Lonchocarpus* = lance-shaped fruit, and *capassa* = Mozambique vernacular name meaning 'of no value'.

trees drop most of their leaves. Animals will eagerly pick these up from the ground. Giraffe are especially partial to the leaves and are usually found in the vicinity of these trees in the veld. As the tree is a real survivor in a drought, it is one that farmers can rely on to produce leaves for browsing. An excellent pollen and nectar source for honeybees. Often used by cavity nest builders like barbets, owls and rollers. The larvae of the large blue charaxes (*Charaxes bohemani*) feed on the leaves.

Plant apple-leaf trees in scattered clumps of up to 10 in a suitable habitat. It is always wise to water the plants every so often initially, but once they are established, nature will take over. Although somewhat slow initially, it makes an interesting street tree, giving a stunning display when in flower. The root system is not aggressive.

Other uses Wood used for carvings, grain mortars and tool-handles. Along the Zambezi and Chobe Rivers it is used for making dug-out canoes. Inhalation of the smoke of burning roots is said to relieve colds. Powdered rootbark is used to treat snakebite.

Cultivation Easily grown from seed. Seed must first be soaked in hot water and left overnight and the soaked seed planted the next morning in seedling trays filled either with river sand or a mixture of river sand and potting soil (4:1). Cover seed lightly with river sand and keep moist. To speed up germination a sheet of polythene or clear glass can be placed over the seedling tray. Seeds usually germinate 4–6 days after being sown. Plant into black nursery bags when they reach the 2-leaf stage. Young plants are often attacked by the white orthezia scale. Keep in 30% shade for 3–5 weeks before taking them into full sun. A relatively fast grower in frost-free areas. Not frost-resistant but will survive in colder regions if properly protected during the first 2–4 years.

A protected tree in South Africa.

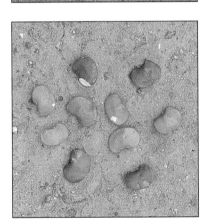

BAOBAB

Description A massive deciduous tree up to 20 m tall with a round or spreading crown. Trunk stout, tapering or cylindrical and abruptly bottle-shaped or short and squat up to 12 m in diameter. **Bark** smooth, reddish brown and heavily folded. **Leaves** alternate and hand-shaped, with 3–9 sessile tapering leaflets (simple on young trees) at the ends of branches, leaf stalk up to 160 mm long. **Flowers** mostly solitary, pendulous and up to 200 mm in diameter, the flower stalks up to 200 mm long. Calyx deeply lobed. Petals waxy, white and crinkly. Stamens numerous and united below into a staminal tube. **Fruit** variously shaped but mostly ovoid, 100–150 mm long, with a hard woody shell covered with velvety hairs. The kidney-shaped seeds embedded in a powdery pulp. **Wood** whitish, spongy and light (air-dried 320 kg/m³).

Afrikaans	Kremetart
Northern Sotho	motsoo
Botanical name	*Adansonia digitata*
Family	Baobab Family (Bombacaceae)
National tree list no.	467

Name derivation *Adansonia* = named after the French surgeon Michel Adanson (1727–1806), and *digitata* = hand-shaped, referring to the shape of the leaf.

Diagnostic features Massive trunk, smooth and folded bark; deciduous, digitately 3- to 9-foliate leaves with long leaf stalk; pendulous waxy white flowers with numerous stamens; pendulous ovoid fruit with a hard woody shell covered with velvety hairs.

Flowering time October to December.
Fruiting time April to May.

Distribution Occurs in most countries south of the Sahara but in South Africa restricted to the Northern Province and Mpumalanga.

Habitat
Occurs in dry woodland, mostly in rocky well-drained soil.

Economic value During the rainy season when the trees are in leaf, it is a good fodder tree, especially for game (elephant, kudu, nyala and impala). At the end of the season cattle eat the fallen leaves. Various game species and cattle relish the fallen flowers. Elephant sometimes destroy vast numbers of baobab trees by tearing off pieces of the stem for moisture. The only way to save these trees is to restrict the number of elephant in the area. The roots can be tapped for water and the young roots cooked and eaten. Fibre from the inner bark is used for rope, baskets, nets and fishing lines. The young leaves are cooked and eaten as spinach or can be dried and powdered to be used later. The leaves are rich in vitamin C, sugars and potassium tartrate. The acid pith of the fruit is rich in ascorbic acid and can be used to make a refreshing drink. Seeds can be eaten fresh or dry or roasted to provide a substitute for coffee. The pulp and seeds have a high nutritional value and are recommended for feeding to stock late in the dry season when grazing is poor. The baobab is a popular species for bonsai specimens. The South African 'Baobab Style' originated from this species.

Other uses It provides food, shelter, clothing and medicine as well as material for hunting and fishing.

Cultivation Seed can be collected from picked or fallen fruit. After crushing the hard woody shell of the fruit, the seeds can be extracted from the dry acidic pulp. The seeds are kidney-shaped, with a smooth, dark brown to blackish seedcoat. It should be soaked in hot water overnight and planted in a soil mixture of washed river sand and compost (5:1). Plant the seed no deeper than 10 mm. Seedlings have flattened hypocotyls and the first leaves are petiolate (with a leaf stalk), generally simple and narrowly linear.

Seed sown during the summer months is likely to germinate within two weeks. Germination is usually 90–100%. Seedlings can be transplanted when they are 60 mm tall. Weaning of the plants is critical before planting them out into the full sun. The growth rate is moderate to fast (500–800 mm) per year, especially for the first 5 years.

Areas where the baobab can be grown are restricted to those with not more than 1 day frost per year.

This is a protected tree in southern Africa.

BEAD-BEAN TREE

Description An evergreen tree up to 15 m tall with a dense, roundish canopy. **Bark** on young stems purplish to yellowish with light grey corky spots (lenticels), on older stems it is smooth and grey to rough and dark grey, peeling off in small flakes. **Leaves** simple, dark green and glossy, the surface covered in short hairs, leaf blade up to 70 x 13 mm, the base rounded but with a conspicuous hair-like growth at the tip, paler below with a light-coloured midrib which is prominent on the undersurface, venation on the upper surface prominent. Leaf stalk 18–30 mm long, with a thickening at the base of the leaf blade and a distinct bend near the leaf base. **Flowers** borne in terminal clusters and sweetly scented, without petals but the sepals are green and the stamens many, 40–50 mm long, whitish to pink, the ovary borne on a long stalk (gynophore). **Fruit** a non-splitting pseudo-pod, up to 160 mm long and markedly constricted around the seeds. **Wood** white and moderately heavy (air-dry 830 kg/m^3).

Diagnostic features Bark smooth with prominent lenticels; leaf tip with a conspicuous hair-like growth, midrib prominent on lower surface, venation marked on upper surface; leaf stalk with diagnostic swelling just below leaf blade and a prominent bend near leaf base; flowers without petals, stamens very long and many, ovary on a long stalk (gynophore); fruit a pseudo-pod, markedly restricted around the seeds.

Flowering from July to December.
Fruiting from September to April.

Distribution From Ethiopia in the north to KwaZulu-Natal in the south.

Habitat Various types of woodland, wooded grassland and evergreen scrub. Mostly on sandy, loamy and rocky soil.

Economic value A valuable tree to have on the farm for it provides fodder and shade to animals. The leaves are eagerly eaten by domestic stock and game (elephant, giraffe, kudu, nyala, bushbuck, duiker and klipspringer). Kudu, nyala and bushbuck eat the bark of this tree,

Afrikaans	Knoppiesboontjieboom
Zulu	umEnwayo
Botanical name	*Maerua angolensis*
Family	Capparaceae (Caper Family)
National tree list no.	132

Name derivation *Maerua* = drooping, referring to the drooping foilage, and *angolensis* = from Angola.

presumably for the control of internal parasites. Most adult specimens of this species show a distinct browse line. The larvae of various butterfly species feed on the leaves of the bead bean tree, e.g. the zebra white (*Pinacopteryx eriphia*), scarlet tip (*Colotis danae annae*), small orange tip (*Colotis evagore*), veined tip (*Colotis vesta*), diverse rainforest white (*Appias epaphia*) and the forest white (*Belenois zochalia*). The instar larvae of these butterflies sometimes defoliate a tree completely. The leaves will grow out again, sometimes during the same season.

Plant this tree in groves in suitable places in camps where they can be utilised by stock and game. It is a rewarding garden subject with its dark green leaves and the masses of whitish flowers attracting a myriad of insects and they, in turn, many insect-eating birds. An ideal tree for the smaller garden, forming a neat shade tree. This tree is a must in the garden if one wants to attract butterflies and insect-eating birds. The root system is not aggressive.

Other uses A thick paste is prepared from the leaves and applied to cancerous areas on the skin and an extract from fresh leaves is used as a mild purgative in adults. Leaves and pieces of bark are heated over a fire without water and given to a child with convulsions to inhale the steam. Similarly steam inhaled from leaves is used by adults for relief of headaches. A decoction of the leaf and bark is taken as a remedy for stomach aches.

Cultivation Easily cultivated from seed. Sound seed is commonly available in the veld. Remove all fruit pulp around the seeds for it contains a growth inhibitor that will block germination. Sow the seed in flat seedling trays filled with river sand and cover with a thin layer of sand or compost. Seeds usually germinate within 12–20 days. Transplant seedlings into black nursery bags filled with a mixture of sand, loam and compost (3:1:1). Young plants grow fast. The growth rate is usually around 800 mm per year and later reduces with age to 500 mm per year. Flowering begins when the plant is 3–4 years old. It is frost and drought-resistant and grows equally well in shade and full sun.

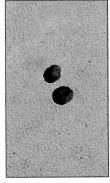

BLACK MONKEY-THORN

Description A deciduous tree up to 25 m tall with a rounded, flattened or open crown. **Bark** on the young branches greyish yellow to reddish brown and velvety but pale or dark greyish yellow to dark brown, irregularly fissured and flaking on the older branches and stems. Prickles in pairs below the nodes and strongly recurved, mostly black, 3–9 mm long. **Leaves** twice-compound, 35–70 mm long, subglabrous to densely hairy, with a gland at the junction of the top pinnae pairs. Inflorescence a 15–85 mm long spike. **Flowers** yellowish white, sessile, with a distinct pinkish to pinkish-red calyx. Pods in drooping clusters, reddish or dark purplish brown, up to 170 x 24 mm, conspicuously veined, straight, with a pointed tip, thinly textured, splitting on the tree. **Wood** with a thin yellowish sapwood and a golden- to dark brown, strong and heavy (air-dry 910 kg/m³) heartwood.

Afrikaans	Swartapiesdoring
Northern Sotho	mokwaripa
Zulu	umKhaya wehlalahlati
Botanical name	*Acacia burkei*
Family	Pod-bearing Family (Fabaceae)
National tree list no.	161

Name derivation *Acacia* = derived from the Greek word 'akis', a point or barb, and *burkei* = named after Joseph Burke (1812–1873), a botanical collector who collected this tree near the Magaliesberg in 1840.

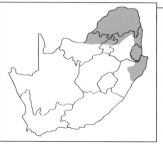

ture of *riempie* benches and chairs. The wood is termite-resistant and therefore makes lasting fence posts. The leaves on the tree are eaten by black rhino, giraffe, kudu, nyala and impala, and the dropped leaves by steenbok and grey duiker. The dry pods have a high nutritional value and are eagerly eaten by cattle and game. It is a valuable shade tree in warm sandveld areas where farmers can plant it in scattered groups of 10–30 as shade for livestock during the hot summer months. It is popular with bonsai growers for the ease with which it can be trained into a shape resembling the adult trees in nature. It should be borne in mind that the root system can become rather aggressive and the black monkey-thorn should not be planted close to paving or buildings.

Diagnostic features Bark flaking; prickles black, in pairs below nodes, strongly recurved; leaves hairy, gland at junction of leaflet pairs; inflorescence a spike, calyx distinctly pinkish; pods thinly textured, with a pointed tip, splitting on tree.

Flowering from October to January.
Fruiting from December to May.

Distribution From south-eastern Zimbabwe in the north to KwaZulu-Natal in the south.

Habitat Occurs on a variety of soil types and on rocky slopes in dry river valley scrub, thornveld or in mixed woodland.

Economic value This was a popular furniture wood at the turn of the century, especially in the manufac-

Other uses The hard and heavy heartwood makes a good-quality fuel with coals that last for a long time.

Cultivation Collect fresh seed from the trees. Seed collected on the ground is usually 80% or more infested with insects. Soak seed in hot water and leave overnight. Sow the swollen seeds in flat seedling trays filled with river sand or a mixture of river sand and compost (9:1). Cover the seed with a 5 mm thick layer of river sand and keep moist. Germination usually takes place after 3–5 days. All seed should have germinated after 4 weeks. Transplant seedlings when they reach the two-leaf stage into black nursery bags filled with a mixture of river sand, compost and topsoil. If left until later, the taproot can be easily damaged. The black monkey thorn will grow in any type of soil but it should be well drained. It can withstand low temperatures but not cold wind. As the growth rate of this tree is rather slow, 600–800 mm per year, it is one to be planted as a long-term project.

BLACK THORN

Description A deciduous tree up to 9 m tall with a roundish to spreading, much branched crown. Sometimes forming dense thickets. **Bark** on young branches greyish or yellowish brown to purplish black but grey and rougher on older branches and stems. Prickles strongly recurved, black, in pairs just below each node. **Leaves** twice-compound, blueish green, mostly with 2 or 3 pairs of pinnae and 1 or 2 pairs of opposite leaflets per pinna, usually with a gland on the leaf stalk. **Flowers** in creamy-white, sweet-scented (especially at night), short but elongated spikes, flower buds reddish. **Fruit** a splitting, straw-coloured, flat, papery pod. **Wood** with a yellowish sapwood and very dark brown to blackish heartwood.

Afrikaans	Swarthaak
Northern Sotho	mongangatau
Botanical name	*Acacia mellifera* supsp. *detinens*
Family	Pod-bearing Family (Fabaceae)
National tree list no.	176.1

Name derivation *Acacia* = from the Greek word 'akis' meaning hook or barb, *mellifera* = honey-bearing, and *detinens* = the Latin word for 'to hold'.

and steenbok. The stems are very strong, pliable and used for tool, axe, pick and instrument handles. The dry wood makes an excellent fuel. The heartwood is termite- and borer- proof, the larger stems making excellent fencing-posts. Trees flower in profusion, producing copious nectar and pollen and tend to be a favourite with bee farmers.

Plant a few black thorn trees scattered in the veld, but remember to prune them regularly to form valuable fodder trees which will also provide shade to animals with short hair in the hot summer sun in the arid areas. If left unattended, they may spread to form impenetrable thickets, slowly taking over good grazing areas. An excellent choice if one needs an impenetrable screen. The plants react well to pruning. A good bonsai subject. It has an aggressive root system, limiting its use in gardens.

Diagnostic features Bark smooth; prickles strongly recurved and in pairs; leaves blueish green, twice-compound with 1 or 2 pairs of opposite leaflets per pinna; flowers in elongated spikes; fruit a papery pod.

Flowering from September to November.
Fruiting from January to April.

Distribution From Tanzania in the north to the western Free State in the south.

Habitat Occurs in dry thornveld, wooded grassland and woodland. Common on brackish soils and Kalahari sand.

Economic value One of the most valuable fodder trees on cattle and game farms in semi-arid to arid areas. The leaves, young twigs, flowers and pods are very nutritious with a high percentage of raw protein and make an excellent stock and game feed. Plants are browsed by black rhino, giraffe, eland, kudu, blue wildebeest, gemsbok, impala, springbok, grey duiker

Other uses Gum collected from injured stems is edible and relished by children, animals and birds. A decoction made from the roots is used for the relief of stomach pains.

Cultivation Seed must be soaked in hot water, left overnight and planted the next morning. Sow the seeds in seedling trays filled with river sand and cover with a thin layer of sand. Seeds usually germinate from the fifth day onwards. Transplant into nursery bags when the first leaf unfolds or sow directly into the open soil where the trees are to grow. Seedlings form a long taproot and if damaged the young plant may die. Young trees are prone to heavy browsing by stock and game and must be protected for the first two seasons. The black thorn has a moderate growth rate, up to 500 mm per year. It is a hardy plant and can tolerate extreme drought conditions and various degrees of frost.

BLADDER-NUT

Description An evergreen tree up to 15 m tall with a dense roundish to pyramidal crown. **Bark** on the young branches yellowish green, with dense rusty hairs but smooth and blackish grey on the older stems and branches. **Leaves** simple, alternate, in two ranks, leathery, very glossy dark green above and lighter below, the midrib conspicuous on both sides, margin smooth but sometimes wavy and covered with long rusty hairs. Leaf stalk up to 2 mm long. Young leaves reddish turning green with age. **Flowers** single or in few-flowered groups in the leaf axils, male and female flowers on different trees, pendulous, 5–10 mm long, white to creamy-yellow and sweetly scented, flask-shaped, corolla lobes curving backwards. **Fruit** a roundish red fleshy berry up to 20 mm long, completely enclosed in an enlarged and inflated papery calyx drying red. **Wood** yellowish white with brownish markings, hard and moderately heavy.

Diagnostic features Evergreen; bark smooth and grey to blackish; leaves very glossy dark green above; flowers scented and with recurved corolla lobes; fruit a red fleshy berry enclosed in an enlarged and inflated papery calyx drying red.

Flowering from July to November.
Fruiting from November to June.

Distribution From Ethiopia in the north to the Western Cape in the south.

Habitat Grows in forests, scrub forests, shady kloofs or on mountain slopes. Mostly in shade along mountain streams.

Economic value Leaves are browsed by stock and game (kudu, nyala, klipspringer and Sharpe's grysbok). In certain areas it is browsed to such an extent that the plants hardly ever get a chance to grow to their normal shape and size. It is popular with fruit-eating birds (Rameron pigeons, African green pigeons, louries,

Afrikaans	Swartbas
Northern Sotho	mohlatsane
Zulu	uManzimane
Botanical name	*Diospyros whyteana*
Family	Ebony Family (Ebenaceae)
National tree list no.	611

Name derivation *Diospyros* = 'divine pear', and *whyteana* = named after Alexander Whyte (1834–1908), a Scottish plant explorer and collector.

barbets and bulbuls) which open the papery calyx as soon as it starts to turn red to get at the fleshy red berries. The ripe red fruit is edible but with a bitter-sweet taste and therefore not very popular. The yellowish seeds can be roasted, ground and used as a substitute for coffee with an agreeable taste. A good furniture wood for making small household articles. It polishes well and furniture oil darkens the wood slightly. It makes excellent pick handles.

The bladder-nut makes an attractive garden subject with its neat habit, glossy dark green leaves and the masses of red fruit. It can be planted either as an accent plant or it can be grown as an attractive hedge that takes pruning well. Makes an attractive container plant for the patio but care must be taken not to let the soil dry out for long periods. A popular species for making bonsai for it is easy to style and the leaves reduce considerably in size. The root system is not aggressive.

Other uses An enema is made from the bark to treat impotency and infertility. An itchy rash on the skin is treated with an infusion of the leaf and root.

Cultivation Collect fruits from the tree and dry in the shade. Remove the seeds, soak them in hot water and leave overnight. Plant the next morning in seedling trays that are at least 60 mm deep and filled with a mixture of river sand and compost (1:1). Press the seeds into the mixture and cover with a layer of either fine sand or compost and keep moist. Seeds should start to germinate within 3–5 weeks. Germination tends to be erratic. Transplant the seedlings into nursery bags filled with a compost-rich mixture when they reach the two-leaf stage. It is fairly fast-growing, especially when young, with a growth rate of 500–800 mm per year. Protect the young plants from frost and cold winds for the first year. The bladder-nut can survive a long drought period and moderate frost, but it grows best if watered often during the growing season.

BRANDYBUSH

Description Mostly a shrub but sometimes a tree up to 4 m tall with an open crown. **Bark** on the young branches grey and covered with dense short hairs but smooth and dark grey on the older branches and stems. **Leaves** simple, alternate, grey to greyish green and finely hairy but paler green below, with a rounded tip, margin toothed, the leaf blade with 3 prominent veins from the leaf base. Leaf stalk 1–2 mm long. **Flowers** in branched heads, yellow, 10–15 mm in diameter, the sepals yellow, longer and wider than the petals. **Fruit** mostly 2-lobed, 6–8 mm in diameter, reddish-brown when mature. **Wood** with a light-coloured sapwood and a brown, fine-grained, hard heartwood.

Afrikaans	Wilderosyntjie
Northern Sotho	mothetlwa
Zulu	umHlwampunzi
Botanical name	*Grewia flava*
Family	Linden Family (Tiliaceae)
National tree list no.	459.1

Name derivation *Grewia* = named in honour of Nehemiah Grew (1641–1712), an English physician, and *flava* = yellow, in reference to the flower colour.

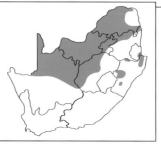

semi-arid areas during late spring and early summer when other food is scarce. The young leaves are more readily eaten than the mature ones. Larvae of the white-cloaked skipper (*Leucochitonea levubu*) and the spotted velvet skipper (*Abantis tettensis*) butterflies use this as a food plant.

Plant in groups of 5–10, scattered in camps where the soil is sandy. Water these plants once a week for up to five weeks or until the plants show signs of growing. It makes an attractive display in a shrubbery when in full flower. The root system is non-aggressive.

Diagnostic features Bark smooth, dark grey; leaves grey with fine hairs and short leaf stalk, with 3 veins from the leaf base; flowers yellow with sepals yellow and larger than the petals; fruit 1- or 2- lobed, reddish brown when mature.

Flowering from October to March.
Fruiting from December to April.

Distribution From Zambia in the north to the Northern Cape in the south.

Habitat Common in open deciduous woodland and Kalahari veld. Mostly on sandy soils. The heavier the soil, the more shrub-like the brandybushes.

Economic value The young shoots, leaves and fruit are relished by all domestic stock, game (giraffe, kudu, sable, nyala, grey duiker and steenbok) and birds (grey louries, helmeted guineafowl, black korhaan and various francolin species). A must in the garden to attract birds. It is considered an important fodder plant in the

Other uses The bark provides a strong fibre for rope. Beer is brewed from the ripe fruit and in certain areas fruit is still being used to distil a type of brandy or mampoer. The ripe fruits have a thin layer of sweet flesh and are edible. The fresh fruit contains 74.7 g/100 g of moisture and 29.8 mg/100 g vitamin C. Dried fruit can be ground to a meal and a porridge made from it. The dried fruit yields 63.8% sugar and 4% protein. The long, straight branches are popular for walking sticks. Bushmen use the thick, long branches to make their bows and the thinner ones for arrow shafts.

Cultivation Fresh seed must be cleaned and dried in the shade. Soak seed in hot water, leave overnight and sow the next morning in seedling trays filled with river sand. Cover the seeds 5 mm deep with river sand and keep moist. Germination is usually erratic, 50–70%. Seedlings should be planted out into black nursery bags when they reach the 2-leaf stage. Take care not to overwater. The brandybush can withstand drought and several degrees of frost. It is fairly slow growing with a growth rate of 400–500 mm per year.

BROOM CLUSTER FIG

Description An evergreen tree up to 35 m tall with a dense rounded crown with milky latex in all parts. **Bark** smooth and light grey. **Leaves** copper-coloured when young, simple, midrib and main veins very conspicuous on both surfaces, with a quilted appearance, margins wavy and irregularly toothed. Leaf stalk 30–40 mm long, furrowed on upper surface. Stipules enveloping the growth tips, thinly textured, 8–10 mm long, falling early. **Figs** borne in large clusters on long, branched stalks on the old wood or sometimes on the roots, roundish, 25–40 mm in diameter, reddish mottled with cream when ripe. **Wood** soft and without heartwood, grey-white, light (air-dry 450 kg/m³) and porous.

Afrikaans	Besemtrosvy
Northern Sotho	mogo-tshetlo
Zulu	umKhiwane
Botanical name	*Ficus sur*
Family	Fig Family (Moraceae)
National tree list no.	50

Name derivation *Ficus* = the classical name for the cultivated fig, and *sur* = named after the Sur area in Ethiopia.

blue (*Myrina dermaptera*) and the African map butterfly (*Cyrestis pantheus sublineatus*) feed on the leaves of this tree.

It can be planted in scattered groups near moist areas to provide shade for livestock. Protect the young plants for the first season from animals browsing the leaves. The root system is aggressive and the broom cluster fig is not suitable for planting in the small garden or near the house, walls, swimming pools or pipes.

Diagnostic features Milky latex in all parts; leaf margin wavy and irregularly toothed; stipules enveloping the growth tips; figs borne in large clusters on branched stalks.

Flowering and fruiting from September to March.

Distribution From the Yemen in the north to the Western Cape in the south.

Habitat Forests and in riverine bush or wooded grassland, always in moist spots.

Economic value Leaves are eaten by cattle and sometimes by elephant, kudu, nyala and blue duiker. Fruits are a favourite with vervet and samango monkeys and baboons. The fallen fruit are eagerly eaten by bushpigs. Fruit-eating birds (African green pigeons, Cape parrots, Meyer's parrots, brown-headed parrots, Knysna, grey and purple-crested louries) and fruit-eating bats relish the ripe fruit. It is a valuable shade tree on the farm for cattle and other stock. One of the most successful trees for attracting fruit-eating birds. The wood is of little commercial value but can be used as a general timber on the farm. The larvae of the common fig tree butterfly (*Myrina silenus ficedula*), lesser fig tree

Other uses The ripe figs are edible, with a sweetish, white to pink pulp but are nearly always infested by insects. These can easily be flicked off the fruit. Jam can be made from the figs when they turn pink or reddish but while the flesh is still firm. Dry pieces of wood from this tree are used as the base wood when making fire with sticks by friction and are carried on the person. The upper or drill-stick is usually from one of the raisin bush species. Mortars for grinding flour and the major part of drums are made from this wood. A good-quality rope can be made from the inner bark. Lung and throat problems are treated with the milky latex. A decoction of the root is administered to a cow with a retained placenta to assist its expulsion.

Cultivation The seed is very fine. After 15–30 days seed shows a germination percentage of 20–40%. The easiest and fastest way to propagate this tree is either by cuttings or by truncheons. Stem cuttings can be treated with a root-stimulating hormone for better results. Plant the cuttings in river sand and keep moist. When the cuttings are ready, transplant them into black nursery bags filled with a mixture of river sand and compost (3:1). If truncheons are used (stem diameter 100–150 mm), place some river sand in the bottom of the hole to keep it from rotting and assist in root formation. The broom cluster fig is not resistant to cold. In areas with frost it should be planted in a protected spot. A fast-growing species with a growth rate of 1 m per year. Can be grown in full sun but grows best in shade and sandy soils.

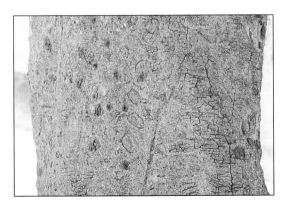

BROWN IVORY

Description A semi-deciduous to evergreen tree up to 20 m tall with a dense roundish crown. **Bark** smooth and grey-green on young twigs, with conspicuous lenticels, older branches and stems dark grey cracking into small rectangular pieces. **Leaves** simple, opposite to sub-opposite, tips blunt or sometimes rounded, the base broadly tapering, thinly textured and glossy dark green above and lighter below, margins smooth, midrib and veins yellowish and the secondary veins sunken on the upper surface but raised on the lower, in a herring bone pattern ending at the margin. Leaf stalks 4–6 mm long, with a prominent groove on the upper side. **Flowers** in small clusters in the axils of the leaves, yellowish green, 4–5 mm in diameter. **Fruit** fleshy, blue-green turning yellow when mature, up to 20 x 8 mm. **Wood** with a pale brown sapwood and a hard, heavy (air-dry 992 kg/m³), fine-grained, yellow-brown heartwood with a reddish tinge.

Afrikaans	Bruin-ivoor
Northern Sotho	mogokgomo
Zulu	uMumu
Botanical name	*Berchemia discolor*
Family	Dogwood Family (Rhamnaceae)
National tree list no.	449

Name derivation *Berchemia* = named after M. Berchem, a French botanist, and *discolor* = the upper and lower surfaces are of a different colour.

Diagnostic features Lenticels conspicuous; bark cracking into small rectangular pieces; leaves mostly opposite, secondary veins yellowish, parallel and ending at the leaf margin, leaf stalk grooved above; flowers yellowish green; fruit yellow when mature.

Flowering from October to January.
Fruiting from January to July.

Distribution From Ethiopia in the north to KwaZulu-Natal in the south.

Habitat On well-drained soils in woodlands and along drainage lines.

Economic value A valuable shade tree in the warmer areas. Many fruits are dropped by birds and monkeys during the fruiting period and then eaten by various animals from small mammals and birds to larger game. Fruits are eaten by baboons, vervet monkeys and various fruit-eating birds, especially louries, pigeons, starlings, barbets and hornbills. Leaves and young branches are eaten by elephant, giraffe, kudu, bushbuck, impala and Damara dik-dik. Humans find the sweet date-like taste quite pleasant. The sugar content of the pulp is as high as 30%. The seeds taste like walnuts. Large quantities of the fruit are collected, dried and stored for later use by the people in the lowveld areas. The ripe fruits are sometimes pounded into a cake and dried. The vitamin C content of the pulp is 65 mg/100 gram. A strong alcoholic drink is distilled from this fruit. It has an excellent wood for making furniture such as tables, chairs and benches.

Plant groups of this tree in protected areas in well-drained soil. Water the young trees during the first year. A good tree to plant at or near watering points. It makes a splendid shade tree. The roots are not aggressive.

Other uses This tree will prove to be a challenge to anyone trying to make a bonsai from it. If successful, this is one of the best indigenous trees for this form of art.

Cultivation Fresh seed can be sown in flat seedling trays filled with a mixture of river sand and compost (5:1). Germination is usually good, between 80–100%. Transplant the seedlings into black nursery bags filled with a well-drained mixture of river sand, loam and compost (2:2:1). The growth rate is relatively fast, 600–800 mm per year. Brown ivory is not resistant to frost and/or cold wind. Clearly a tree for the frost-free areas. It is drought-resistant.

BUFFALO THORN

Description A deciduous tree up to 17 m tall with an open, round to spreading crown. **Bark** on the young branches smooth and reddish brown but rough, dark grey to brown and longitudinally fissured on the older branches and stems. Spines paired, one hooked, 5–7 mm long and the other straight, 10–20 mm long, some forms with hardly any spines. **Leaves** alternate, simple, smooth and shiny, up to 70 x 50 mm, toothed margin in the upper two-thirds, leafbase asymmetrically round. **Flowers** in clusters in the leaf axils, yellowish green, with short flower stalks. **Fruit** a round, reddish brown, glossy drupe. Trees with two types of fruit, the small type 7–10 mm in diameter and the large type 15–25 mm in diameter, all often remaining on the tree after the leaves have fallen. **Wood** with a pale yellow brown sapwood, the heartwood light brown tinged red, heavy (air-dry 880 kg/m^3), hard and often with a twisted grain.

Afrikaans	Blinkblaar-wag-'n-bietjie
Northern Sotho	mokgalô
Zulu	umLahlankosi
Botanical name	*Ziziphus mucronata* subs. *mucronata*
Family	Dogwood Family (*Rhamnaceae*)
National tree list no.	447

Name derivation *Ziziphus* = Latinised version of the Arabic vernacular name 'zizouf' for *Ziziphus jujuba*, and *mucronata* = refers to the shape of the leaf tip.

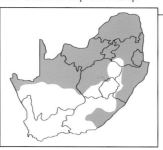

Diagnostic features Leaves glossy, three veins from the leaf base, margin toothed for the upper two-thirds; spines paired, the one straight and the other hooked; leaf base asymmetric; fruit glossy reddish brown.

Flowering from October to April.
Fruiting from February to August.

Distribution From Arabia in the north to the Western Cape in the south.

Habitat Found under nearly all ecological conditions. Occurs mostly in woodland and wooded grassland.

Economic value A valuable fodder tree, especially in the drier areas. Stock and game (giraffe, eland, kudu, sable, black wildebeest, nyala, impala, klipspringer, springbok, Sharpe's grysbok, steenbok, Damara dik-dik and warthog) relish the highly nutritious leaves and fruit. Many species of birds (guineafowl, francolins, Meyer's parrots, purple-crested and grey louries and Burchell's coucal) eat the fruit. The flowers attract masses of insects and they in turn attract various insect-eating birds. Larvae of the black pie (*Tuxentius melaena*), common dotted blue (*Tarucus sybaris sybaris*), Hintza pie (*Zintha hintza*) and the white pie (*Tuxentius calice calice*) butterflies feed on the leaves. Beekeepers consider this a valuable source of nectar.

A useful species to plant as a hedge around camps. It forms an impenetrable hedge for at least 10 years before the crown is too high off the ground to act as a barrier. However, it would still be used as a fodder tree. Trees can also be planted as scattered groups of 10–20 individuals to act initially as fodder trees and protection of small game and later as shade trees for cattle and game. Young trees must be protected against cattle eating the leaves and thus retarding the growth. It is also a useful tree to plant as a background plant. This tree is a must for the bird garden. The root system is not aggressive.

Other uses The fruit is edible, with a thin meal-like flesh and a sweetish taste. It can be dried and ground to a meal and cooked to produce a kind of porridge. Seeds can be roasted, crushed and used as a coffee substitute. The young leaves can be cooked and eaten as spinach, not very palatable though, but nutritious. The bark contains 12–15% tannin. The powdered leaf and bark in water is taken as an emetic for chest troubles. A poultice of the leaves is applied to septic swellings of the skin. An infusion of the root is taken for dysentery. The wood is hard and makes good fuel.

Cultivation Grows easily from seed, with a minimum of 75% germination. Between 700 and 1 100 fruits weigh 1 kg. Sow in seedling trays in pure river sand. Cover the seed with a thin layer of river sand and keep moist. Seeds usually germinate in 2–3 weeks. Seedlings have long taproots and care should be taken not to damage these while they are being transplanted into black nursery bags. Seedlings transplant easily though. A fast-growing tree with a growth rate of 4–6 m in four years. A very hardy species, resistant to both frost and drought.

A protected tree in the Free State.

BUSHMAN'S TEA

Description An evergreen tree up to 25 m tall with a slender and upright canopy, resembling a bluegum tree from a distance. **Bark** on the young branches smooth and green to pinkish but smooth, grey and sometimes rough and darker on older branches and stems. **Leaves** simple, opposite, elliptic to oblong, erect or pendulous, glossy green above but lighter below, leathery and stiff tapering to both ends, the margin evenly toothed, midrib level with the leaf blade on the upper surface but conspicuously raised on the undersurface. Leaf stalk pinkish, 3–10 mm long. **Flowers** pale greenish yellow to lemon-yellow, in dense branched axillary clusters, margins of petals deeply cut in. **Fruit** a smooth and narrow three-lobed capsule, up to 10 x 3 mm, brown when mature, splitting to release narrowly winged reddish seeds. **Wood** with no distinct difference between sapwood and heartwood, pale to golden brown, moderately heavy (air-dry 800 kg/m³), hard and strong, with a very fine texture.

Diagnostic features Canopy slender and upright; bark grey and smooth; leaves opposite with evenly toothed margins, midrib level with leaf blade on upper surface but raised on lower surface; flowers in dense branched clusters; fruit a narrow three-lobed capsule; seeds with narrow wings.

Flowering from April to June.
Fruiting from June to August.

Distribution From Arabia in the north to the Eastern Cape in the south.

Habitat Edges of evergreen forests, woodlands and rocky wooded hillsides.

Economic value Bushman's tea can be planted in a plantation format. The trees react well to pruning and produce long, straight stems in only a few years. This will provide durable poles and furniture wood. Leaves are not known to be eaten by livestock or game. It can be grown as an effective windbreak and can be planted

Afrikaans	Boesmanstee
Northern Sotho	mohlatse
Zulu	umHlwazi
Botanical name	*Catha edulis*
Family	Stafftree Family (Celastraceae)
National tree list no.	404

Name derivation *Catha* = based on the Arabic word 'khat', and *edulis* = edible, referring to the leaves.

along fences. In this way the trees can be harvested for poles when needed. The trees sprout vigorously after cutting, much the same way as bluegum trees. The borer-proof wood is strong, pliable and finishes very smoothly. It is commonly used for rafters, building posts and poles for general purposes on the farm. Furniture from this wood is durable and has a beautiful yellowish lustre. It has been used for cabinet making in the past. Wood pulp made from Bushman's tea produces a high-quality paper. The wood is popular for small household articles such as handles for pots and pans, rolling pins, forks and spoons, handles for hammers and chisels and for rulers. The larvae of the foxy charaxes (*Charaxes jasius saturnus*) feed on the leaves. The root system is non-aggressive.

Other uses Preparations made from leaves and roots are used as a remedy for influenza and the treatment of coughs, asthma and other chest complaints. The root is used for stomach troubles, and an infusion is taken orally to treat boils and infertility in men. In the northern countries in Africa the leaves are brewed as a tea, the dried leaves smoked and green leaves chewed as a stimulant and produce an artificial feeling of wakefulness, well-being and mental alertness. The plant has a narcotic-stimulating effect much like cocaine. The actual long-term effect is harmful. This custom has not been verified for southern Africa.

Cultivation The easiest way to propagate Bushman's tea is by root cuttings and root suckers. A fairly fast-growing species, up to 2 m per year under garden conditions but as slow as 1 m under field conditions. It is difficult to obtain viable seeds, most of which are infested with small beetles. Seed should be sown in seedling trays filled with a mixture of river sand and compost (4:1). Cover the seed with a thin layer of sand and keep moist. Germination is erratic, the first seedlings appearing after two weeks and the last ones usually six weeks later. Seedlings transplant easily. Transplant into nursery bags and plant out into the garden or veld when 200 mm high.

CAMEL'S FOOT

Description An evergreen to semi-deciduous tree up to 12 m tall with a roundish open crown. **Bark** on young branches covered with rusty hairs but rough and longitudinally fissured on older branches and stems. **Leaves** alternate, simple, leaf blade 50–150 x 60–160 mm, deeply bilobed, with 5 or 6 secondary veins radiating from the base of each lobe, underside with conspicuous net veining. Leaf stalk 20–40 mm long and hairy. **Inflorescences** with male (50–190 mm long) and female (20–70 mm long) on separate trees. **Flowers** with calyx 8–15 mm long covered with rusty hairs, petals crisped and white to pinkish, 12–20 mm long. **Pods** woody, thick and non-splitting, 130–220 x 30–70 mm, seeds embedded in the pulp, stipe 2–3 mm long. **Wood** soft and moderately heavy (air-dry 752 kg/m^3) without a distinctive heartwood, darkening in colour from pale brown at outer edge to dark brown with a reddish tinge in the centre.

Afrikaans	Kameelspoor
Northern Sotho	mukolokote
Botanical name	*Piliostigma thonningii*
Family	Pod-bearing Family (Fabaceae)
National tree list no.	209

Name derivation *Piliostigma* = cap-like stigma, and *thonningii* = commemorates Peter Thonning (1775–1848), a Danish botanist .

Diagnostic features Bark rough; young branches with rusty hairs; leaf stalk 20–40 mm long, leaf blade bilobed, with prominent venation underneath; petals white to pinkish; pods thickly woody and broad, with seeds embedded in pulp.

Flowering from November to April.
Fruiting from June to September.

Distribution From the Sudan in the north to Mpumalanga in the south.

Habitat Grows in open woodland and wooded grassland of medium to low altitudes. Often on stream banks. Prefers sandy soils.

Economic value The leaves are eaten by cattle and game (elephant, kudu). The young pods are eagerly eaten by baboons. The large, flat pods are valuable fodder for stock. Many farmers in the lowveld collect the pods and grind them into a meal to feed their cattle during the dry winter months. The tough inner bark produces a rope of good quality. The macerated and boiled bark contains 18–20% tannin and is used for tanning leather, producing a red-brown colour. The pods and seeds produce a blue dye, giving a blackish colour to the leather. Larvae of the bushveld charaxes (*Charaxes achaemenes achaemenes*) feed on the leaves.

In frost-free areas the camel's foot makes an interesting shade tree for the garden. The interesting growth habit, large bi-lobed leaves and the broad pods all add to the uniqueness of this tree. The roots are not aggressive and it can be planted close to paving and walkways.

Other uses The pulp and seeds are edible. The young leaves can be chewed to relieve thirst. The root heated in fat can be applied as a poultice over the spleen to relieve pain in that area. Extracts made from the roots are used to kill hookworms. An infusion made from roots is used to treat ketosis in cattle. A concentrated infusion of the bark is used to treat inflamed gums. A cold infusion made from the bark is used as an anti-diarrhoeic, anti-emetic and an anti-dysenteric. A decoction made from root, bark and leaves is used to ease coughs. The unripe pod can be used as a substitute for soap.

Cultivation Easily grown from seed. Seeds should be removed from the dry pods by breaking them with a hammer. Soak seeds overnight in hot water and plant the next morning in seedling trays filled with river sand. Press the seeds into the sand so that they are flush with the surface, cover with a thin layer of sand and keep moist. The first seedlings should appear approximately 5–10 days after sowing. Transplant the seedlings when the first adult leaves appear, first into nursery bags, and eventually into open soil. Fill the bags with a mixture of river sand, loam and compost (2:1:1). Young plants must be planted out after only one season in the bag. This species is not suitable for areas that receive frost. In cold areas without frost it will have a slow growth rate. The camel's foot can withstand prolonged periods of drought. The growth rate is relatively slow, up to 600 mm per year.

A protected tree in South Africa.

CAMEL THORN

Description An evergreen to semi-deciduous tree up to 20 m tall with a wide spreading crown and the young branches prominently zig-zagged. **Bark** on the young branchlets smooth and reddish brown but dark brown to grey and deeply furrowed on the older branches and stems. Thorns in pairs, almost straight, up to 60 mm long, usually swollen and fused together at the base into a large 'ant-gall'. **Leaves** twice-compound, with 2–5 pairs of pinnae each bearing 8–15 pairs of leaflets. **Flowers** in a round, bright golden-yellow, sweetly scented inflorescence up to 15 mm in diameter. **Fruit** non-splitting, hard, very broad and curved, up to 130 x 70 mm, covered with grey velvety hairs, spongy within. **Wood** with a very thin light-coloured sapwood and a dark reddish brown, hard and heavy (1 144 kg/m³) heartwood.

Afrikaans	Kameeldoring
Northern Sotho	mogôtlhô
Botanical name	*Acacia erioloba*
Family	Pod-bearing Family (Fabaceae)
National tree list no.	168

Name derivation *Acacia* = from the Greek word 'akis' meaning a point or a barb, *erio* = woolly, referring to the covering of the fruit, and *loba* = lobe, referring to the fruit.

Diagnostic features Older bark deeply fissured; stout spines that are often basally enlarged into 'ant-galls'; leaflets with prominent venation; bright yellow flowers; pods broad and curved, covered with dense grey velvety hairs.

Flowering from July to September.
Fruiting from December to April.

Distribution From Angola and Zambia in the north to the Northern Cape in the south.

Habitat Dry woodland along dry river beds where underground water is present and on sandy loams and deep Kalahari sand.

Economic value Livestock and game browse the leaves but the sweetish and astringent pods are excellent fodder (elephant, giraffe, eland, kudu, gemsbok and grey duiker) and are highly nutritious. Pods are sometimes milled and given as fodder during periods of drought. It is said that cows feeding on the pods show an increase in milk production. Young leaves and pods may cause prussic acid poisoning. Pods have 11.4% crude protein. Seed yields up to 33% crude protein and 3.5% of bright orange fat. The shell of the pod yields 1.2% fat and has a herb-like odour.

The camel thorn is one of the best shade trees in the drier areas and provides shade for man and animal alike during the hot summer months. It is a popular firewood resulting in very hot coals lasting a long time. Larvae of the topaz blue butterfly (*Azanus jesous*) feed on the inflorescences.

Farmers can plant groups of up to 15 trees in a suitable habitat to provide fodder, protection and shade to animals. It makes an attractive and interesting garden tree, with birds nesting in it from an early stage. The root system is, however, rather aggressive and the tree should not be planted close to buildings and paving.

Other uses The gum is eaten by man, animals and birds. The stripped and pounded inner bark produces a good-quality rope. Burnt and powdered bark is used as a remedy for headaches. Dried and powdered pods are used to treat discharging and infected ears. The roasted seed can be used as a substitute for coffee.

Cultivation Seed is frequently destroyed by beetles and other insects but sound seed is easily obtainable. Seed must be soaked in boiled water and left overnight. The next morning, place it on river sand and cover lightly with sand. Germination tends to be erratic. Seedlings should be planted out when they are no taller than 40 mm. Later the long taproot makes it difficult to transplant. Trees coppice and sucker freely. A relatively slow grower with a growth rate between 300 and 500 mm per year. Well adapted to very dry and heavy frost conditions.

It is a protected tree in South Africa.

CAMPHOR BUSH

Description Evergreen shrub or tree up to 9 m tall with a dense crown and drooping branches. **Bark** on young branches very velvety and pale cream to white but brownish grey and furrowed lengthwise on the older branches and stems. **Leaves** simple, alternate, elliptic, up to 150 x 40 mm, leathery, green to grey-green above but velvety and grey underneath, aromatic, the crushed leaf smelling of camphor, margin smooth or sometimes with small teeth, the venation prominent underneath. Leaf stalk 1–7 mm long. **Inflorescence** a branched spray up to 90 mm long, covered in whitish woolly hairs, borne at the end of branches, flowerheads thistle-like, with cream- coloured flowers in groups of 3–5 and 8–12 mm long. Male and female flowers on separate trees. **Fruit** a nutlet covered in long white woolly hairs. **Wood** with a thin, light brown sapwood and a greyish brown heartwood, close-grained and hard, heavy.

Afrikaans	Kanferbos
Northern Sotho	sefahla
Zulu	iGqeba-elimhlophe
Botanical name	*Tarchonanthus camphoratus*
Family	Daisy Family (Asteraceae)
National tree list no.	733

Name derivation *Tarcho* = based on the Arabic name 'Tarchon', and *-nanthus* = the Greek name 'anthos' meaning flower, and *camphoratus* = like the smell of camphor.

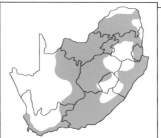

Diagnostic features All parts smell strongly of camphor; bark brownish grey, rough; leaves aromatic, leathery, green above and greyish below; inflorescence a branched spray covered in whitish woolly hairs; flowerhead thistle-like; male and female flowers on separate trees; fruit a nutlet covered in long woolly hairs.

Flowering mainly from March to June.
Fruiting from June to September.

Distribution Widespread from Somalia in the north to the Western Cape in the south.

Habitat Occupies a wide variety of habitats, from Kalahari veld, various woodland types, wooded grassland to montane thicket. Grows from sea-level to an altitude of 1 800 m. Where this tree occurs in extensive stands it is regarded as an indicator of Kalahari type soils.

Economic value The leaves are palatable and domestic stock browse them from the tree as well as from the ground where they fall. A valuable fodder tree, especially in the more arid areas. The leaves can taint milk if the animal consumes large quantities. Game (giraffe, eland, kudu, gemsbok, sable, black wildebeest, nyala, impala, springbok and grey duiker) also utilise this tree. In arid and semi-arid areas, poles from the tree make long-lasting fence posts as they are termite-proof. A good fuel that burns even if it is semi-dry.

Makes a worthy garden subject and can be planted for its bark, bicoloured foliage and general shape of the plant. Camphor bushes can be planted in scattered groups in camps to provide fodder. Because of its soil-binding ability, it can be used successfully to combat erosion. Plant trees in areas directly above gully erosion as well as in the eroded areas. It has a rather aggressive root system. A favourite species for making bonsai.

Other uses The fine-grained wood can be used for musical instruments and cabinet work. The green branches are burnt and the smoke inhaled to cure blocked sinuses and headaches. A hot poultice of the leaves is applied to the chest for asthma and other chest problems. A hot ointment is rubbed on for the relief of chilblains. Tea is made from the leaves and is a good cure for stomach ache. Makes excellent walking-sticks.

Cultivation Seed germinates within 8 weeks after sowing. Usually only 30–40% of the seedlings survive. Seedlings transplant well. It can also be grown from cuttings. Take cuttings from the soft wood and treat with a root-stimulating hormone before planting. It has a moderate growth rate, 600–800 mm per year. One of the few plants that can tolerate sea-breezes and withstand severe frost and drought.

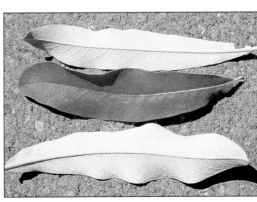

CAPE ASH

Description An evergreen tree up to 20 m tall with a roundish crown. **Bark** various shades of grey, smooth with the second year branches having conspicuous white lenticels and marked by old leaf scars. **Leaves** drooping, spirally arranged, compound, with 3–7 pairs of leaflets plus a terminal leaflet, glossy dark green above and lighter underneath, the margins smooth and sometimes wavy. **Flowers** in loose sprays at the tips of the branches, sweetly scented, small and white, the male and female flowers on different trees. **Fruit** almost spherical, fleshy (coastal plants having more fleshy fruit), red when mature, with a whitish flesh. **Wood** without a clear distinction between sapwood and heartwood, soft, pale brown to light reddish brown, with an even grain and light (air-dry 592 kg/m^3).

Afrikaans	Essenhout
Northern Sotho	mmidibidibi
Zulu	umNyamathi
Botanical name	*Ekebergia capensis*
Family	Mahogany Family (Meliaceae)
National tree list no.	298

Name derivation *Ekebergia* = named in honour of Captain Carl Gustaf Ekeberg (1716–1784), and *capensis* = from the Cape.

nyala eat the fallen fruit underneath the tree. A useful tree to attract fruit-eating birds (Knysna and purple-crested louries, barbets, hornbills, bulbuls and mousebirds). Larvae of the white-barred charaxes (*Charaxes brutus natalensis*) feed on the leaves of the Cape ash.

A worthwhile tree to plant for shade, fodder and a must in the garden to attract birds. A very successful street tree and it is planted along streets in various towns throughout South Africa. The shape and size of this tree makes it ideal for a park. The Cape ash has a non-aggressive root system. Plant it in suitable spots, especially near or at waterpoints. Protect young trees for the first two years from cattle and game.

Diagnostic features Bark grey, smooth; young twigs with prominent leaf scars and lenticels; leaves compound, with 3–7 pairs of leaflets and ending in a leaflet; male and female flowers on different trees; fruit a fleshy red berry.

Flowering from September to December.
Fruiting from November to April.

Distribution From Ethiopia in the north to the Western Cape in the south.

Habitat Mostly evergreen woodland, riverine, coastal sandveld or montane forests above 1 200 m altitude. Always in well-drained soil.

Economic value A good furniture and panelling wood. When cut, the wood must be treated with a 10% solution of zinc chloride to protect it against insects. It makes a good general timber, especially for beams. Can be used successfully as a street tree or shade tree in parking lots. Domestic stock and game (kudu, nyala, bushbuck) readily browse the fresh and the fallen leaves, especially during times of drought. Baboons, vervet and samango monkeys, bushpig, bushbuck and

Other uses The bark contains 7.23% tannin and is used for tanning leather. The bark is also used as an emetic and in the treatment of dysentery. The leaves are used as a remedy for intestinal worms. A decoction of the root is used for a chronic cough and taken orally for the relief of headaches.

Cultivation Fresh seed germinates in 4–8 weeks, but the fleshy part must be removed from the seed. If seeds are collected on the ground beneath the trees, the germination is usually 40–50% but it can be as high as 90% if collected off the trees (October). About 6 000 seeds make up one kilogram. Sow the seed during October and November in flat seedling trays filled with a mixture of river sand and compost (5:2) and cover with sand not deeper than 5 mm and keep moist. It is best to transplant seedlings when they are 100–150 mm tall. The Cape ash can also be propagated from cuttings. A fast-growing species with a growth rate of up to 1 m per year.

It can tolerate light drought conditions and very light frost but is sensitive to heavy frost and grows best if given lots of water.

A protected tree in South Africa.

CAPE BEECH

Description An evergreen tree up to 20 m tall with a dense narrow to spreading crown. **Bark** on the square, thick, soft young branches smooth and pinkish grey with raised corky dots (lenticels) but grey-brown, rough, thickly corky and fissured on the older branches and stems. **Leaves** alternate, simple, clustered towards the ends of branchlets and thickly textured with light-coloured gland dots visible when held against the light, dark green, the midrib flat above and prominent on the lower surface, margin smooth and rolled under, young leaves and twigs purplish. Leaf stalk purplish, grooved above, up to 15 mm long. **Flowers** in dense clusters in the leaf axils and above leaf scars below the leaves, greenish white. **Fruit** clustered close to the stems, a round purple berry up to 5 mm in diameter. **Wood** hard, pinkish brown, with a reticulate texture and moderately heavy (air-dry 737 kg/m^3).

Afrikaans	Kaapse boekenhout
Northern Sotho	mogônô
Zulu	isiCalabi
Botanical name	*Rapanea melanophloeos*
Family	Myrsine Family (Myrsinaceae)
National tree list no.	578

Name derivation *Rapanea* = from 'la Rapane' the French name for a species in Guinea, and *melanophloeos* = black bark.

Diagnostic features Evergreen; young branches and leaves pinkish; leaves clustered towards ends of branches, thickly textured, with gland dots in leaves, leaf stalk purplish and grooved above; flowers in clusters mostly below the leaves; fruit purple and clustered close to the stems.

Flowering from May to August.
Fruiting from August to March.

Distribution From Zambia in the north to the Western Cape in the south.

Habitat In all types of forest and evergreen scrub and in woodland on mountain slopes and wooded montane grassland.

Economic value The flowers attract many insect species and they in turn many insect-eating birds. A must in the garden to attract birds. The ripe fruits are eaten by birds (crested guineafowl, African green pigeons, Rameron pigeons, Knysna and purple-crested louries and barbets), baboons, samango and vervet monkeys and bushpigs. A must for the game farm. Wood very popular for making furniture, especially dining room tables and chairs. The reticulated effect of the wood gives a beautiful texture to the furniture. Parquet floors made of Cape beech are still in demand. The texture of the wood makes it popular for cabinet work and panelling. For the past 15 years, more and more violins and other musical instruments have been manufactured from Cape beech. It gives a similar quality of sound to those made from European woods.

Cape beech trees can be planted in high rainfall areas in a plantation as a long-term project. Remember to clean the stems of the plants from an early stage to force the plants to form a single, straight stem. It is also a neat small tree to use as an accent plant on the lawn. Plant a few Cape beech trees in the garden to attract insects and birds. An ideal tree for the smaller garden as it has a non-aggressive root system.

Other uses A decoction of the bark is used as an expectorant and an emetic. Pieces of bark are chewed or dried and powdered to treat sore throats and wounds. The bark contains 12–15% tannin.

Cultivation The Cape beech grows easily from seed. Collect the purple fleshy fruit from the trees and dry in the shade. Sow in seedling trays filled with seedling mix or a mixture of river sand and compost (1:1). Cover the seed lightly with either fine compost or river sand and keep moist. Germination is usually between 60–80%. Transplant the seedlings into nursery bags when they reach the 2-leaf stage. Seedlings and young plants transplant easily. The growth rate is moderate, up to 600 mm per year. It can withstand moderate drought and a fair degree of frost. It grows very well in shade and full sun and is tolerant of sea winds.

CAPE CHESTNUT

Description Depending on the habitat, it is an evergreen to deciduous tree up to 25 m tall with a roundish dense canopy. **Bark** on the young branches hairy but smooth and light to dark grey on older branches and stems. **Leaves** opposite, simple, shiny and dark green above but lighter below, with a smooth margin, the lateral veins running parallel to one another and nearly at right angles to the midrib, venation and midrib conspicuous beneath, leaf blade with prominent scattered gland dots (visible as transparent dots if the leaf is held to the light), with a strong citrus smell when crushed. **Flowers** in large (up to 150 mm long) and branched sprays at the tips of the branches, light to dark pink with 5 petals and 5 petal-like staminodes spotted with deep maroon glands, staminodes longer than the petals, stamens the same length as the petals and scented. **Fruit** a 5-lobed, strongly warty and splitting capsule up to 40 mm in diameter, splitting from below with the 5 valves remaining attached at the top of a central column, with large, shiny, black, angular seeds. **Wood** with little difference between sapwood and heartwood, whitish to pale yellow, sometimes with brown markings, hard, tough and moderately heavy (700–800 kg/m³).

Afrikaans	Wildekastaiing
Northern Sotho	mookêlêla
Zulu	umBhaba
Botanical name	*Calodendrum capense*
Family	Citrus Family (Rutaceae)
National tree list no.	256

Name derivation *Calodendrum* = from the Greek word 'kalos' meaning beautiful, *dendron* = tree, and *capense* = from the Cape.

Diagnostic features Bark smooth and grey; leaves with scattered gland dots, crushed leaves smelling like citrus; flowers pink with purple glands on petal-like staminodes; fruit a warty 5-lobed capsule splitting from the back.

Flowering erratic but mostly from July to March.
Fruiting from January to May.

Distribution From Kenya in the north to the Western Cape in the south.

Habitat Not restricted to any specific habitat. Trees in forests tend to have straight stems, sometimes buttressed, but trees growing in hot and dry valleys are low and gnarled with dark grey bark and small leaves and flowers.

Economic value The wood was, and still is in certain areas, very popular for furniture. The furniture is light-coloured and moderately heavy with a smooth finish. It is also used for cabinet work, turning and shelving. The tough and pliable wood is also popular for implement handles. A valuable shade tree on the farm, attracting various insects and butterfly species to the flowers with the instar larvae of the citrus swallowtail (*Papilio demodocus*), green banded swallowtail (*Papilio nireus lyaeus*) and emperor swallowtail (*Papilio ophidicephalus*) butterflies feeding on the leaves. Thirteen other insect species have been identified as feeders on the Cape chestnut. Fruits are eaten by samango and vervet monkeys but also by various bird species (Cape parrots, Rameron pigeons and cinnamon doves).

Suitable for street and parking lot plantings at the coast where it is evergreen. It makes an attractive specimen tree, especially on a lawn with the light grey bark, large leaves, masses of large pink flowers and knobbly fruit. It has a non-aggressive root system.

Other uses The crushed seeds can be boiled and soap made from the resultant oils.

Cultivation Easily cultivated from seed. There are ± 600 seeds per kilogram. Fresh seed can be sown in deep seedling trays filled with river sand. The seeds usually germinate in 10–40 days, with a 80–90% germination. Germination is sometimes very erratic if old seeds are sown. It can be propagated successfully from cuttings made from half-grown shoots but they must be treated with a root-stimulating hormone. Young plants transplant easily. In warm areas with a high rainfall the growth rate can be up to 850 mm per year. Trees grown from seed will flower only after 6–7 years, but those grown from cuttings after 4 years. Trees flower in profusion and this makes them conspicuous in forests, standing out in their pink colour and easily identifiable from kilometres away. Cape chestnut trees can withstand temperatures as low as -5°C. It can be planted in either light shade or in full sun. It likes deep soil with regular watering. Cut flowers are long-lasting in water.

CAPE HONEYSUCKLE

Description An evergreen scrambler to small tree up to 5 m tall with a roundish crown. **Bark** pale brown with many lenticels (corky spots) and longitudinally furrowed on old stems. **Leaves** opposite, unevenly compound, up to 130 mm long, with 2—5 pairs of leaflets, the terminal leaflet the largest, margins coarsely toothed, glossy green above but lighter below, with hairs in the axils of the veins. **Flowers** yellow, orange, red or salmon-pink, in long clusters of stalked flowers at the ends of the branches, calyx bell-shaped, the corolla up to 50 mm long, tubular, curved and widening at the mouth with rounded lobes, two-lobed with the upper lobe hooded and four protruding stamens. **Fruit** a narrow, flat pod-like capsule up to 130 mm long, splitting to release seeds with large papery wings.

Afrikaans	Kaapse kanferfoelie
Northern Sotho	morapa-sitsane
Zulu	uMunyane
Botanical name	*Tecomaria capensis*
Family	Jacaranda Family (Bignoniaceae)
National tree list no.	673.1

Name derivation *Tecomaria* = like the genus *Tecoma*, and *capensis* = from the Cape.

Diagnostic features Evergreen; many lenticels on bark; leaves compound with the terminal leaf the largest, hairs in axils of veins on underside; corolla tube curved and widening at tip, two-lobed with rounded lobes, stamens protruding; fruit a flattened capsule; seeds with papery wings.

Flowering from June to November.
Fruiting from October to February.

Distribution From Tanzania in the north to the Western Cape in the south.

Habitat It occurs on forest margins but more commonly along drainage lines in dense woodland. Grows well in moist areas and in dry scrub and woodland. Not restricted to any soil type.

Economic value Readily browsed by stock and game (kudu, nyala, bushbuck, klipspringer, red and grey duiker). Commonly planted as a hedge and reacts well to pruning. Pruning stimulates flowering. An attractive garden subject that can be used in a shrubbery and as a background plant. If it is pruned often it is ideal for the small garden. The trumpet-shaped flowers contain nectar rich in sugar thus attracting many species of birds, especially sunbirds. The darker red the colour, the more sunbirds it attracts. Birds with short bills (starlings and orioles) remove the flower tube to reach the nectar. Larvae of the common pea blue (*Leptotes pirithous*) and Barker's smokey blue (*Euchrysops barkeri*) butterflies use this as a food plant. The Cape honeysuckle can be planted scattered in camps in suitable spots as a fodder plant but also to give colour to the bush and to provide nectar for birds. The Cape honeysuckle does not have an aggressive root system.

Other uses The powdered bark is used for the treatment of fever, pneumonia and stomach troubles and is also rubbed on bleeding gums to promote coagulation of the blood. A decoction of the leaf is used for diarrhoea and for inflammation of the intestines.

Cultivation Easily grown from seed, however, cuttings are a more successful method. Ideally seed should be sown in early spring or summer. Rub the seed between the hands to remove the wings. Sow in a mixture of compost and river sand (1:1) and cover with a thin layer of sand and keep moist. Seedlings can be transplanted when they reach the 2-leaf stage. Cuttings should be taken from either semi-hardwood or hardwood during autumn after the plants have flowered. Make the cuttings 100 mm long, removing all leaves except for the top two and place in river sand. Cuttings should be misted at regular intervals to prevent drying out. Another successful method of propagation is layering. A branch can be bent over until it touches the ground, and covered with soil at this point. Within a few weeks roots will have formed at this point. Detach the rooted part from the mother plant and plant out into the garden or into black nursery bags. The Cape honeysuckle grows well in semi-shade or full sun. The growth rate is fast, at least 1 m per year. Plants usually flower in their second year. Frost-tender but can withstand temperatures as low as 0°C. It is surprisingly drought- and wind-resistant, thus ideal for coastal gardens. If planted in the garden, it must be pruned to attain a neat shape. Protect the young plants from frost during the first two winters.

There are three garden cultivars, namely 'Coccinea' with light red flowers on a bushy plant, 'Lutea' with bright yellow flowers on a spreading bush and 'Salmonii' with salmon-coloured flowers.

CHEESEWOOD

Description An evergreen tree up to 15 m tall in woodlands, but up to 30 m in forests, with a dense roundish to upright crown. **Bark** on young stems pale grey, on old stems grey, rough becoming somewhat flaky, seamed crosswise and with a faint liquorice smell and bitter taste. **Leaves** alternate, simple, obovate, the tip rounded to bluntly pointed, shiny dark green above and lighter green below, with prominent venation on the undersurface, margin characteristically semitranslucent, leaf blade tapering to the base. **Flowers** in dense terminal clusters, creamy-yellow to greenish, with a sweet honey scent. **Fruit** in dense clusters, capsules yellowish, 6–10 mm in diameter, with the two valves opening to show the sticky, resinous, red flesh around the seed. **Wood** off-white, with little difference between sapwood and heartwood.

Afrikaans	Kasuur
Northern Sotho	kgalagangwe
Zulu	umFusamvu
Botanical name	*Pittosporum viridiflorum*
Family	Pittosporum Family (Pittosporaceae)
National tree list no.	139

Name derivation *Pitta* = resin, *sporum* = seed, and *viridiflorum* = with green flowers.

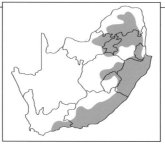

Diagnostic features Bark grey and smooth, seamed crosswise on older branches; liquorice smell and bitter taste; venation prominent on undersurface, margin semitranslucent; capsules 2-valved, with red resinous flesh around seed.

Flowering from September to December.
Fruiting from December to April.

Distribution From Arabia in the north to the Western Cape in the south. Eastwards through Madagascar to India.

Habitat Grows in forests to wooded grassland. Sometimes conspicuous along streambanks and riverine fringes. Full sun to light shade but always in well-drained soil.

Economic value Cattle, goats and especially game (kudu, nyala, bushbuck, klipspringer and grey duiker) browse the leaves. The smaller game species prefer to browse the young and tender leaves. Trees from the drier Karoo regions tend to be more palatable than those from the high rainfall areas in KwaZulu-Natal and the Northern Province. In the Karoo, cheesewood trees tend to have long stems with a roundish but dense crown providing much needed shade for goats, sheep and various game species. It is much valued here by farmers. Seeds are eagerly eaten by birds (red-eyed doves, turtle doves, Rameron pigeons, grey louries, pied barbets, crested barbets, black-collared barbets, bulbuls, redwinged starlings and Cape glossy starlings). Dropped fruits are eaten by crested francolins and guineafowl. The wood is still used for kitchen furniture and shelving.

Cheesewood is a must in any bird garden and a bonus on a game farm. Useful to plant as a hedge along driveways or along fence lines in camps or along drainage lines and at watering points. It makes a good garden subject with the glossy foliage, greenish yellow flowers and the mass of reddish fruit attracting many bird and insect species. It is a good subject to plant in the small garden as it does not have an aggressive root system. For those with space problems, it is ideal as a container plant on a patio.

Other uses The root or bark of cheesewood is dried, ground, and the powder taken in beer as an aphrodisiac. An infusion made from the roots is taken orally for chest complaints or used as an enema to treat dizziness. A decoction made from the bark is used as an emetic and sometimes as an enema for treating stomach complaints, malaria and other fever-related diseases.

Cultivation Easily grown from seed. Unparasitised seed is readily available from trees in the veld (± 6 000 seeds per kilogram). Sow seeds in flat seedling trays filled with a mixture of river sand and compost (3:2). Cover the seeds lightly with fine compost and keep moist. Seeds take 8–12 weeks to germinate, with a germination percentage of 80–90%. The seedlings grow relatively fast and must be planted out into nursery bags filled with a similar mixture when they reach the two-leaf stage. It may also be propagated by means of softwood or semi-hardwood cuttings. Use of a root-stimulating hormone is recommended. Seedlings and young plants transplant well. The growth rate is moderate, 400–700 mm per year. This tree is fairly frost- and drought-hardy and grows equally well in full sun or light shade. It prefers well-drained soils and does best with a reasonable amount of water.

COMMON CABBAGE TREE

Description An evergreen tree up to 18 m tall with long bare stems and a much branched roundish to cylindrical crown. **Bark** grey and smooth on young stems but yellowish grey and thickly corky on old stems. Stems becoming buttressed in old specimens.

Leaves crowded at the end of branches, palmately compound, leaf blade up to 700 mm in diameter, with 7–9 leaflets arising from the leaf stalk, leaflets glossy dark to light green, twice-compound, lobed and dissected, the margins mostly toothed, the midribs prominent. Leaf stalk 200–600 mm long, **Flowers** greenish yellow, 6–8 mm in diameter on branched inflorescences made up of 5–11 branches, with 5–9 thick spikes. **Fruit** fleshy and purple when mature, 6–8 mm in diameter. **Wood** with no distinction between sapwood and hardwood, whitish, light (air-dry 500 kg/m^3), soft and coarsely grained.

Diagnostic features Long bare stems with a much branched roundish crown; bark corky; leaves palmately (hand-shaped) compound, with leafstalk 200–600 mm long, leaflets 7–9 and deeply dissected and twice-compound; flowers in thick tightly packed spikes.

Flowering from April to May.
Fruiting from June to September.

Distribution From the Sudan in the north to the Western Cape in the south.

Habitat On rocky outcrops, wooded grassland, mountainsides and in montane forests.

Economic value The leaves are eagerly browsed by domestic stock and game, especially in predominantly shrubveld areas. Leaves of the cabbage tree are eaten throughout the year but more so during the dry winter months. It can be a valuable source of fodder and shade during the hot summer months. Roots and bark are eaten by black rhino, bushpigs and baboons. Leaves are eaten by elephant and kudu. Ripe fruits are eaten by many fruit-eating bird species, especially louries, bulbuls, starlings, barbets and mousebirds. A must for the bird garden.

Afrikaans	Gewone kiepersol
Northern Sotho	mosêtshê
Zulu	umSenge
Botanical name	*Cussonia spicata*
Family	Ivy Family (Araliaceae)
National tree list no.	564

Name derivation *Cussonia* = named after Pierre Cusson (1727–1783), Professor of Botany, University of Montpellier, and *spicata*, referring to the spike-like inflorescences.

The cabbage tree can be planted in suitable habitats in the veld, especially along drainage lines in hills or mountains and near watering points. It is a worthwhile garden subject and ideal as an accent plant with its typical shape and glossy dark green leaves. It is very successful as a container plant placed either along the edge of a swimming pool or on the patio. The common cabbage tree has an invasive root system and should not be planted close to buildings or paving.

Other uses The succulent roots are eaten for their moisture content, but the above-ground roots are slightly bitter and hard, the roots in the ground being softer, more crispy and more palatable. Pieces of the root are chewed, the liquid swallowed and the dry pieces of fibre spat out. Various decoctions are used to treat amenorrhoea, convulsions, heart pains, painful legs, madness, venereal disease and a painful uterus.

Cultivation Germinates easily from fresh seed sown in flat seedling trays filled with a mixture of sand and compost (1:1). Germination usually takes anything from 15–30 days and is initially erratic, most of the seed germinating in the third week. It can also be grown from truncheons but this method is not always very successful. Truncheons must be planted in a shady area. The cabbage tree has a fast growth rate and can grow up to 1 m per year. It is quite hardy and can survive Highveld conditions but does not like cold winds. It is quite drought-resistant but requires somewhat more water than the usual garden tree.

A protected tree in South Africa.

COMMON CORAL TREE

Description A deciduous tree up to 12 m tall with an open but sparse roundish crown. **Bark** on young branches smooth and greenish to pale grey-brown, but on older branches and stems pale grey-brown with lengthwise grooves and scattered hooked thorns. **Leaves** with 3 leaflets which are almost heartshaped, tips drawn out, with smooth margins. **Flowers** appearing before the leaves in compact, erect heads up to 90 mm long, bright red, the standard petal long and narrow enclosing the other petals. **Fruits** when mature, a black narrow curved pod up to 210 mm long and constricted between the seeds, splitting open to reveal the shiny orange to red seeds. **Wood** without a defined heartwood but whitish, soft and light (air-dry 350 kg/m³).

Afrikaans	Gewone koraalboom
Northern Sotho	mmalê
Zulu	umSinsi
Botanical name	*Erythrina lysistemon*
Family	Pod-bearing Family (Fabaceae)
National tree list no.	245

Name derivation *Erythrina* = from the Greek word 'erythros' meaning red, and *lysistemon* = with a loose stamen.

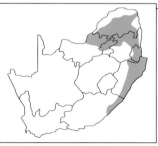

Diagnostic features Deciduous; hooked spines on stems; leaves compound, with 3 heart-shaped leaflets, leaf stalk up to 160 mm long and with small prickles, two glands at top of leaf stalk; flowers red, in compact erect heads, standard petal enclosing other petals and stamens.

Flowering from June to October, usually before the new leaves appear.

Fruiting from September to February.

Distribution From Tanzania in the north to the Eastern Cape in the south.

Habitat Covers a wide range of altitudes and habitats. Not restricted to any soil type but most specimens occur on well-drained soils.

Economic value The adaptability of this tree to various climatic and soil conditions and the high growth rate makes it suitable to plant on cattle or game farms to provide very necessary shade and shelter for animals during the hot summer months. Straight stems can be cut and planted as fence poles which will later root and grow, reducing maintenance of the fence. Many insect and bird species (various sunbird species) are attracted to the tree. The insects in turn attract many species of insect-eating birds. The brown-headed parrot feeds on the unripe seeds and nectar from the flowers, with grey louries feeding on the flower buds and flowers. Barbets and woodpeckers usually nest in these trees, because the soft fibrous wood is easy to excavate. Roots are unearthed and eaten by bushpigs and porcupines. Leaves and bark are eaten by elephant, black rhino, kudu, nyala, klipspringer and baboons. Vervet monkeys regard the flower buds as a delicacy and sometimes destroy more than 50% of the flowers on a tree. In spite of the leaves which drop during the winter months, it makes an attractive street tree delivering a stunning display of red flowers when no other trees are in flower. The common coral tree grows well in a container and if pruned often, will take on a much-branched shape and give a beautiful display of red flowers on the grey leafless branches. The root system is aggressive. Larvae of the giant charaxes butterfly (*Charaxes castor flavifasciatus*) feed on the leaves.

Other uses The bark is used for treating rheumatism and arthritis. Crushed leaves are applied to festering sores to remove inflammation. Open wounds are treated with powdered burnt bark to counteract inflammation. An infusion made from boiled or soaked bark is a remedy for toothache and an infusion from the leaves is used as eardrops to relieve earache.

Cultivation Easily grown from seed, cuttings or truncheons. Seed should be soaked in warm water, left overnight and the swollen seeds then sown in river sand the next morning. Seeds will usually germinate after 7–20 days. For the best results seed should be sown in spring. Cuttings are equally successful and can be made from semi-hardwood or hardwood. Place the cuttings in very coarse river sand to prevent rotting. Cuttings should also ideally be planted in late spring or during early summer. Large branches or truncheons can be cut off and placed in a mixture of river sand and compost. Spring or summer is the best time. The common coral tree can survive in areas with light frost. When planted in an area where frost is experienced, protect the young plant with either grass or any other suitable material. The growth rate is fast, up to 1.5 m per year for the first four years after which it slows down to about 1 m per year. Very drought-resistant.

COMMON HOOK THORN

Description A deciduous tree up to 14 m tall with an open roundish to spreading crown.
Bark on the young branches smooth and reddish brown but dark brown and rough on the older branches and stems, sometimes peeling in long strips. Thorns paired, recurved, brown, borne just below each node, mature branches nearly thornless.
Leaves twice-compound, drooping, up to 230 mm long, with 8–26 pairs of pinnae and 13–50 pairs of leaflets, prickles on lower surface of leaf stalks and rachis, sometimes distinctly blueish green. **Flowers** in spikes up to 140 mm long, creamy-white turning yellowish with age.
Fruit a straight, flat, brown, narrow, splitting pod up to 190 mm long and 13 mm broad produced in drooping clusters. **Wood** with a thin cream-coloured sapwood and a dark brown, hard and heavy (air-dry 980 kg/m³) heartwood.

Diagnostic features Young branches smooth and reddish brown; bark on stems rough; with paired recurved prickles; leaves with 8–26 pairs of pinnae and 13–50 pairs of leaflets; inflorescence a cream-coloured spike; pods thin.

Flowering from September to November, mainly October.

Fruiting from January to May.

Distribution From Botswana in the north to the Western Cape in the south.

Habitat Found in various habitat types including coastal scrub, mountain slopes, woodland, wooded grassland and along drainage lines.

Economic value The leaves, especially the young

Afrikaans	Gewone haakdoring
Northern Sotho	mositsana
Zulu	umTholo
Botanical name	*Acacia caffra*
Family	Pod-bearing Family (Fabaceae)
National tree list no.	162

Name derivation *Acacia* = from the Greek word 'akis' meaning a point or a barb, and *caffra* = from Kaffraria (Eastern Cape).

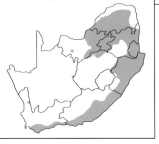

leaves, are relished by black rhino, giraffe, kudu, impala, reedbuck and grey duiker. Leaves and pods are eaten by livestock, especially in times of drought when farmers cut the lower branches for cattle to browse on. The hard wood makes good fence posts for it is termite and borer-proof. Small pieces of furniture made from this wood are durable, with a pleasing dark brown colour and satin lustre. The dry wood makes good fuel, with coals lasting for a long time. Larvae of the Van Son's playboy (*Deudorix vansoni*) and Amakosa rocksitter (*Durbania amakosa penningtoni*) butterflies use the seed pods of this tree.

This very decorative tree is an excellent garden subject, the open crown permitting grass to grow beneath it. One of the best indigenous trees to use for a bonsai. The common hook thorn has a rather aggressive root system.

Other uses In the Eastern Cape the wood is sought after for making tobacco pipes. The bark is sometimes used for tanning leather. Long and thin branches are pliable and used for making baskets. An infusion made from the bark is used for blood cleansing. Abdominal disorders in infants are treated with an enema made from leaves and milk.

Cultivation It is easily cultivated from seed. The seed can be soaked in hot water, left overnight and then sown directly into black nursery bags. Seedlings form a very long taproot, and should therefore be transplanted into larger bags as soon as they reach the two-leaf stage. It is relatively fast-growing, with a growth rate of 700–900 mm per year and reacts very well to pruning. The common hook thorn is frost and drought-resistant.

COMMON ROTHMANNIA

Description An evergreen tree up to 10 m tall in woodland but reaching 20 m in forests, with a dense roundish crown. **Bark** on the slightly angular young branches smooth and grey-brown but darker grey on older branches and stems, flaking in small blocks.

Afrikaans	Wildekatjiepiering
Northern Sotho	modulatshwene
Zulu	umPhazane-mkhulu
Botanical name	*Rothmannia capensis*
Family	Gardenia Family (Rubiaceae)
National tree list no.	693

Name derivation *Rothmannia* = named in honour of Georgius Rothman (1739–1778), and *capensis* = from the Cape.

Leaves crowded towards ends of branches, simple, opposite, with leaflike bracts between the leaf stalks (interpetiolar stipules), leaf blade up to 120 x 40 mm, leathery, dark glossy green, with prominent pockets in axils of veins on underside, margin smooth. Leaf stalk very short. **Flowers** singly in leaf axils, calyx lobes awl-shaped. Corolla bell-shaped, up to 80 mm long and 70 mm in diameter, white to light yellow with purplish red streaks and spots on inside of flower tube, with a strong sweet scent. **Fruit** round and up to 70 mm in diameter, with many flat seeds embedded in the pulp. **Wood** hard and close-grained, heavy, pale brown tinged reddish.

Diagnostic features Evergreen; leaves opposite with leaflike bracts between the leaf stalks, piths in axils of primary and secondary veins; flower large and bell-shaped, whitish with purple markings in throat, sweetly scented; fruit spherical and up to 70 mm in diameter.

Flowering from December to February.
Fruiting from January to October.

Distribution From the Northern Province southwards to the Western Cape.

Habitat Cliffs, rocky hillsides, wooded valleys and evergreen forests. It will grow in most soil types except clay soil. Plants in the dry and rocky woodlands of Sekhukuneland reach a maximum height of 2 m.

Economic value Pieces of wood that are large enough are used for engraving in the printing industry. The hard, pliable wood is popular for instrument handles but also for making various household utensils. It makes durable spoons for cooking and stirring sticks for porridge. The dry, dense wood gives a hot fire. The fruit is edible but not very tasty. Green and ripe fruit are eaten by baboons, vervet and samango monkeys. Dropped fruit in forests are immediately devoured by bushbuck, grey duiker and bushpig.

The glossy dark green leaves and the large whitish flowers make this an ideal specimen tree for the garden. The best effect is obtained when three or more trees are planted in a group on a lawn. Common rothmannia can be used most effectively as a shade tree in the small garden as it has a non-aggressive root system.

Other uses The powdered root is used for treating leprosy and rheumatism by rubbing it into tiny incisions made into the skin over the affected parts. Juice from the fruits is heated and applied to wounds and burns to speed the healing process.

Cultivation Collect the fruit when it turns brown and remove the seeds. Plant the seeds in a flat seedling tray filled with a mixture of river sand and compost (3:1) and keep moist. It is very important that the mixture never dries out. Seeds usually germinate from 14 days onwards. It grows well in light shade or in full sun. The growth rate is moderate, up to 700 mm per year. Some plants flower in their second year but most do so in the third year. It is frost and to some extent drought-resistant.

COMMON WILD FIG

Description An evergreen tree up to 15 m tall, with a rounded to spreading and dense crown. **Bark** on young branches hairy, with a stipular cap covering the growth tip, but smooth and grey on older branches and stems, the whole plant exuding a milky latex. **Leaves** simple, with a rounded base and a rounded to pointed tip, glossy dark green and leathery, margin smooth, venation prominent on both surfaces. **Fruit** a fig enclosing many small flowers, mostly hairy and borne in the leaf axils, reddish when ripe and only on the new growth. **Wood** moderately hard and whitish to pale brown, with a rough texture and light (air-dry 510 kg/m³).

Afrikaans	Gewone wurgvy
Northern Sotho	moumo
Zulu	umBombe
Botanical name	*Ficus thonningii*
Family	Fig Family (Moraceae)
National tree list no.	48

Name derivation *Ficus* = the classical Latin name for the cultivated fig, and *thonningii* = named in honour of Peter Thonning (1775–1848).

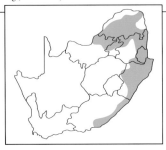

starlings, barbets and bulbuls. One of the best tree species to attract fruit-eating birds. The figs are edible but mostly infested with insects. A good quality jam can be cooked from the ripe fruit. Straight planks can be cut and used on the farm as general timber. Larvae of the lesser fig tree blue (*Myrina dermaptera*) and the common fig tree blue (*Myrina silenus ficedula*) butterflies feed on the leaves.

Plant groups of these trees in camps where shade is needed for stock and game or near watering points. It makes an ideal shade tree in a large garden or in a park. This tree has an aggressive root system and should not be planted in a small garden or near buildings, swimming pools or paths. It makes a successful container plant for the patio. Plants up to 4 m tall can be grown in containers. Ideal for use as a bonsai specimen. Truncheons can be planted close to each other in dongas to help control erosion. This tree is a must for the bird garden – space permitting!

Diagnostic features Starts life as a strangler on other trees or on rocks; bark smooth and grey; branchlets hairy; leaf stalk 7–45 mm long; fruit a fig, 7–11 mm in diameter, bracts in the pore of the fruit descending into the fig.

Flowering and fruiting for most months of the year with a peak period during October.

Distribution From Zaïre and Tanzania in the north to the Eastern Cape in the south.

Habitat Grows in wooded grassland, woodland and on the edges of forests. Also found in ravines and on rocks. It favours humus rich or deep loamy soil.

Economic value A most useful tree on the farm to provide shade during the hot summer months and shelter during the winter months. Livestock eat the dry leaves on the ground and to a lesser degree fresh leaves. This tree will always be an asset to the game farmer. It grows into a prominent specimen, provides shelter for many insects, birds, reptiles and other animals and provides fodder for various animals. Leaves and twigs are eaten by elephant, giraffe, kudu, nyala, bushbuck, impala and Damara dik-dik. Dropped fruits are eaten by baboons, vervet- and samango monkeys, porcupines, civets, slender mongoose, rock and tree dassies, bushpigs, warthogs, grey duiker, Damara dik-dik, impala, bushbuck, nyala and kudu. The ripe fruits are eaten by fruit-eating bats, louries, parrots, pigeons,

Other uses An infusion of the root and fibre is taken orally to prevent abortion. The powdered root is taken in porridge to stop bleeding of the nose (epistaxis). The milky latex is dropped into the eye to treat cataracts. An infusion of the bark is taken to prevent constipation and to stop bleeding of the nose, and a decoction of the bark is also used for colds and throat infections. Bark fibre is used for making mats. The twined bark produces a strong rope which is mostly used for fastening bundles of firewood in the veld before they are carried to the homestead or for fastening slats onto a roof.

Cultivation This tree grows easily from cuttings and truncheons. Make cuttings ± 200 mm long and remove most of the leaves, leaving only a few at the top. Plant in river sand and keep moist. Leave truncheons in the shade for a few days to dry before planting. Place river sand in the bottom of the hole before planting, to prevent the bottom of the truncheon from rotting. It grows very quickly into a fair-sized tree but is sensitive to cold winds. In the colder regions, the young plants must be protected for the first two to three years. Relatively drought-resistant.

CORK BUSH

Description An evergreen to semi-deciduous tree up to 5 m tall with a shapeless to roundish crown. **Bark** on young branches smooth and covered with silky hairs but becoming grey, thickly corky, very rough and deeply furrowed on older branches and stems. **Leaves** unevenly compound with 4–11 pale green leaflets covered in long silvery silky hairs and with narrowly rounded tips and smooth margins. **Flowers** in terminal sprays up to 140 mm long, flowers mauve to purple, up to 20 mm in diameter. **Fruit** a flat greyish brown pod up to 100 mm long, with thickened rims and covered with golden-brown velvety hairs, taking some time to split. **Wood** light yellow, hard and strong.

Afrikaans	Kurkbos
Northern Sotho	mosetla-tlou
Zulu	umHlalantethe
Botanical name	*Mundulea sericea*
Family	Pod-bearing Family (Fabaceae)
National tree list no.	226

Name derivation *Mundulea* = neat, and *sericea* = Latin for silky.

(*Leptotes pirithous*) feed on the leaves. Various sunbirds (greater doublecollared sunbird, Marico sunbird and shortbilled sunbird) visit the flowers for nectar. The bark and seed are pounded, placed in a bag and thrown into the water; this does not merely stupefy the fish but actually kills them. This method is used for collecting fish throughout the distribution range of the cork bush.

The cork bush makes a superb accent plant if planted on the lawn with a few large rocks contrasting with the silvery foliage and dark mauve flowers. It is always a feature on a ridge or on the rockery. One of the best plants to grow as a container plant. It always looks neat, dwarfs easily (that is why it makes beautiful bonsai) and is interesting with or without flowers. Young plants start to flower even when they are only 150–200 mm tall. A hedge of these plants look neat and colourful and of course attracts a myriad of insects and sunbirds. A perfect plant for the small garden as it does not have an aggressive root system.

Diagnostic features Thick corky bark; leaves covered with silvery silky hairs; flowers pea-shaped, mauve; pod covered with dense golden-brown velvety hairs, pod taking a long time to split.

Flowering from October to February.
Fruiting from November to April.

Distribution From Tanzania in the north to KwaZulu-Natal in the south and eastwards to India and Sri Lanka.

Habitat Usually on rocky ridges in open woodland or in wooded grassland.

Economic uses Leaves are browsed by stock and game (elephant, giraffe, eland and impala). Larvae of the Natal bar (*Spindasis natalensis*), dusky blue (*Pseudonacaduba sichela*) and the common pea blue butterfly

Cultivation Seeds germinate easily. Soak seeds in hot water, leave overnight and sow the next morning in seedling trays filled with a 1:1 mixture of river sand and compost. Cover the seeds lightly and keep moist. The seeds usually germinate after 4–10 days. Transplant the seedlings into nursery bags when they reach the 2-leaf stage but take care not to damage the taproot whilst transplanting. It prefers well drained soil and full sun. A very hardy plant, not affected by either drought or frost. The growth rate is moderate, 0.5 – 1 m per year, initially slow but speeding up later on.

CROSS-BERRY

Description An evergreen to semi-deciduous tree that can grow up to 10 m tall, usually with an open but somewhat tangled crown with a spread of up to 5 m. In certain areas tending to scramble, main stems somewhat angular. **Bark** smooth and grey to grey-brown. **Leaves** simple and alternate, light green and thinly textured but smooth, with 3 prominent veins from leaf base, leaf base symmetrical, with sharp or blunt teeth on leaf margin, tip either bluntly pointed or drawn out to a slender point. Leaf stalk up to 13 mm long and smooth. **Flowers** up to 35 mm in diameter, borne in 1–3-flowered clusters situated opposite the leaves, pink to dark mauve, showing yellow stamens in a central mass; sepals green outside and pink to dark mauve inside. **Fruit** 4-lobed and square, up to 25 mm in diameter, reddish brown, slightly fleshy and shiny when mature. **Wood** with a whitish sapwood and a dark brown heartwood, hard with a fine grain and moderately heavy.

Afrikaans	Kruisbessie
Northern Sotho	motshwarabadikana
Zulu	iLalanyathi
Botanical name	*Grewia occidentalis*
	var. *occidentalis*
Family	Linden Family (Tiliaceae)
National tree list no.	463

Name derivation *Grewia* = named after Nehemiah Grew (1641–1712), an English physician, and *occidentalis* = west.

times boiled in milk – this beats any milkshake! Beer is brewed from the ripe fruit in certain areas. Ripe fruits are also eaten by various birds (Knysna louries, speckled mousebirds, black-eyed and Cape bulbuls and barbets). Instar larvae of the rufous-winged elfin butterfly (*Eagris nottoana*) and buff-tipped skipper butterfly (*Netrobalane canopus*) live on the leaves of this tree.

The cross-berry can be planted along the edges of camps to provide additional food for stock, but also as protection and food for various birds and insects. It takes pruning well and should be trimmed once a year to keep it in a neat shape. It can be used very effectively in a shrubbery, giving a delightful display of glossy leaves and mauve flowers. The cross-berry flowers throughout the year with a peak during spring and early summer. The root system is not aggressive and it can therefore be planted close to structures. A must in the garden to attract birds and butterflies.

Diagnostic features Bark smooth and grey-brown; 3 main veins from leaf base, leaves thinly textured, flowers pink to mauve; fruit 4-lobed.

Flowering from October to January.
Fruiting from January to May.

Distribution From Zimbabwe in the north to the Western Cape in the south.

Habitat Grows in a wide variety of habitats from arid karoo, coastal dune bush to evergreen montane forests.

Economic value The leaves are browsed by cattle, goats and game (black rhino, giraffe, kudu, nyala and grey duiker). The ripe fruits are eagerly eaten by humans who enjoy its sweet fruity taste. In certain areas where the sugar content of the fruits is high, fruits are collected and dried for later use; dried fruits are some-

Other uses Bruised bark soaked in hot water is used for dressing wounds. Assegai handles and walking sticks are made from the branches of this tree in the Eastern Cape and in Zimbabwe.

Cultivation Collect fresh seed and sow it in a 5:1 mixture of river sand and compost. Take care not to plant the seed too deep! Germination is usually in the order of 70–80%. Transplant the seedlings into nursery bags filled with a mixture of sand, compost and loam. Keep them in the bags for not longer than one season before planting out into open ground. Seedlings transplant well. This plant thrives in either full sun or shade. It can withstand several degrees of frost, especially if the plants have been grown from seed collected on the highveld. Drought-resistant. The growth rate is fast, up to 1.5 m per year for the first 3–5 years but it slows down to 1 m per year thereafter.

DOGWOOD

Description An evergreen bush to small tree up to 7 m high with a dense roundish crown. **Bark** smooth and green on young stems but grey-brown to dark brown and covered with corky dots (lenticels) on the older branches and stems. **Leaves** simple, alternate, very glossy and dark green above but duller green below, midrib sunken on upper surface, net-veining distinct, tip and base tapering, margin finely toothed over the upper two-thirds. Leaf stalk up to 10 mm long. **Flowers** in sparse clusters in axils of leaves, on slender stalks, petals greenish. **Fruit** a round fleshy berry ± 5 mm in diameter on a long, thin stalk, nearly black when ripe. **Wood** white streaked brown to reddish, hard and heavy.

Afrikaans	Blinkblaar
Northern Sotho	mofifi
Zulu	umNyenye
Botanical name	*Rhamnus prinoides*
Family	Dogwood Family
	(Rhamnaceae)
National tree list no.	452

Name derivation *Rhamnus* = Greek word meaning 'a tuft of branches', and *prinoides* = resembling the evergreen oak *Prinos*.

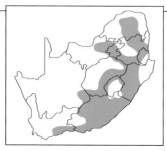

The dogwood can be planted as a hedge along camp fences or along the edges of crops to act as a low windbreak. A good tree to plant along drainage lines or furrows to protect the stream banks. It can be used effectively as a hedge or screen plant in the garden. A perfect plant for the small garden with its low growth, non-aggressive root system, glossy dark green leaves and purple berries. A must for the bird garden! Plants in containers grow well and with constant pruning will form a dense bush. Plant it at a fishpond to give texture and colour but also protection and shade for the fish. The dogwood is easily grown and can be trained in various bonsai styles. Young plants are available at many nurseries.

Diagnostic features Evergreen with very glossy dark green leaves with a sunken midrib; flowers greenish and on long slender stalks; fruit a fleshy purple to blackish berry.

Flowering from October to January.
Fruiting from December to June.

Distribution From Ethiopia in the north to the Western Cape in the south.

Habitat Along drainage lines, riverine forest and along forest margins. Thrives in humus-rich soil.

Economic value The ripe fruit is edible, with a slightly tart taste. Many fruit-eating birds (starlings, bulbuls, barbets and francolins) enjoy the ripe purplish to black fruit. A popular plant with bee farmers for nectar and pollen. Good walking sticks are made from the long, straight branches. Larvae of the forest-king charaxes (*Charaxes xiphares*) feed on the leaves.

Other uses A decoction made from the root bark is used as a blood purifier and to treat pneumonia. Sprains are treated with a paste made from the green leaves and an extract of the wood is used for the relief of muscular rheumatism.

Cultivation Collect fresh seed by picking fruit from the trees, removing the fleshy part (it contains a growth inhibitor) and drying the seeds in the shade. There are ± 60 000 seeds per kilogram. Most of the seeds germinate, taking from 2–6 weeks with some still germinating after 8 weeks. Germination is usually between 80–90%. The growth rate is fast, ± 1 m per year. Trees planted in dry areas and without additional water, will grow far more slowly than plants in high rainfall areas. The dogwood can withstand a fair amount of frost. This, together with the fast growth, glossy leaves and attractive berries, makes it a popular garden subject. It grows well in light shade under trees and equally well in full sun. It grows well in most soil types and thrives in moist conditions.

DUNE SOAP-BERRY

Description An evergreen tree up to 9 m tall with an open rounded canopy. **Bark** on young branches smooth and greyish green to smooth and grey-brown on older branches and stems. **Leaves** in clusters at tips of branches, evenly compound with 5–10 pairs of opposite to sub-opposite, glossy, pale green, smooth, hard-textured leaflets with yellowish veins and very short twisted stalks, margins smooth, leaflets held at an angle to the leaf stalk giving a louvre appearance. Leaf stalk up to 90 mm long. **Flowers** borne on a many-flowered, dense inflorescence up to 350 mm long at tips of branches, individual flowers white to cream, flask-shaped, up to 10 mm in diameter, flower stalk and sepals covered with dense silvery to golden-red hairs. **Fruit** berry-like, fleshy, pale yellow to yellowish orange, up to 10 mm in diameter, in clustered terminal heads.

Afrikaans	Duineseepbessie
Zulu	iQinisamasimu
Botanical name	*Deinbollia oblongifolia*
Family	Litchi Family (Sapindaceae)
National tree list no.	430

Name derivation *Deinbollia* = named after P.V. Deinboll, a Danish botanist, and *oblongifolia* = oblong leaves.

rior. One of the best trees to plant in the garden to attract insects, especially butterflies. Larvae of the violet-spotted charaxes (*Charaxes violetta*), forest queen butterfly (*Euxanthe wakefieldii*), gold-banded forester (*Euphaedra neophron*), and purple-brown hairstreak (*Hypolycaena philippus philippus*) eat the leaves, and larvae of the coastal hairstreak (*Hypolycaena lochmophila*) eat the flowers, with larvae of the black-and-orange playboy (*Deudorix dariaves*) and the orange playboy (*Deudorix dinomenes*) butterflies eating the unripe fruit.

The dune soap-berry is a must in the garden to attract birds and butterflies. The berries remain on the tree for up to 10 weeks, thus providing the birds with food for a long period. The interesting shape, long bare stems with leaves clustered at the top and the shiny leaves make it an excellent specimen plant, especially if planted on a lawn grouped with some rocks. Its non-aggressive root system together with the slow growth rate makes it suitable for the small garden.

Diagnostic features Evergreen; bark smooth; leaves in clusters at tips of branches, evenly compound, with hard-textured leaflets set at an angle to the leaf stalk giving it a louvre effect; flowers in dense erect inflorescences at tips of branches, flower stalk and sepals covered with dense hairs; fruit yellowish and berry-like.

Flowering from March to June.
Fruiting from July to October.

Distribution From Mozambique in the north to the Eastern Cape in the south.

Habitat A coastal species but occurs inland as far as Barberton in the Mpumalanga Province. Mainly in dune bush, woodland and along streams in thick bush.

Economic value Leaves browsed by game (kudu, nyala, bushbuck, impala, grey duiker and red duiker) and the ripe fruit by bushpigs, baboons, samango and vervet monkeys and birds (black-eyed bulbuls, speckled and red-faced mousebirds, glossy starlings, Cape white-eyes and masked weavers). The ripe fruits are edible and enjoyed by humans. The leaves are edible and can be prepared like spinach but the taste is infe-

Other uses An infusion made from the root is used for treating diarrhoea and dysentery. The fruits and especially the seeds lather in water and are used as soap.

Cultivation Collect seeds on the tree as soon as they start to dry. Fruit on the ground is mostly parasitised at this stage of development. Sow the cleaned seed in trays filled with a 1:1 mixture of river sand and compost. Press the seeds into the soil mixture until they are flush with the soil surface and cover with either a thin layer of compost or river sand and keep moist. Some batches of seed germinate as soon as 3 weeks after sowing while others take as long as 12 weeks. Transplant the seedlings into nursery bags filled with a mixture of river sand, loam and compost after the first adult leaf is formed. Unfortunately the growth rate of this beautiful tree is slow, up to 400 mm per year. It can tolerate mild frost but it is mainly a plant for the warm frost-free garden, especially along the coast.

DWARF CORAL TREE

Description A deciduous tree up to 4 m tall with an open crown. **Bark** on young branches grey-green with scattered hooked thorns but grey and smooth on older branches and stems. **Leaves** with three leaflets with scattered hooked thorns on stalks and main veins, light-coloured glands present at base of leaflets, middle leaflet the largest, leaflets triangularly three-lobed with tip long and drawn out. **Flowers** in long narrow flowering heads up to 300 mm long at tips of branches, flowers brilliant red. **Fruit** a splitting pod up to 160 mm long, dark brown when ripe, with red seeds. **Wood** white and very soft.

Afrikaans	Kleinkoraalboom
Northern Sotho	mokhupye
Zulu	umSinsana
Botanical name	*Erythrina humeana*
Family	Pod-bearing Family (Fabaceae)
National tree list no.	243.1

Name derivation *Erythrina* = based on the Greek word *erythros* meaning red, and *humeana* = named after Sir Abraham Hume.

seeds by brown-headed parrots.

The dwarf coral tree can be planted as a specimen tree at the focal point of the garden. Plant a group of about three trees next to some boulders where the grey stems and the drooping pods will contrast well with the boulders in winter. The red flowers will catch the eye in spring and early summer. The size of the tree is such that it can be used in a small garden. One of our indigenous plants for a container on the patio. Plants will flower profusely if kept in full sun and watered well.

Diagnostic features Deciduous; scattered hooked thorns on young bark; leaflets triangularly three-lobed, leaflet tip long and drawn out, middle leaflet the largest; flowering heads up to 300 mm long, flowers brilliant scarlet red; pods dark brown, seeds red.

Flowering from September to April.
Fruiting from December to May.

Distribution From Mozambique in the north to the Eastern Cape in the south.

Habitat Occurs mostly in wooded grassland and in deciduous scrub or woodland on rocky hill and mountain slopes.

Economic uses One of the best bird trees for the garden. The brilliant red flowers attract masses of birds (sunbirds, black-eyed bulbuls, Cape white-eyes). The flowers are eaten by the grey lourie and the unripe

Other uses An extract made from the root is placed on sprained limbs and taken with water to treat tuberculosis and bronchitis.

Cultivation Fresh seed can be collected from the tree but seeds up to two years old still have a high germination rate. Seeds must be soaked overnight in hot water and planted in trays filled with river sand. Press the seeds into the sand as deep as the seed is thick and cover with a thin layer of sand and keep it moist. Place the trays in a hot area to speed up germination. Seeds usually germinate after 2–3 weeks. Transplant the seedlings when they reach the 2-leaf stage. After a year the young plants can be planted out into the open ground. The fastest way of propagating this tree is by truncheons which strike fairly easily and are best planted in August. Remember to place some river sand at the bottom of the hole before planting the truncheon. This will help with root formation and prevent rotting. The dwarf coral tree is frost- and drought-hardy.

EAST AFRICAN MAHOGANY

Description An evergreen tree up to 60 m tall (up to 30 m in the garden) with an elongated or rounded, much branched crown. **Bark** on the young branches smooth and greyish brown but smooth to sometimes mottled grey and brown and flaking on the older branches and stems, stems of large specimens buttressed. **Leaves** alternate, evenly compound with 3–7 pairs of leaflets, 150–300 mm long and dark glossy green, base broadly tapering to round and slightly asymmetric, smooth and glossy, veins distinct on the lower surface, margin smooth. **Flowers** in branched sprays at tips of branches, white and sweetly scented, up to 10 mm in diameter, male and female flowers separate but on the same tree, stamens joined to form a tube up to 6 mm long. **Fruit** a splitting, oval, hard and woody capsule up to 60 mm in diameter with 4 or 5 valves. **Wood** dark reddish brown, hard and moderately heavy (air-dry 620 kg/m³), with an attractive grain.

Diagnostic features Evergreen; long straight stem, bark smooth; leaves evenly compound with 3–7 pairs of leaflets; male and female flowers separate on the same tree; fruit a woody capsule splitting; with 4 or 5 valves.

Flowering from September to December.
Fruiting from March to September.

Distribution From Zaïre in the north to Zimbabwe in the south.

Habitat The East African mahogany occurs in evergreen and riverine forest, nearly always near water.

Economic value A very important timber wood in

Afrikaans	Oos-Afrikaanse mahonie
Botanical name	*Khaya anthotheca*
Family	Mahogany Family (Meliaceae)
Zimbabwe tree list no.	422

Name derivation *anthotheca* = the Greek for the container of the flower.

tropical and southern Africa. The dark reddish wood makes beautiful bench tops, furniture, cabinets and panelling. It is frequently used in the building trade for beams, window frames, doors and for shelving. Popular as a general timber on the farm. Borer, ant and termite-resistant. Farmers in the warm, high rainfall areas can consider planting this tree in a plantation. It is a fast grower and compares favourably with eucalyptus in growth and wood quality. It makes an effective windbreak for at least the first 8 years and can be cut for timber at a later stage. Larvae of the whitebarred charaxes (*Charaxes brutus natalensis*) butterfly feed on the leaves of this tree. A neat and decorative tree for the larger garden and park. Its fast growth rate makes it ideal for establishing shade and protection for other plants in the new garden. The root system of this tree is not particularly aggressive.

Other uses An infusion made from the bitter-tasting bark is used to relieve colds. Popular in some areas (Mozambique, Zambia and Zaïre) for making dugout canoes.

Cultivation Grows easily from seed sown during spring. Soak the seeds in warm water and leave overnight to speed up germination. Plant them the next morning in seed trays filled with seedling soil or a mixture of river sand and compost (1:1) and keep moist. Seeds germinate within 2–6 weeks. As soon as they reach the 2-leaf stage they must be planted out into nursery bags or any other suitable container. Transplant the young trees when they reach a height of ± 300 mm. Protect from the cold for the first few seasons. It is able to withstand some drought but not frost. A very fast grower, up to 1.5 m per year.

FALSE MARULA

Description A deciduous tree up to 15 m tall with a spreading open crown, slightly aromatic. **Bark** on young stems green and hairy with very prominent leaf scars, but grey and flaking in rectangular pieces giving the stem a mottled appearance on older branches and stems. **Leaves** borne at tips of branches, unevenly compound, with leaflets in 1–3 pairs plus a large terminal one, leaflets sessile, leaf 100–200 mm long, woolly when young but adult leaflets smooth and shiny dark green, leaf stalk long and slender, woolly. **Flowers** in long spikes (male inflorescence 130 mm long, female 80 mm long) in axils of leaves, creamy yellow, ± 7 mm in diameter, sexes on different trees. **Fruit** oval and slightly flattened, up to 25 mm long, tipped with four papillae, fleshy and reddish purple with an orange flesh. **Wood** with no distinction between sapwood and heartwood, off-white and light (air-dry 570 kg/m³).

Afrikaans	Bastermaroela
Northern Sotho	mmopu
Zulu	umGanunkomo
Botanical name	*Lannea schweinfurthii* var. *stuhlmannii*
Family	Mango Family (Anacardiaceae)
National tree list no.	363

Name derivation *Lannea* = the Latin for wool, *schweinfurthii* = named after Dr G. Schweinfurth, naturalist and explorer, and *stuhlmannii* = named after Franz Ernest Stuhlmann, acting Governor in Tanzania.

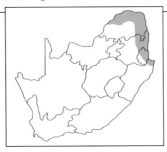

birds (grey hornbills, grey louries, pied, black-collared and crested barbets, Meyer's and brown-headed parrots and red-faced mousebirds). The dropped fruits are eaten by Swainson's and crested francolins and guineafowl. Bark, twigs and roots eagerly eaten by elephants. In the Transvaal Lowveld and in Zimbabwe this is regarded as one of the best fodder trees for cattle and game. Small household articles such as spoons are made from the wood but it can also be used for general purpose timber on the farm. The chopped bark is left in water for a few days and then used for tanning leather, giving it a purplish brown colour.

Diagnostic features Plant slightly aromatic; leaf scars prominent on young branches, bark on old stems flaking; leaves compound with 1–3 pairs of leaflets, no petiolules except terminal one, woolly when young; male and female flowers on separate trees; fruit with four papillae on top.

Flowering from October to January.
Fruiting from November to March.

Distribution From Tanzania in the north to KwaZulu-Natal in the south.

Habitat Grows in well drained sandy to gravelly soil derived from igneous rocks. In deciduous woodland. Often associated with termitaria.

Economic value Leaves eagerly browsed by cattle. The browse line on these trees is made by cattle and not game. Cattle will even eat the dry leaves on the ground. Leaves also browsed by giraffe, kudu, nyala, bushbuck and grey duiker. Ripe fruits eaten by kudu, bushpigs, warthogs, baboons, vervet monkeys and

Plant scattered groups of this tree in camps in areas with sandy soil. The young trees can grow up to 200 mm per year if given enough water. A worthwhile tree to plant in the garden to attract fruit-eating birds. The false marula has a non-aggressive root system.

This is one of the best indigenous trees to grow as a bonsai specimen, with a shape resembling the adult tree attained in two years.

Other uses A paste is made from the leaves and applied as a dressing to sores and abscesses. An infusion made from the root is taken orally to treat diarrhoea. Although the skin is not eaten, the fruit is edible, with a pleasant mango-like taste.

Cultivation Collect ripe fruit from various trees and dry in the shade. It is best to remove the dry fruit pulp from the seeds. Sow in a seedling tray in a mixture of river sand and compost (4:1). Press seeds lightly into the sand mixture and cover with a thin layer of sand. The seeds usually take 10–30 days to germinate. Transplant into nursery bags when they reach the 2-leaf stage. Cuttings can be made from semi-hardwood but must be treated with a growth stimulating hormone before planting. Cuttings must be 80–100 mm long. This tree is very frost-sensitive but can survive in colder areas if planted in a warm, protected spot. Will grow much slower than those planted in a frost-free area.

FALSE OLIVE

Description An evergreen tree up to 10 m tall with a much branched crown with drooping branches. **Bark** on the ± 4-angled young branches scaly and on the fluted to twisted stems and older branches pale grey-brown, fissured and flaking in long pieces.
Leaves opposite and simple, upper surface smooth and dark green with impressed venation, lower surface light coloured with dense star-shaped scales, net-veining prominent and the side veins forming a line more or less parallel to the margin, margin smooth and usually rolled inwards. **Flowers** clustered in much branched panicles up to 120 mm long in axils of upper leaves, flowers small, ± 2 mm long, white to cream-coloured and honey-scented. **Fruit** a 2 mm long capsule slightly longer than the persistent calyx. **Wood** with a cream-coloured sapwood and a dark brown heartwood, fine-grained, hard and heavy (± 1 100 kg/m³).

Afrikaans	Witolien
Zulu	iGqeba-elimhlope
Botanical name	*Buddleja saligna*
Family	Wild Elder Family (Loganiaceae)
National tree list no.	636

Name derivation *Buddleja* = named in honour of Rev. Adam Buddle (1660–1715), an amateur botanist, and *saligna* = willow, the leaves likened to that of a willow tree.

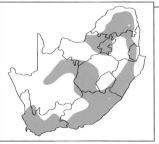

Diagnostic features Evergreen; bark on stems fissured and flaking in long pieces, stems twisted; leaves dark green on upper surface but light grey to white on the undersurface with prominent venation and side veins forming a line roughly parallel to the margin.

Flowering from August to January.
Fruiting from September to March.

Distribution From Zimbabwe in the north to the Western Cape in the south.

Habitat Grows in most habitat types except in forests. Very common in dry deciduous woodland along drainage lines.

Economic value The straight stems are used for fence poles and the heavy, dense wood makes an excellent fuel generating intense heat. In the past the wood was used for small pieces of furniture. The wood produces an extremely fine finish. The masses of small white flowers make this one of the best trees to plant to attract butterflies. A favourite with bee farmers as the mass of flowers produce copious nectar and pollen.

The false olive tends to become untidy and woody after a season or two and should be pruned back fairly hard after flowering to ensure a neat, compact shape the next season. It makes an excellent hedge or screen and reacts well to pruning. When in flower, it makes a superb focal point in the park or garden. It does not have an aggressive root system and can be planted near buildings and pools without any fear of damage!

Other uses Scrapings of the root are used as a purgative and to induce vomiting. A decoction made from the leaf is used to treat coughs and colds.

Cultivation Easily grown from seed or cuttings. The very fine seed should be mixed with fine river sand before sowing to ensure even distribution. After sowing, place the seedling tray in a shallow container with water – once the surface is moist, it can be removed. Germination is erratic but most of the seeds should germinate after four weeks. Seedlings transplant well if watered after planting. Fast-growing, up to 800 mm per year. Very drought and frost-resistant and always a winner in any garden, even in areas experiencing frost during winter.

FEVER TREE

Description A semi-deciduous to deciduous tree up to 30 m tall with an open, rounded to spreading crown. **Bark** lemon- to greenish yellow, becoming powdery. **Stipules** spinescent and in pairs, white and straight, 10–85 mm long. **Leaves** twice compound, with 3–7 pairs of pinnae each with 8–20 pairs of leaflets, glands present at bases of upper pinnae pairs. **Inflorescence** round, bright yellow and sweetly scented, borne on shortened side shoots represented by clustered scales. **Fruit** a thin non-splitting yellowish brown to brown pod slightly constricted between the seeds, breaking transversely into segments. **Wood** pale brown with a reddish tinge, hard and heavy (air-dry 910 kg/m³).

Afrikaans	Koorsboom
Northern Sotho	mooka-kwena
Zulu	umHlosinga
Botanical name	*Acacia xanthophloea*
Family	Pod-bearing Family (Fabaceae)
National tree list no.	189

Name derivation *Acacia* = from the Greek word 'akis' meaning a point or a barb, and *xanthophloea* = yellow bark.

Diagnostic features Bark greenish yellow; spines paired and straight; flowers in bright yellow balls; pod breaking up in segments.

Flowering from September to November.
Fruiting from January to April.

Distribution From Kenya in the north to KwaZulu-Natal in the south.

Habitat The fever tree occurs in low-lying swampy areas, margins of lakes and pans and along river banks. Often forms dense stands in seasonally flooded areas.

Economic value The young branches and leaves are eaten by elephant and the leaves and pods by giraffe and vervet monkeys. The wood is a useful general purpose timber but must be seasoned.

Probably one of the best indigenous trees for the garden, with its contrasting bark and very fast growth rate. Plant them in groups of up to 5 trees for the best effect. Groves of this tree can be planted next to dams and streams on the farm for both aesthetic and functional purposes. It will provide nesting sites for birds. This tree does not have an aggressive taproot, but because of its large size should not be planted close to the house.

Cultivation Easily grown from seed. Despite the production of a large number of flowers, often only a few pods develop. Seeds are therefore generally not easy to come by. Soak seeds in hot water, leave overnight and sow the next morning in seedling trays filled with a mixture of river sand and compost (3:1). Cover the seeds with a thin layer of sand and keep moist. Transplant the seedlings into nursery bags filled with a mixture of river sand and compost (5:1) when they reach the 2-leaf stage. Be careful not to damage the long taproot in the process of transplanting. Seedlings and young trees transplant well. One of the fastest growing thorn tree species in southern Africa with a growth rate of 1–1.5 m per year. It can withstand cold but no cold winds or frost.

FOREST ELDER

Description An evergreen tree up to 20 m tall with a dense rounded crown. **Bark** on young angled branches smooth or finely hairy but grey-brown, fissured and flaking on older branches and stems. **Leaves** simple, mostly in whorls of three, light green, glossy and thinly textured with raised venation underneath, margin smooth or slightly toothed, leaf stalk up to 45 mm long. New growth purplish. **Flowers** in much branched heads up to 300 mm in diameter, individual flowers tubular, white and scented, flower buds sticky and resinous. **Fruit** a capsule splitting into two valves. **Wood** with no clear distinction between sapwood and heartwood, pale yellowish brown, finely textured, heavy (air-dry 994–1 074 kg/m³) and hard.

Afrikaans	Bosvlier
Northern Sotho	motlhabare
Zulu	umHlamban dlazi
Botanical name	*Nuxia floribunda*
Family	Wild Elder Family (Loganiaceae)
National tree list no.	634

Name derivation *Nuxia* = named for M. de la Nux, amateur botanist from Réunion, and *floribunda* = many-flowered.

insects and they in turn many insect-eating birds. The copious nectar in the flowers makes this a good honey tree. The wood can be used for parquet floors, turnery and furniture. These pieces are relatively heavy, but with a pleasing light colour and a very fine finish. The colour of oiled furniture deepens to a light brown after about 10 years.

The forest elder makes an attractive street and garden tree with its evergreen foilage and masses of white flowers. The root system is non-invasive and it can be planted next to paved areas and buildings. When in full flower, it is an eye-catcher in the garden!

Diagnostic features Young branches angular, with conspicuous leaf scars; leaves in whorls of three, light green, with venation raised underneath; flowers scented, white to cream-coloured and in much branched heads; fruit a two-valved capsule.

Flowering from May to August.
Fruiting from June to October.

Distribution From northern Zambia and Malawi in the north to the Western Cape in the south.

Habitat In evergreen montane forests and along rivers in high-lying areas.

Economic value Leaves browsed by stock and game (kudu, bushbuck, nyala, klipspringer, red and grey duiker). The bunches of flowers attract all kinds of

Cultivation Grown either from seed or cuttings. The viability of seed collected in its natural habitat is low. Collect the fruit capsules as they start to discolour, dry them in a cool place and shake out the fine seed. Having mixed this seed with very fine river sand, it can then be sown in seedling trays filled with a mixture of river sand and compost (1:1). Fine seed is usually mixed with very fine river sand to ensure even distribution of seed when sowing. Cover the tray with a pane of glass. Germination can take up to 12 weeks. Make cuttings from hardwood or semi-hardwood. Cuttings must not be longer than 100 mm. For the best results, treat cuttings with a root-stimulating hormone powder (e.g. Seradix). A fast grower, up to 800 mm per year. Plant in a protected position in deep soil, with an abundance of compost and regular watering throughout the year.

Not recommended for areas experiencing heavy frost.

Description A deciduous tree up to 30 m tall with a spreading crown. **Bark** on young branches covered with orange hairs but older branches and stems grey and rough to slightly fissured and strongly aromatic. **Leaves** simple, alternate, smooth, dark green, 3–5-nerved from base, margin shallowly toothed, leaf tip much pointed. Leaf stalk up to 100 mm long, with two prominent knob-like glands at junction of stalk and leaf blade. **Flowers** cream-coloured, on long terminal inflorescences up to 200 mm long, male flowers at top and female flowers at lower part of inflorescence. **Fruit** a soft, roundish, orange to reddish orange capsule up to 10 mm long, with a slightly warted surface, clustered on long terminal stalks, hanging. **Wood** yellowish to white, soft and light.

Afrikaans	Boskoorsbessie
Northern Sotho	moêma
Zulu	umHloshozane
Botanical name	*Croton sylvaticus*
Family	Spurge Family (Euphorbiaceae)
National tree list no.	330

Name derivation *Croton* = Greek for a tick, referring to the shape of the fruit, and *sylvaticus* = woodland.

trumpeter hornbills and forest weavers). Fallen fruits are eaten by bushbuck, blue duiker and bushpigs. Larvae of the green-veined charaxes butterfly (*Charaxes candiope*) feed on the leaves.

The forest fever-berry makes a beautiful shade tree in the garden or park. It can be planted as a specimen tree, the showy, orangy fruit being visible from a distance. An ideal tree to plant along a drive-way. The root system is not very aggressive but it is always wise not to plant it too close to buildings and pools. One of the best trees to plant if you want to attract birds to the garden. It can also be planted in protected kloofs on the game farm to supply food for birds and game.

Diagnostic features Young branches covered in orange hairs; bark aromatic; leaves 3–5-nerved from base, leaf tip much pointed, two prominent glands at base of leaf blade; male and female flowers; fruit orange.

Flowering from September to January.
Fruiting from December to May.

Distribution From Ethiopia in the north to the Eastern Cape in the south.

Habitat In forest and evergreen woodland.

Economic value The wood is ideal for making furniture (kitchen and side tables), shelves and fruit boxes. The flowers are visited by masses of insects and they in turn attract various insect-eating birds. The fruits are very popular with birds (African green pigeons, cinnamon doves, tambourine doves, red-eyed doves,

Other uses The root is a remedy for indigestion and the bark is used for chest problems and for treating rheumatism. The bark is also used as a fish poison in certain areas. The leaves are made into a poultice to treat pleurisy.

Cultivation Collect fresh fruit in the veld and remove the seeds. Sow them in containers filled with a mixture of river sand and compost (1:2). Cover the seeds lightly with fine compost and keep moist. The seeds usually take between 2 and 3 weeks to germinate, with a surprisingly even germination. Transplant the seedlings when they reach the 2-leaf stage, either into the open ground or into bags filled with a 1:1 mixture of river sand and compost. A tree for light to deep shade conditions but it will survive if planted in full sun. It can tolerate moderate frost but no cold wind. If planted in the colder areas the young plants must be protected against cold winds and frost for the first two seasons. The growth rate is very fast, up to 1.5 m a year.

FOREST FEVER TREE

Description An evergreen tree up to 30 m tall with a long clean stem and roundish crown. **Bark** with leaf scars prominent on young stems, smooth and grey. **Leaves** borne at tips of branches, simple, opposite, with one pair at right angles to the next, with the upper half broader than the lower half, very large, up to 1 500 x 450 mm, dark glossy green and soft, with a smooth and slightly thickened margin, tips round, venation prominent on the undersurface, leaf stalk short. **Flowers** in branched inflorescences at tips of branches or in axils of upper two pairs of leaves, flowers white turning yellow with age but very fragrant, flower tube up to 30 mm long, the 8–13 petals curving backwards, stamens well exserted, calyx four-lobed and green. **Fruit** oval-shaped, up to 30 x 20 mm, with a conspicuous calyx at the base, glossy dark green to brown when mature. **Wood** soft, moderately heavy (air-dry 730 kg/m^3) and light brown.

Afrikaans	Boskoorsboom
Northern Sotho	mophala
Botanical name	*Anthocleista grandiflora*
Family	Wild Elder Family (Loganiaceae)
National tree list no.	632

Name derivation *Anthocleista* = closed flower, and *grandiflora* = large flowers.

Diagnostic features Tall tree with a clean stem; leaves opposite and very large (1 500 x 450 mm), with round tips; flowers large with a 30 mm long tube, white and fragrant, petals 8–13, curving backwards; fruit oval; always found in moist areas.

Flowering from September to January.
Fruiting from January to June.

Distribution From Kenya in the north to Swaziland in the south.

Habitat Along perennial streams and springs in forests. In humus-rich soils.

Economic value The best application of a forest fever tree is for shade. The fast growth rate and dense crown formed by the exceptionally large leaves can provide much needed shade for farm animals and game in frost-free areas. It has a light wood which does not crack when nails are driven through it, and was used by fruit and vegetable farmers for making fruit boxes. Elephants eat the leaves and young branches and in the process destroy many of the smaller trees, but fortunately they coppice freely. Bushpigs eat the ripe fruit dropped by monkeys and birds on the forest floor. This tree attracts many species of insects when in flower and in the process these in turn attract many insect-eating birds. A worthwhile tree to plant along streams. Cattle eat the leaves that drop to the ground.

On the farm, the best effect is achieved when these trees are planted in groves of up to 20 in a suitable habitat. This is one of the most decorative trees for a garden or park. It can be used most successfully for creating a tropical effect in the garden and is stunning planted next to a swimming pool. Although a very large tree, its root system is not aggressive.

Other uses People in the Lowveld areas drink a decoction of the bark and leaves to treat malaria, diarrhoea, diabetes, high blood pressure, venereal diseases and to get rid of roundworm.

Cultivation Although easily cultivated from seed, it is difficult to find fruits that are not infested by insects. Remove the seeds from the fruit and dry in a cool, shady place. The fruit pulp contains a germination inhibitor and must be removed to ensure germination. Sow the seeds in seedling trays filled with a mixture of river sand and compost (5:1). Cover the seed with a thin layer of sand or compost, keep moist and do not allow the medium to dry out. Seedlings should emerge after 15–30 days. Transplant the seedlings into black nursery bags into a mixture of sand and compost (4:1). Keep the young plants in light shade or under 30–40% shade cloth. Young plants transplant easily and need regular watering. A very fast growing species that can grow up to 2 m per year in the shade and up to 1.5 m in full sun. Plants in full sun tend to have smaller and lighter green leaves than those growing in the shade. The forest fever tree thrives on lots of water during the summer months. Frost and cold winds usually kill the above-ground parts.

This is a protected tree in South Africa.

GIANT RAISIN

Description A small evergreen tree up to 6 m tall with an open crown. **Bark** on young branches covered with long rusty hairs, but reddish brown and smooth with conspicuous pale lenticels becoming dark grey and rough on thicker branches and stems. **Leaves** simple, leathery, up to 100 x 60 mm, rounded or acute at the tip and markedly asymmetric at the base, upper surface glossy dark green with sunken veins, lower surface covered in very dense yellowish hairs with veins conspicuous, margin toothed, leaf stalk up to 6 mm long. **Flowers** honey-scented, in groups of 2 or 3 together in leaf axils, 40–50 mm in diameter, sepals with fine golden-brown hairs on the back, smooth and yellow within, petals small and yellow, stamens many and forming a large central mass, the ovary and stamens borne on a stalk called an androgynophore. **Fruit** deeply divided into two golden reddish brown, shiny, globose lobes, 15–20 mm in diameter, covered with scattered longish hairs. **Wood** with a yellowish brown sapwood and a buff-brown, heavy (air-dry 960 kg/m^3) and fine-grained heartwood.

Afrikaans	Reuserosyntjie
Zulu	umLalampunzi
Botanical name	*Grewia hexamita*
Family	Linden Family (Tiliaceae)
National tree list no.	460

Name derivation *Grewia* = named in honour of Nehemiah Grew (1641–1712), an English physician, and *hexamita* = Greek for 6 stamens.

Diagnostic features Conspicuous lenticels on bark; leaves leathery with upper surface glossy dark green, lower surface with raised venation; petals small, sepals bright yellow inside, velvety and dull outside; fruit with two globose lobes.

Flowering from September to November.
Fruiting from December to June.

Distribution From Tanzania in the north to KwaZulu-Natal in the south.

Habitat Deciduous woodland, on rocky hillslopes and in river valleys in warm, low-lying areas.

Economic value Leaves are browsed by livestock and game (elephant, black rhino, buffalo, giraffe, eland, kudu, Lichtenstein's hartebeest, impala, bushbuck, duiker and steenbok). A worthwhile tree to have on a game farm. The fallen fruits are eagerly eaten by helmeted and crowned guineafowl and various francolin species.

A very decorative plant for the garden, with its glossy dark green leaves and masses of large deep yellow flowers which attract many insects. It can be successfully incorporated into a shrubbery and will give a splash of bright yellow colour. It has a non-aggressive root system. Plant scattered groups of this tree in suitable areas (rocky with sandy soil) on the farm. It is advisable to water the transplanted trees for the first three months after planting until they have become established.

Other uses The ripe fruit is edible, the thin sweetish layer of flesh having a high sugar content. An intoxicating drink can be made from the ripe fruit.

Cultivation Cultivate the giant raisin from fresh seed. Leave seed to soak in water for 2–3 days before sowing. Sow either directly into black nursery bags or in seedling trays filled with pure river sand. The seedlings from the trays can be planted out into black nursery bags when they reach the 2-leaf stage. This is a species for frost-free areas only. They transplant well but are initially slow-growing. After two years the growth rate speeds up considerably.

JACKAL-BERRY

Description A semi-deciduous to evergreen tree up to 25 m tall with a dense rounded to spreading crown and a tall bare stem. Sexes on different plants. **Bark** on young twigs green and hairy but dark brown, rough, fissured and peeling in thin sections on the older branches and stems. **Leaves** simple, alternate, leathery, dark green with a dull shine, tip rounded to broadly tapering, margins smooth, leaf stalk 5–10 mm long. Young leaves reddish. **Flowers** fragrant, cream-coloured and bell-shaped, 10–12 mm long, male flowers in stalked bunches and the female flowers solitary. **Fruit** a fleshy berry 20–25 mm long, with persistent style and enlarged calyx, yellowish to orange-yellow when ripe. **Wood** with a light-coloured sapwood and a dark brown, fine-grained, hard and heavy (air-dry 850 kg/m³) heartwood.

Afrikaans	Jakkalsbessie
Northern Sotho	motlouma
Botanical name	*Diospyros mespiliformis*
Family	Ebony Family (Ebenaceae)
National tree list no.	606

Name derivation *Diospyros* = 'divine pear', and *mesos* = half + *pilos* = bullet, referring to the shape of the fruit.

The fruit contains –

protein .... 1.1 g/100 g
carbohydrate .... 22 g/100 g
sodium .... 13.7 mg/100 g
potassium ...... 417 mg/100 g
phosphorus .. 27.8 mg/100 g
vitamin C .... 25 mg/100 g

Fruits remain on the tree for a very long time. The fruit can be successfully dried for later use and can be made into a type of porridge or more commonly mixed in with mealie meal. The wood is suitable for floors and produces good-quality furniture. Dugout canoes are made from this wood especially in Botswana and Namibia. Stamping blocks and pestles are made from the wood in certain areas.

This large tree is suitable for the very large garden or farm garden. It has a taproot and a non-aggressive root system.

Diagnostic features Dense crown, tall bare stem, bark dark brown and fissured; leaves leathery, dark green with a dull shine, young leaves reddish; male and female flowers on separate trees, flowers bell-shaped; fruit fleshy and yellow, with persistent style and calyx.

Flowering from October to November.
Fruiting from April to September.

Distribution From Ethiopia in the north to Swaziland in the south.

Habitat Favours heavy soils on river banks but also occurs in open woodland. Commonly found on termite mounds.

Economic value Leaves eaten by elephant, giraffe, black rhino, buffalo, eland and kudu. Fruit eaten by kudu, klipspringer, warthog, baboons, vervet monkeys, yellow-spotted rock dassies, pigeons, parrots, hornbills, louries and bulbuls. A definite asset to any farm. Fruit edible, with a soft and sweet flesh.

Other uses Beer is made from the fermented ripe fruit. All over Africa the jackal-berry is used as medicine. The crushed young shoot is applied to wounds and sores to speed up healing. A decoction made from the crushed root is applied to get rid of ringworm, and pieces of bark are placed over coals, the resultant steam inhaled to treat coughs and sinus infections. An extract from the bark is applied to bruises.

Cultivation Viability of the seed is high for a long period. The seed can be placed in boiling water and left to soak overnight. Sow seed during spring in flat seedling trays filled with river sand. Seedlings should be planted out when they reach the 3-leaf stage; if left longer the taproot may be damaged. They are rather slow-growing initially but the growth speeds up considerably after a year. They prefer deep soil and sheltered conditions in colder areas. A fast grower in frost-free areas.

A protected tree in South Africa.

JACKET-PLUM

Description An evergreen to semi-deciduous tree up to 9 m tall with a dense much branched roundish crown. **Bark** on the young branches light-grey but grey to light-brown and mostly smooth on the older branches and stems. **Leaves** towards tips of twigs, alternately arranged and simple, oblong, with fairly parallel secondary veining, margin of young leaves prominently toothed but that of mature leaves nearly entire, variable in size, up to 60 x 40 mm, leaf stalk up to 15 mm long. **Flowers** in long spike-like heads, scented, yellowish green, sexes on different trees. **Fruit** a roundish velvety green capsule 10–15 mm in diameter, splitting open to expose the fleshy orange-red flesh around the seed. **Wood** with little difference between sapwood and heartwood, light-brown with a reddish tinge, hard, tough, grain twisted, heavy (air-dry 864 kg/m³).

Afrikaans	Doppruim
Northern Sotho	mongatane
Zulu	umQhokwane
Botanical name	*Pappea capensis*
Family	Litchi Family (Sapindaceae)
National tree list no.	433

Name derivation *Pappea* = named after Dr Ludwig Pappe, Colonial Botanist at the Cape, and *capensis* = of the Cape.

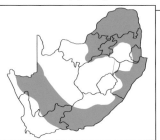

Diagnostic features Smooth grey stem; leaves with secondary veining parallel, margin of young leaves prominently toothed; male and female flowers on different trees; fruit with orange-red flesh.

Flowering time From September to May.
Fruiting time From December to July.

Distribution From Ethiopia in the north to the Western Cape in the south.

Habitat Occurs in most habitat types except forests. Ecologically a most adaptive tree. Trees in the arid areas tend to be smaller, with the leaves far smaller than their Mpumalanga counterparts along rivers.

Economic value An excellent fodder tree for livestock and game (elephant, giraffe, kudu, nyala, bushbuck, impala and grey duiker) throughout its distribution range. Most fruit-eating birds visit these trees, especially mousebirds, starlings and barbets. The orange-red flesh is edible, with a pleasant sourish taste. It can be made into a jelly which complements pork very well. Some people still make vinegar from the orange-red flesh. Larvae of the pearlspotted charaxes (*Charaxes jahlusa*), common hairtail (*Anthene definita*) and brown playboy (*Deudorix antalus*) butterflies feed on the tree.

Jacket plum trees can be planted at the beginning of the rainy season in groups of five or more in suitable rocky habitats in camps with natural grazing. It may be necessary to water the young plants until they produce new leaves.

An excellent specimen tree for the garden, with its grey stem and neat, compact crown. The new leaves make patches of bronze colour in the crown. It does not have an aggressive root system and is well suited to a small/medium garden. An essential addition to a bird garden!

Other uses The golden-yellow, non-drying and fairly viscous oil (up to 74%) from the roasted seeds can be used to oil rifles. The oil is used topically in the treatment of ringworm and baldness. An infusion of the root is given orally or as an enema for purging cattle.

Cultivation Seed may be collected by picking fruit from the tree and then removing the flesh from the shiny, black seed. Seeds lying beneath the tree are mostly parasitized. Remember to use fresh seed only. No special treatment of the seed is necessary. Seed can be sown in seed trays. The growing medium can be made up of a mixture of (1:3) compost and sand and should drain easily. One can also use a commercial 'Seedling Mix' available at most nurseries and garden centres.

The seed is pressed into the mixture lightly so that it is flush with the surface of the mixture and covered with a thin layer of either the seedling mixture or fine river sand. The seed trays should be placed under conditions conducive to germination and kept moist.

Seed sown during the summer months is likely to germinate within two weeks, with a germination rate of 70–80%. Seedlings can be transplanted when they are 50 mm tall or alternatively when they reach the 4-leaf stage. Care must be taken not to damage the taproot during transplanting. The plants should be properly weaned before being planted out into full sun. The growth rate is moderate, 500–800 mm per year. Young plants withstand the cold quite well.

Adult trees are both frost and drought-resistant.

KAREE

Description An evergreen tree with a loose, rounded crown up to 9 m tall. **Bark** on young branches smooth and reddish brown but rough and dark brown on older branches and stems. **Leaves** drooping, with three leathery, glossy and dark green leaflets up to 150 mm long, middle leaflet the longest, leaf stalk up to 50 mm long. **Flowers** small, up to 3 mm in diameter, yellow-green, in much-branched sprays at ends of branchlets, with male and female flowers on different trees. **Fruit** round and slightly flattened, up to 5 mm in diameter, with a thin layer of flesh, glossy brown when ripe. **Wood** reddish brown, hard, tough, close-grained and heavy (air-dry 1 040 kg/m³).

Afrikaans	Karee
Northern Sotho	mokalabata
Botanical name	*Rhus lancea*
Family	Mango Family (Anacardiaceae)
National tree list no.	386

Name derivation *Rhus* = the classical Greek name for *Rhus coriaria*; *lancea* = refers to the lance-shaped leaflets.

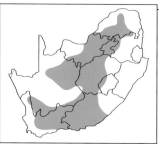

Can be used successfully as termite-proof fence posts. The bark can be used for tanning. The leaf and twig yield 5.1% tanning material. Several bird species eat the fruit. Bulbuls eat the ripe fruit on the tree, with guineafowl and francolin eating the dropped and dry fruit on the ground underneath the tree.

Plant karee trees along fences as hedges or around drinking troughs. In the Karoo and Kalahari the karee is a valuable shade tree. For this purpose, plant them in groups of 10–20 individuals. A neat and worthwhile garden subject, especially for areas with water restrictions or prolonged drought. It has a non-aggressive root system. Trees in gardens sometimes have a disease in which the terminal leaves are stunted and bunched together – this also occurs in trees in the wild and the disease should be left to run its course.

Diagnostic features Bark rough and dark brown; leaves leathery, with three glossy leaflets up to 150 mm long; small greenish yellow flowers, male and female flowers on different trees; fruit round and slightly flattened.

Flowering from June to September.
Fruiting from September to January.

Distribution From Zambia in the north to the Western Cape in the south.

Habitat Mostly in *Acacia* woodland or along drainage lines. Grows in practically any soil type. Thrives in poorly drained soils, i.e. black cotton soil.

Economic value A valuable fodder tree especially in areas hard hit by drought. In some areas this is the only tree that stock can use as fodder or shade. In most areas the leaves are browsed by domestic stock and game (kudu, roan and sable). When eaten in large quantities, the resin in the leaves can taint the milk.

Other uses The ripe fruit is edible, with a sour taste. Tea made from the dried fruit has an agreeable taste.

Cultivation Grows easily from seed, cuttings or layers. There are approximately 30 000 seed per kilogram. Sow ripe seed in flat seedling trays in a mixture of river sand and compost (8:1). Cover seed with a 5 mm layer of pure river sand. Seedlings can be planted out into black plastic nursery bags when they have reached the 2-leaf stage. Transplant into the veld or garden when ± 300 mm tall. Cuttings must be made from young branches from September to October. Transplant as for seedlings from December to January. Can be grown from truncheons but they do not strike easily. Fairly fast-growing, up to 800 mm per year. The karee is drought and frost-resistant.

A protected tree in the Northern Cape and the Jacobsdal district in the Free State.

KAROO RHIGOZUM

Description A deciduous shrub to small tree up to 4 m tall with opposite pairs of branches. **Bark** grey and smooth. **Leaves** simple or sometimes with three leaflets up to 13 x 5 mm, leaflets egg-shaped and greyish green, with smooth margins and a rounded tip, clustered on spiny lateral branches. **Flowers** bright yellow and conspicuous, up to 35 mm in diameter. **Fruit** a splitting flattened capsule tapering to both ends, up to 80 x 10 mm, brown to purplish brown, seed with a broad papery wing.

Afrikaans	Geelberggranaat
Botanical name	*Rhigozum obovatum*
Family	Jacaranda Family (Bignoniaceae)
National tree list no.	675

Name derivation *Rhigozum* = from the Greek 'rhigos' meaning rigid, referring to the rigid branches, and *obovatum* = egg-shaped, referring to the shape of the leaf.

ers and fruit. Plants are usually browsed to such an extent that they appear stunted. In most areas stock and game keep the plants to a height of ± 1 m except for some protected specimens in hilly country. Kudu, goats and sheep in particular eat the flowers.

A very rewarding garden subject that requires little attention. Combine it into a shrubbery with other flowering shrubs, or into a rockery – it thrives in well-drained soil and is very drought-resistant. It does not have an invasive root system. A good plant to use as a protective barrier in certain areas to keep out man and animal. Planted as a hedge, it looks splendid when in flower after the first good rains of the season.

Diagnostic features Spiny lateral branches bearing simple leaves or leaves with three leaflets; bright yellow flowers and flat splitting pods.

Flowering from September to November, usually after good rains.

Fruiting throughout the year.

Distribution From Namibia in the north to the Western Cape in the south.

Habitat Dry, rocky places in deciduous woodland and karroid vegetation.

Economic value A valuable fodder plant, with both domestic stock and game browsing the leaves, flow-

Cultivation Can be grown from seed with ease. Fresh seed should be harvested and preferably sown during early spring. No special pre-sowing treatment is needed. The seed is merely placed on the surface of a sand-compost mixture (8:1) and covered lightly with river sand. This can be done either in seed trays or directly in black nursery bags. If sown during spring, the first seedling is likely to emerge within seven days of sowing. A 100% germination rate is not unlikely. The seedlings may be planted out within a few weeks, and weaned accordingly. The young plants withstand cold, heat and drought very successfully. At first it has a rather slow growth rate until it becomes established.

KEI-APPLE

Description An evergreen tree up to 9 m tall with a dense and much branched crown. Male and female flowers on separate trees. **Bark** grey and smooth on young branches but grey, fissured and flaky to corky on old branches and stems, young branches heavily armed with long (40–70 mm) spines, but main stem with few spines. **Leaves** simple and in clusters on dwarf side branches but alternate on young shoots, dark green with a waxy lustre, with 3–5 prominent veins from base on both sides, leaf tip rounded to notched, leaf margin smooth, slightly rolled under and base tapering to a leaf stalk up to 5 mm long. **Flowers** in dense clusters, creamish green with male flowers 3 mm long in dense clusters of 5–10 but female flowers solitary or in groups of up to three on stalks 4–10 mm long in leaf axils. **Fruit** almost spherical, up to 60 mm in diameter, fleshy, with a velvety surface and orange-coloured, containing 10 mm long woolly seeds. **Wood** white, dense and heavy.

Afrikaans	Keiappel
Northern Sotho	motlhono
Zulu	umQokolo
Botanical name	*Dovyalis caffra*
Family	Kei-apple Family (Flacourtiaceae)
National tree list no.	507

Name derivation *Dovyalis* = based on the Greek word for spear, and *caffra* = from Kaffraria (Eastern Cape).

Diagnostic features Male and female plants; spines up to 70 mm long; leaves in clusters on dwarf side branches, with a waxy lustre, 3–5 veins from leaf base; male flowers in dense clusters of 5–10, female flowers solitary or in groups of up to three on 4–10 mm long stalks; fruit fleshy, velvety and orange; seeds woolly.

Flowering from November to January.
Fruiting from November to February.

Distribution From Malawi in the north to the Eastern Cape in the south.

Habitat Grows in Valley Bushveld, woodland, wooded grassland, rock outcrops and on forest edges.

Economic value Leaves are eaten by cattle but mostly by goats and game, such as kudu, nyala, bushbuck, grey duiker, vervet monkeys and baboons. The ripe fruits are edible, with a high vitamin C content (83 mg/100 g). The fruits can be eaten fresh, the slightly acidic flavour being most refreshing, or they can be cooked into a jelly or jam. To neutralise the acidic taste (high malic acid content), mix with grapes when making a preserve. The ripe fruits are popular with birds (purple-crested louries, Knysna louries, grey louries and the black-eyed bulbuls), so plant at least one Kei-apple tree in the garden. Larvae of the African leopard butterfly (*Phalanta phalantha*) feed on the leaves.

An attractive, drought- and frost-resistant addition to any garden. Plants can be spaced close together to form an impenetrable hedge around homesteads, gardens and croplands to keep unwanted animals and people out. A non-aggressive root system.

Cultivation Collect ripe fruit and dry them in a shady spot. Remove the seeds and sow them in flat seedling trays filled with river sand. Press the seeds down into the sand until they are level with the surface of the sand and cover with a layer of fine sand and keep moist. Seedlings transplant well. The Kei-apple can also be propagated from hardwood cuttings, but remember to treat the cut tips with a root-stimulating hormone before planting into river sand. The Kei-apple thrives in loamy or sandy soil with added compost. It has a moderate growth rate of up to 600 mm per year. Plants will fruit when at least three years old. They are drought-resistant and can take very light frost, except the young plants which must be protected for the first two years. Reacts well to pruning. It grows well in either full sun or light shade. Tolerates sea breezes and salt spray.

The Kei-apple has been grown in England and Australia since 1878 and is now grown as a garden plant in the U.S.A. and Israel.

KNOB THORN

Description A deciduous tree up to 30 m tall with a rounded or spreading crown. Young twigs growing in a zig-zag fashion. **Bark** yellowish and peeling on young twigs but dark brown with black prickles on prominent knobs on older branches (these disappearing with age), paired black hook thorns on young branches. **Leaves** twice compound with 2–4 pairs of grey-green pinnae each having 1 or 2 pairs of nearly circular leaflets up to 25 x 22 mm and asymmetric at base, leaf stalk very thin. **Flowers** in cream to yellowish white spikes up to 100 mm long, appearing before or with new leaves, made up of sessile flowers. **Fruit** a dark brown, thinly textured, splitting pod borne in pendant clusters. **Wood** with a yellow sapwood and a dark brown, hard, strong and tough, heavy (air-dry 1 120 kg/m³) heartwood.

Afrikaans	Knoppiesdoring
Northern Sotho	mokgalô
Zulu	umKhaya
Botanical name	*Acacia nigrescens*
Family	Pod-bearing Family (Fabaceae)
National tree list no.	178

Name derivation *Acacia* = derived from the Greek word 'akis' meaning a point or a barb, and *nigrescens* = becoming black.

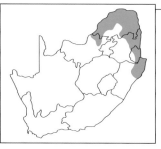

furniture wood but difficult to cut. Popular as fencing posts as the wood is hard and durable. During late summer and autumn, cattle eat the fallen leaves. Leaves and pods of the knob thorn form part of the primary and/or secondary diet of elephant, giraffe, kudu, impala, grey duiker and steen-bok. Most of these animals eat the leaves on the tree as well as the fallen leaves and sometimes also the young branches. The pods are a favourite with the brown-headed parrot which opens it up to get to the unripe seeds. The larvae of the dusky charaxes (*Charaxes phaeus*) butterfly live on this tree.

Diagnostic features Knobs with black hooked thorns on stem and branches; 1 or 2 pairs of roundish leaflets; creamy-white spikes.

Flowering from August to November.
Fruiting from January to June.

Distribution From Tanzania in the north to KwaZulu-Natal in the south.

Habitat Low-altitude woodland and wooded grassland, especially near or along drainage lines. Mostly on clay soils.

Economic value Grows in association with rooigras (*Themeda triandra*) or Smuts finger grass (*Digitaria eriantha*) and marula and is an indicator of sweetveld. West and north of the Waterberg the vegetation is known as Knob thorn or Knoppiesdoring veld. A good

Plant groups of this tree around or near water points in camps. A most beautiful and distinctive tree for the larger or farm garden. Also attractive when planted in a group of 3 or 5 on the lawn. It gives a 'bushveld' feeling to the garden. It has a taproot and is not aggressive.

Other uses A good-quality firewood producing long-lasting coals which give off intense heat. The bark contains 15% tannin compounds and is used by some tribes for tanning leather. It is one of the most popular and easiest indigenous trees to train as a bonsai specimen.

Cultivation Easily cultivated from seed. There are ± 6 200 seeds per kilogram. Soak seed in hot water, leave overnight and plant in separate black plastic nursery bags the next morning. Seedlings form a long taproot and must be planted into larger bags when they reach the 3-leaf stage. Seedlings transplant easily. A fast-growing species, up to 700 mm per year. Drought-resistant and can withstand cold, but sensitive to frost.

KOOBOO-BERRY

Description An evergreen tree usually up to 6 m tall but reaching up to 15 m, with a roundish crown. **Bark** on young branches green and softly hairy but dark grey and rough on older branches and stems. **Leaves** simple, alternate and leathery, dark green and slightly glossy above, dull lighter green underneath, tips round or bluntly pointed, margins with round to pointed teeth or sometimes smooth, side veins conspicuous. Leaf stalk up to 8 mm long. **Flowers** yellowish green on short stalks, borne in clusters in leaf axils, strongly scented. **Fruit** a fleshy oval to round red to purple drupe up to 20 mm in diameter. **Wood** with little distinction between sapwood and light brown heartwood which has a fine grain.

Afrikaans	Koeboebessie
Northern Sotho	monamane
Zulu	umNqayi
Botanical name	*Cassine aethiopica*
Family	Staff-tree Family (Celastraceae)
National tree list no.	410

Name derivation *Cassine* = a Florida Indian name, and *aethiopica* = African.

Diagnostic features Bark smooth and dark grey; leaves dark green and leathery, side veins prominent; flowers on short stalks and in tight clusters in leaf axils; fruit a red to purplish drupe.

Flowering from October to December.
Fruiting from January to May.

Distribution From Ethiopia in the north to the Western Cape in the south but also occurring on Madagascar, the Comoro Islands and the Seychelles.

Habitat Occupies a wide variety of habitats from very dry scrub to forest margins but most common in woodland and on termite mounds.

Economic uses The bark and leaves are eaten by black rhino and the leaves by stock and game (kudu, blue wildebeest, nyala, impala, grey and red duiker). Cattle and goats favour the young leaves but seldom eat the adult leaves. The ripe fruit on the tree but more so those on the ground are eaten by kudu, nyala, bushpigs, warthogs, grey duiker, red duiker, baboons, samango and vervet monkeys. The ripe fruits are popular with birds (purple-crested louries, Cape parrots, African green pigeons, black-eyed bulbuls and Swainson's francolins). The bark is used in tanning leather giving it a characteristic light brown colour. The wood is sometimes used for making carvings, small household articles and it makes a good fuel. The red to purplish ripe fruit is edible, with a somewhat tart taste but is bitter when not fully ripe.

This tree is an asset on any game farm and can be planted along stream beds and on termite mounds. The kooboo-berry can be used to fill openings in a shrub bed, giving colour during the fruiting period. Planted alone or in a small group it makes a beautiful specimen plant which is very attractive especially when laden with red fruit attracting man, bird and animal. A must in the garden to attract birds. It lends itself to container planting, reacting well to pruning. The root system is not aggressive at all.

Other uses An infusion made from the root bark is used for treating diarrhoea and dysentery and is sometimes used as an enema.

Cultivation Remove any flesh from the seeds for it contains a growth inhibitor. Sow the seed in trays filled with a mixture of river sand and compost (1:1) and keep moist and in a warm spot. Seeds usually take 2–3 weeks to germinate, germination being erratic. Transplant the seedlings into nursery bags filled with a mixture of river sand, loam and compost (1:2:1). Keep them in light shade for a month or two before gradually moving them to full sun. The young trees can be planted into open ground after one season. The growth rate is moderate, 400–500 mm per year. It tolerates mild frost and is very drought-hardy.

LARGE FEVER-BERRY

Description Depending on the locality, it is a semi-deciduous to evergreen tree up to 15 m high with a round densely leafy crown. **Bark** on young branches green and covered with star-shaped hairs and light-coloured corky dots (lenticels), but older branches and stems pale grey to greyish brown, smooth and with prominent light-coloured corky dots (lenticels). **Leaves** simple, alternate, roughly triangular, young leaves covered in star-shaped hairs, mature leaves smooth, with 4 or 5 pairs of side veins, leaf margin irregularly and roughly toothed, leaves sometimes turning a beautiful yellow to orangy brown during autumn. Leaf stalk up to 100 mm long, with two prominent glands at base of leaf blade. **Flowers** on 80–160 mm long spikes, yellowish green, separate male and female flowers, female flowers usually on lower part of inflorescence. **Fruit** a yellowish brown, three-lobed, non-splitting, pear-shaped, woody capsule up to 35 mm long, with brown and white mottled seeds. **Wood** with no clear distinction between sapwood and heartwood, whitish yellow, light (air-dry 600 kg/m^3).

Afrikaans	Grootkoorsbessie
Northern Sotho	motsibi
Botanical name	*Croton megalobotrys*
Family	Spurge Family (Euphorbiaceae)
National tree list no.	329

Name derivation *Croton* = Greek for a tick, referring to the shape of the fruit, and *megalobotrys* = Greek for a large cluster, referring to the flower head.

Diagnostic features Bark smooth and grey; leaf triangular in shape with 3 veins from the leaf base, 2 conspicuous glands at leaf base; spikes 80–160 mm long; fruit pear-shaped up to 35 mm in diameter; seeds mottled.

Flowering from September to November.
Fruiting from December to February.

Distribution From Tanzania in the north to Swaziland in the south.

Habitat Always associated with flood areas along streams and rivers, mostly forming dense stands.

Economic value The leaves and young branches are eaten by elephant and black rhino, and the leaves browsed by kudu, nyala, impala and bushbuck. Tree squirrels go to great lengths to open the fruit and eat the mottled seeds. The large fever-berry produces a useful general timber that can be used for shelving. It is often used for carving household articles and as the bottom piece in the fire-by-friction method. Larvae of the green-veined charaxes butterfly (*Charaxes candiope*) feed on the leaves.

The large fever-berry can be planted on the banks of streams and rivers in frost-free areas as browsing for game and as shade for cattle during the hot summer months. Planted on a lawn or open area in the garden, it will make an attractive shade tree. It has a non-invasive root system. The flowers attract a large variety of insects and they in turn insect-eating birds. This tree is not recommended for the highveld or other cool inland areas.

Other uses An infusion made from the root is used to treat abdominal pains, and the bark and seeds are used as a purgative and also to treat fever attacks. The seeds contain more active ingredients than the bark. The golden-yellow semi-drying oil extracted from the seeds is known as 'Croton oil', a strong purgative. The crushed seed is taken in water. In certain areas the powdered bark is thrown into pools to poison fish.

Cultivation Remove the ripe seeds from the fruit and plant in bags filled with a 1:1 mixture of river sand and compost and keep moist. The seeds should germinate after 3–4 weeks but this can be speeded up considerably if the seeds are first soaked in water overnight. The young plants can be transplanted into the open ground when they are ± 100 mm tall. If planted in colder areas, young plants should be protected against cold wind for the first two years. This species can survive prolonged drought conditions. The growth rate is very fast and can be up to 1.5 m per year.

LARGE-LEAVED CORAL TREE

Description A deciduous tree up to 12 m tall with a roundish to flat, loose to open canopy. **Bark** on young branches grey and slightly corky with spines, but grey, thickly corky and grooved with thorns on older branches and stems. **Leaves** large and compound with 3 leaflets, the side leaflets being smaller than the middle one, grey-green to dark green above and leathery, the surfaces covered with dense woolly hairs in young leaves but less woolly to smooth in adult leaves, venation prominent on undersurface, tips rounded, margin smooth. **Flowers** in cylindrical compact flowerheads on woolly stalks up to 300 mm long at tips of twigs, calyx red, filiform and covered in hairs with, petals deep crimson-red to scarlet. **Fruit** a large cylindrical pod up to 300 mm long, brownish black and deeply constricted between seeds, splitting to expose the large (11–15 mm in diameter) orange-red seeds. **Wood** with no heartwood, yellowish white, soft and light (air-dry 320 kg/m^3).

Afrikaans	Breëblaarkoraalboom
Northern Sotho	mphapha
Zulu	umGqwabagqwaba
Botanical name	*Erythrina latissima*
Family	Pod-bearing Family (Fabaceae)
National tree list no.	244

Name derivation *Erythrina* = from the Greek word 'erythros' meaning red, and *latissima* = very broad, referring to the leaflet size.

species, especially sunbirds, visiting it for the nectar. Young flowers and buds are eaten by the grey lourie and the unripe fruit by brown-headed parrots. The large leaves provide much needed shade for animals during the hot summer months.

This tree can be planted in groups of up to five in suitable habitats to provide shade and shelter. It makes an attractive garden plant that remains decorative throughout the year, with the contrasting bark, large leaves, the crimson flowers followed by the pretty pods and the attractive seed. It creates a stunning focal point on a large lawn. It has a rather invasive root system and should be planted away from buildings and paving and preferably only in large or farm gardens.

Other uses The burnt and powdered bark is used as a dressing for open sores.

Cultivation It is best to soak the seeds in hot water and leave them overnight before planting them in containers filled with river sand the next morning. The seeds can be pressed down into the sand and left like that or covered with a thin layer of river sand or compost. Seeds usually germinate within 2–5 weeks. Seedlings grow rapidly to form a thickened base. This is the best time to transplant them into larger containers. The large-leaved coral tree can also be propagated by truncheons planted during the spring. Cut a branch at least the thickness of your wrist, remove all the leaves and allow to dry for about two days. Plant in a hole with sand at the bottom. This will inhibit fungus growth and supply moisture to the young roots. The growth rate is relatively slow, 500–600 mm per year in the colder areas but faster, up to 900 mm in warmer areas. Can withstand light frost when mature. Plants usually flower during their second or third year.

Diagnostic features Deciduous; bark corky with scattered hooked thorns; leaves compound with 3 leaflets, middle leaflet the largest, leathery, young leaves with dense woolly hairs, venation prominent on undersurface; flowers in compact heads, calyx hairy and filiform, petals crimson; fruit a thick woody pod, seed orange-red.

Flowering from July to October.
Fruiting from November to April.

Distribution From Zimbabwe in the north to the Eastern Cape in the south.

Habitat Occurs mostly in wooded grassland and in scrub forest.

Economic value The bark, leaves and twigs are eaten by elephant. The red tubular flowers attract many bird

LARGE-LEAVED DRAGON TREE

Description Evergreen tree up to 5 m tall with or without a branched stem. **Bark** smooth and whitish to light brown with prominent marks left by the leaf bases. **Leaves** crowded towards top of stems, simple, leathery, broadly strap-shaped, with short broadening sheaths, leaf blade glossy green to bright green, with a smooth cartila-ginous leaf margin, leaves up to 1 m long. **Flowers** 1–4 together on a erect branched panicle up to 1 m long, flowers greenish white, sweet smelling. **Fruit** usually single-seeded, round, bright orange, up to 20 mm in diameter.

Afrikaans	Grootblaardrakeboom
Northern Sotho	photsoloma
Zulu	iThokothoko
Botanical name	*Dracaena aletriformis*
Family	Dragon Tree Family (Dracaenaceae)
National tree list no.	30.9

Name derivation *Dracaena* = from the Greek word for dragon, and *aletriformis* = likened to the genus *Aletris* and referring to the leaves.

used effectively in landscaping and makes an ideal specimen plant on lawns in the more subtropical regions and along the coast. An ideal foliage plant to give height and texture under larger trees, or plant a group of dragon trees of various heights to fill an opening in a shady place. It mixes well with other plants. Planted in a container, it makes a superb indoor plant but it must have a very good flow of air. Grows very well if planted in a container and kept on the patio where it receives shade for some hours during the day. It does not have an aggressive root system.

Diagnostic features Evergreen; bark smooth and whitish with leaf scars; leaves crowded towards tops of stems, leaf margin whitish, venation parallel; groups of 1–4 greenish white flowers on an erect branched panicle; fruit orange.

Flowering from November to February.
Fruiting from February to April.

Distribution From Kenya in the north to the Eastern Cape in the south.

Habitat Coastal dune forests and evergreen montane forests. Always in humus-rich soil.

Economic value Fruit-eating birds (Rameron pigeons, African green pigeons, Knysna louries, purple-crested louries, black-eyed bulbuls) love the ripe fruits. Larvae of the bush nightfighter butterfly (*Artitropa erinnys erinnys*) feed on the leaves of this tree.

A worthwhile tree to plant in the garden to attract butterflies. The conspicuous orange-red fruits attract birds to the garden. The large-leaved dragon tree can be

Cultivation Grows easily from fresh seed. Collect the seeds and remove the sticky orange pulp for it contains a growth inhibitor that will keep the seeds from germinating quickly. Sow the seeds in seedling trays filled with a mixture of river sand and compost (1:2) and cover with either a layer of fine compost or river sand and keep moist. The growth medium must be kept moist under all circumstances. Seeds usually germinate after 15–20 days, but germination is sometimes erratic, especially if the seeds are old. Transplant the seedlings into nursery bags filled with a mixture of river sand and compost (1:1) when they reach the 5-leaf stage. This is a critical period; so ensure that the young plants receive sufficient water and keep them in the shade. Keep them in the bags for at least one season before planting them out into the open ground. Truncheons or stem cuttings will also root but it is preferable to grow it from seed. The growth rate is moderate, up to 800 mm per year if the plants receive enough water. The large-leaved dragon tree needs lots of water during the growing season and less during winter. It grows the best in light to deep shade. Frost- and drought-sensitive.

LARGE-LEAVED FALSE THORN

Description A deciduous tree up to 20 m tall with a spreading rounded to flat crown. **Bark** on young branches covered with dense brownish to yellowish hairs, but corky, greyish brown and rough on older branches and stems. **Leaves** twice compound, up to 300 mm long, with 1–3 pairs of pinnae and each with 3–5 pairs of leaflets, the top pair the largest, hairy, venation prominent and much raised below, margin smooth, new leaves soft and bright reddish brown, autumn leaves yellow. **Flowers** in faintly scented half-spherical heads, creamy white, stamens up to 40 mm long. **Fruit** a large pod, reddish brown when young but pale brown when mature, up to 270 mm long, thinly textured, with thickened margins. **Wood** with a light brown sapwood and a dark to reddish brown, moderately heavy (air-dry 650 kg/m^3) heartwood.

Afrikaans	Grootblaarvalsdoring
Northern Sotho	mokgobongo
Zulu	umVangazi
Botanical name	*Albizia versicolor*
Family	Pod-bearing Family (Fabaceae)
National tree list no.	158

Name derivation *Albizia* = named after F. de Albizzi, nobleman from Florence who brought an Asian species *Albizia julibrissin* into cultivation in Europe in 1749, and *versicolor* = variously coloured, referring to the leaves.

Diagnostic features Deciduous; young branches and leaves covered with rust-coloured hairs; leaves twice-compound with few pairs of broad leaflets, venation prominent below; stamens up to 40 mm long; pod thin with thickened margins.

Flowering from September to December.
Fruiting from December to March.

Distribution From Uganda in the north to KwaZulu-Natal in the south.

Habitat Large-leaved false thorn occurs in deciduous woodland on well-drained soils.

Economic value Leaves and shoots eaten by elephant and kudu. Seeds eaten by brown-headed parrots. Pods, especially the young pods, can cause poisoning of cattle and sheep which is termed albiziosis. Outbreaks of this disease occur in late winter or early spring when pods are blown from the trees. Poisoned animals can be treated with high dosages of vitamin B6. The wood is used for making furniture, cabinets, parquet floors and as a general timber wood on the farm and in the building trade. The termite-resistant wood is often used for beams, doors, window and door frames. When in flower, the large-leaved false-thorn is a source of nectar and pollen for bees.

Makes a beautiful shade tree and can be planted along lands for much needed shade for farm workers during the hot summer months. This tree makes a beautiful specimen plant and is strongly recommended for use in any large garden or park. It does not have an invasive root system.

Other uses The bark contains 4.8% tannin and is used for tanning leather. The inner bark produces a fairly strong rope. The root bark is used as an enema and purgative. The leaves and bark are used to soothe headaches. An infusion made from the bark is used as a wash for sore eyes and to treat skin diseases.

Cultivation Collect the pods while they are still hanging on the tree. Seeds on the ground are usually quickly parasitised. Soak them in hot water, leave overnight and sow the next morning in seedling trays filled with a mixture of river sand and compost (4:1). Sound seed usually gives 80–90% germination. Watch out for damping-off disease when the seedlings are still young. Plant seedlings out when they reach the 2-leaf stage. Be careful not to damage the long taproot while transplanting. Also easily cultivated from cuttings. Make softwood cuttings ± 100 mm long and dip the bottom ends into a root-stimulating hormone powder (e.g. Seradix) and plant in river sand. The growth rate is fast, up to 800 mm per year. It is drought-resistant but frost-sensitive. A beautiful tree for the warmer parts of the country.

A protected tree in South Africa.

LARGE-LEAVED ROCK FIG

Description A deciduous tree up to 10 m tall with a spreading round crown and roots which often grow over rocks and act as 'rock splitters'. Stipules forming a protective hood over the growth tip. All parts of the plant exude a non-toxic white latex. **Bark** on the thick young branches cream-coloured, with prominent leaf scars, but cream-coloured and flaking on older branches and stems. **Leaves** alternate, simple, heart-shaped and up to 160 mm in diameter and almost as long as wide, smooth to somewhat hairy especially on veins, leaf tip rounded to slightly pointed, leaf base distinctly lobed, margin smooth and sometimes wavy, leaf stalk up to 170 mm long. **Figs** in axils of leaves, 10–16 mm in diameter, with a short fruit stalk, greenish with white flecks and slightly reddish when ripe. **Wood** without any heartwood, pale brown, soft and light (air-dry 640 kg/m³).

Afrikaans	Grootblaarrotsvy
Northern Sotho	mphaya
Zulu	iNkokhokho
Botanical name	*Ficus abutilifolia*
Family	Fig Family (Moraceae)
National tree list no.	63

Name derivation *Ficus* = name for the cultivated fig, and *abutilifolia* = with leaves resembling that of the genus *Abutilon*.

Diagnostic features Deciduous; roots growing over rocks; bark cream-coloured; growth tip covered by stipules forming a protective hood; leaves large and heart-shaped with yellowish venation; leaf stalk up to 170 mm long; figs in axils of leaves and 10–16 mm in diameter.

Flowering and fruiting from September to March.

Distribution From Tanzania in the north to KwaZulu-Natal in the south.

Habitat On rocky hills and ridges. Common growing on cliffs.

Economic value The figs are eaten by fruit-eating birds (Rameron pigeons, African green pigeons, brown-headed and Rüppell's parrots, purple-crested and grey louries, barbets, bulbuls and starlings), vervet monkeys and baboons. The fruits that they drop to the ground are eaten by kudu, nyala, bushbuck, klipspringer and grey duiker.

A very useful tree to have on the game farm and in the garden to attract birds. It has a rather aggressive root system and should be kept away from buildings, paved areas and swimming pools. Well-suited to the larger garden. Makes a beautiful container plant with cream-coloured stems in winter and large roundish leaves in summer. It can also be used as an accent plant in the garden on the lawn or planted near a group of rocks.

Other uses The fruits are edible, with a sourish taste and nearly always infested with insects but these can be washed out with water. Figs can be dried and used later.

Cultivation Grows well from seed and cuttings. The seed is very fine and must be mixed with fine river sand before sowing to ensure even distribution. Use fresh seed and sow in flat seedling trays filled with seedling mix obtainable from a nursery or in a mixture of river sand and compost (1:1). Keep moist. The seedlings transplant well. Grows very easily from cuttings which root without special treatment. Growth rate moderate, up to 700 mm per year. Frost-sensitive.

LARGE NUM-NUM

Description An evergreen tree up to 5 m tall with a much branched roundish crown, all parts exuding a non-toxic milky latex. **Bark** on young stems green and smooth, but grey-brown and rough on older branches and stems, spines Y-forked, 20–50 mm long, becoming woody. **Leaves** opposite and simple, leathery and shiny dark green above, tapering into a bristle tip, up to 60 x 35 mm, side veins obscure, base square to rounded, margin smooth, axillary glands conspicuous, leafstalk up to 5 mm long and channelled above. **Flowers** in clusters at the base of or sometimes in the Y-shaped thorns or terminally, white and sweetly scented, up to 35 mm in diameter, with a glabrous corolla which is hairy within, flower tube up to 14 mm long with the spreading lobes overlapping to the left. **Fruit** an oval-shaped, fleshy berry up to 50 x 35 mm, red when mature, with milky latex, many-seeded.

Afrikaans	Grootnoemnoem
Zulu	umThungulu
Botanical name	*Carissa macrocarpa*
Family	Oleander Family (Apocynaceae)
National tree list no.	640.3

Name derivation *Carissa* = probably from the Sanskrit word 'Corissa', a name for one of the Indian species, and *macrocarpa* = large fruit.

and other insect species with insect-eating birds paying regular visits to these plants. The ripe fruits are eaten by baboons, vervet monkeys and fruit-eating birds (Knysna louries, starlings and bulbuls). The edible fruits have a sweetish taste and are rich in vitamin C, calcium, magnesium and phosphorus. The fruits can be eaten raw or made into a dessert or an excellent jam. Raw fruit can be marketed locally and abroad for it has a long shelf life. This fruit should be promoted much more than it is at present.

Diagnostic features Evergreen; with milky latex; young branches green; thorns Y-shaped; leaves opposite and glossy dark green with a bristle tip; axillary glands conspicuous; flowers white and scented, flower tube hairy within; fruit red and many-seeded.

Flowering from July to November.
Fruiting from September to January.

Distribution From Mozambique in the north to the Eastern Cape in the south.

Habitat In coastal bush never far from the sea, mostly on vegetated sand dunes.

Economic value The flowers attract many butterflies

It can be used for protection as impenetrable hedges if the plants are planted ± 1 m apart. These hedges can be clipped to form neat, square shapes. They are very useful around gardens and homesteads to keep unwanted animals and intruders out. It is worthwhile planting the large num-num in coastal gardens for they can withstand heavy winds and salt spray. It is strongly recommended for any garden. Its drought tolerance and ability to grow in most soils make it popular in the garden of today.

Other uses The root is sometimes used medicinally.

Cultivation The large num-num is easily grown from seed, cuttings or layers. Seed should be cleaned and sown in flat seedling trays filled with a mixture of river sand and compost (2:1). Cover the seeds with a thin layer of sand and keep moist. Germination usually takes from 16–30 days. The new leaves are soft, with an attractive shiny red-copper colour. It is usually frost-tender but can tolerate a little frost – but not cold winds. Plants in frost-free areas are fast-growing and flower in the second year.

LARGE SOURPLUM

Description A deciduous tree up to 6 m tall with an open, shapeless, untidy crown. **Bark** on young branches green to pale brown, ridged and covered in dense rusty hairs but dark grey and rough, breaking into small rectangular scales on older branches and stems. The young branches are spine-tipped. **Leaves** alternate, simple, borne in axils of spines or in groups on short side branches, leathery, dark green, smooth, midrib sunken on upper surface, margin smooth, tip rounded to notched, base rounded. Leaf stalk up to 8 mm long, sometimes hairy. **Flowers** borne singly in leaf axils or in clusters in axils of spines, flowers up to 12 mm long, with four cream to greenish petals which are bearded within and with tips recurved; stamens 8. **Fruit** an oval drupe up to 40 mm long, pinkish to deep red with whitish dots, glossy. **Wood** with a whitish sapwood and a reddish brown, hard, moderately heavy (air-dry 830 kg/m³) heartwood.

Afrikaans	Grootsuurpruim
Northern Sotho	morotologa
Zulu	umThunduluka-obomvu
Botanical name	*Ximenia caffra*
Family	Sourplum Family (Olacaceae)
National tree list no.	103

Name derivation *Ximenia* = named after a Spanish monk, Francisco Ximenez, and *caffra* = from Kaffraria (Eastern Cape)

Bowker's sapphire (*Iolaus bowkeri*), saffron sapphire (*Iolaus pallene*), brown playboy (*Deudorix antalus*) and the bush scarlet butterfly (*Axiocerses amanga*) feed on the leaves.

The large sourplum is a worthwhile tree to plant in the garden to attract fruit-eating birds and the various butterflies whose larvae feed on the leaves. It makes an ideal container plant and is particularly pretty when in full fruit. Keep the plant compact by trimming away the excess branches during August to September. It does not have an aggressive root system.

Diagnostic features Untidy crown with spine-tipped branches; petals recurved and bearded within; fruit an oval red drupe with a strong sourish taste.

Flowering from August to October.
Fruiting from November to February.

Distribution From Tanzania in the north to KwaZulu-Natal in the south.

Habitat In woodland or wooded grassland, rocky hillsides or on rock outcrops. Sometimes on termite mounds.

Economic value The leaves are eaten by giraffe, eland, kudu, impala, bushbuck and klipspringer. The ripe fruit is edible, with a refreshing sour taste. Ripe fruit is used for making jam, dessert and jelly. It has a vitamin C content of 27% and the seed has an oil content of 65%. Ripe fruits are eaten by birds (barbets, bulbuls and starlings) and animals (eland, kudu, warthogs, grey duiker and steenbok). Larvae of the Natal bar (*Spindasis natalensis*), silvery bar (*Spindasis phanes*),

Other uses The non-drying oil from the seed, ximenia oil, is used by some people to soften leather and for lamps. It is also used as a cosmetic for rubbing chapped feet and to anoint the body. A decoction made from the leaves is used as a wash to soothe inflamed eyes. An infusion made from the roots is used as a remedy for dysentery and diarrhoea, and together with the leaves is taken for abdominal pains and for bilharziasis. Powdered roots are applied to sores to speed up healing. Dried leaves are powdered and taken orally to break fevers.

Cultivation Collect fresh seed from the trees and sow in seedling trays filled with a mixture of river sand and compost (5:1). Press the seeds into the mix until flush with the surface and cover with a thin layer of sand. Keep moist and never allow the mix to dry out. The seed should germinate after 14–30 days, but germination is usually erratic. Transplant the seedlings into nursery bags when they reach the 2-leaf stage. Take care not to damage the long roots while transplanting. Fill the bags with a mixture of river sand and compost (5:1). Do not keep the plants in the bags for longer than a season before planting them out into open ground. The growth rate is moderate, up to 500 mm per year. The large sourplum can withstand moderate frost and is drought-resistant, but needs full sun. The autumn leaves turn a deep purple colour before they are shed.

LAVENDER TREE

Description A semi-deciduous to evergreen tree up to 15 m tall with a spreading to roundish crown. **Bark** on young branches grey and smooth to flaking in strips, but grey to light-brown flaking in large pieces leaving lighter patches on older branches and stems. **Leaves** simple, alternate, with scattered glands throughout leaf blade, aromatic with a distinct lavender smell, smooth and shiny light green above and much lighter below, tip and base tapering, pockets situated between midrib and side veins, midrib prominent below, leaf stalk 8–25 mm long, young leaves light coppery red, producing beautiful autumn colours ranging from red through to purple. **Flowers** in branched and spreading heads at tips of branches, flowers small, white to pale yellowish cream, fragrant, with a gland-dotted calyx. **Fruit** a capsule splitting at maturity. **Wood** brownish purple, tough, medium hard.

Afrikaans	Laventelboom
Zulu	iNkunzi
Botanical name	*Heteropyxis natalensis*
Family	Lavender Tree Family (Heteropyxidaceae)
National tree list no.	455

Name derivation *Heteropyxis*: 'heteros' = distinct + 'pyxidatus' = a capsule with a box-like lid, and *natalensis* = from Natal.

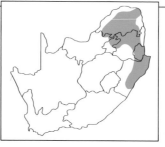

Diagnostic features Bark peeling; leaves glossy and with scattered glands throughout the leaf blade; crushed twigs and leaves with a distinct lavender smell.

Flowering from December to March.
Fruiting from March to May.

Distribution From Zimbabwe in the north to KwaZulu-Natal in the south.

Habitat The lavender tree sometimes occurs in forest margins but mostly on rocky hills and mountainsides in woodland or in wooded grassland.

Economic value Bark and leaves are eaten by black rhino and the leaves by kudu and grey duiker. The masses of small flowers attract many insects and they in turn many insect-eating birds.

The attractive bark, fragrant leaves and beautiful autumn colours make it an attractive garden subject. The lavender tree makes a good container plant and if kept in full sun, will form beautiful red and purple autumn leaves. It is a favourite for making bonsai.

Other uses A medicinal tea is made from the leaves. Bleeding gums and noses are treated by steaming the face in the vapour from a decoction made from the roots. Powdered leaves are administered to cattle to rid them of intestinal worms.

Cultivation Collect fresh seed from the trees. First mix the fine seed with fine river sand to ensure even distribution when sowing onto the seedling mix and keep under glass. The seed usually germinates after 10–14 days. Wait until the seedlings reach the 2-leaf stage before planting them out into black nursery bags filled with a mixture of river sand and compost (4:1). The growth rate is fast, 800–1 000 mm per year. Lavender trees prefer full sun but grow well in light shade. Young trees are frost-sensitive and must be protected for the first year.

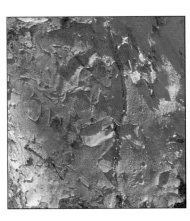

LEADWOOD

Description A semi-deciduous tree up to 20 m tall with a sparse roundish crown, new growth straight with opposite spine-tipped side branches. **Bark** on young branches smooth and covered with dark brown scales, on older stems it is pale grey, cracked into rectangular blocks along deep longitudinal furrows and irregular transverse cracks. **Leaves** on new growth only, simple, mainly opposite, tip broadly tapering to round, midrib protruding below, margin smooth but wavy, leaf stalk 4–10 mm long. **Flowers** in slender 4–8 mm long axillary spikes, flowers greeny white and changing to yellow, sweetly scented. **Fruit** 4-winged, up to 15 x 15 mm, pale yellowish green turning yellowish brown when dry. **Wood** with a thin yellowish sapwood and a dark brown, hard, very heavy (air-dry 1 200 kg/m³) heartwood.

Afrikaans	Hardekool
Northern Sotho	mohwelere-tshipi
Zulu	uMangwenja
Botanical name	*Combretum imberbe*
Family	Combretum Family
	(Combretaceae)
National tree list no.	539

Name derivation *Combretum* = a name that Pliny used for a creeping plant, and *imberbe* = beardless in Latin, and referring to the lack of hairs on the plant.

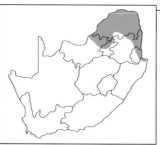

Diagnostic features Bark pale grey and cracked into rectangular blocks; leaves hairless, grey-green and surfaces covered in small silvery scales; fruit 4-winged, yellowish green and densely covered with silvery scales.

Flowering from November to March.
Fruiting from February to August.

Distribution From Tanzania in the north to KwaZulu-Natal in the south.

Habitat In various types of woodland along drainage lines but also in open veld. Common on alluvial soils, sometimes on heavy clay soils.

Economic value This tree is more for the game farmer as it is hardly utilised by cattle for browsing, except for shade to a certain extent. The young leaves of leadwood trees are more readily eaten than the more mature leaves. They are eaten by elephant, giraffe, kudu, red lechwe, impala and grey duiker. The leadwood tree is regarded as an indicator of good grazing areas and sweet veld. Stems are commonly used as fencing posts as the wood is not attacked by termites or borers. Various tribes carve grain mortars from the wood. In the past most of the straight-stemmed specimens were cut for railway sleepers. The wood is becoming increasingly popular for furniture. Although very heavy, it finishes with an extremely smooth surface and will last for generations. The wood becomes dark to blackish brown if treated with oil. Provides an excellent fuel as it burns slowly with an intense heat.

Plant scattered groups of leadwood trees in suitable spots in camps. It is suggested that these group plantings vary from 5–25 individuals. Protect the young plants for the first two years against defoliation by game. Such a group planting provides protection for many small animals and nesting sites for many bird species. Although rather large for the average garden, it makes an interesting subject. It has a non-aggressive root system.

Other uses The gum that exudes from damaged areas on the stem is edible and forms part of the diet of the Bushmen. It has become a popular wood for sculpturing and lathe-work. The ash contains a high percentage of lime and can be used as a substitute for lime to whitewash buildings. Root bark is boiled with water and used for tanning leather. A decoction made from the roots is taken orally to treat diarrhoea and with an infusion made from root bark to treat bilharziasis. Green leaves are placed on hot coals and the resultant smoke inhaled to relieve coughs and colds. Coughs are sometimes treated with an infusion made from the flowers.

Cultivation Unparasitised seeds can be carefully removed from the four-winged fruit. The seed should be planted in seedling trays filled with river sand. Press seeds level with the sand, cover with a thin layer of sand and keep moist. Seedlings usually emerge after 7–15 days. Usually only a few seeds germinate in the first three weeks; therefore many seeds must be sown. Watch out for rodents – they enjoy the seed! Transplant seedlings into nursery bags when they reach the 2-leaf stage. Transplant into open ground when 200–250 mm tall. Relatively quick-growing under favourable conditions, 0.5–1 m per year. A tree for frost-free areas only.

A protected tree in South Africa.

LEMON THORN

Description An evergreen tree up to 5 m tall with a much branched crown. **Bark** smooth and green on young stems but smooth and pale greyish brown on older branches and stems which are covered with simple green spines up to 50 mm long on one side between opposite leaves on the young zig-zag branches. **Leaves** simple, opposite, glossy green above and much duller below, margin smooth or with teeth, tip spiny. Leaf stalk up to 8 mm long. **Flowers** in branched clusters opposite spines, white to cream-coloured, up to 2 mm in diameter and borne on thin stalks that can be up to 10 mm long, sepals and ovary distinctly hairy. **Fruit** a slightly fleshy, smooth, bright orange drupe up to 13 mm in diameter, tipped with remains of style.

Afrikaans	Lemoentjiedoring
Zulu	isiHlokolozane
Botanical name	*Cassinopsis ilicifolia*
Family	White Pear Family (Icacinaceae)
National tree list no.	420

Name derivation *Cassinopsis* = resembling the genus *Cassine*, and *ilicifolia* = leaves resembling those of the holly (genus *Ilex*).

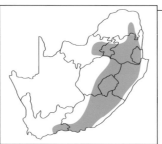

Diagnostic features Evergreen; crown much branched; young branches zig-zag and green; leaves very glossy; sepals and ovary hairy; fruit bright orange.

Flowering from September to November.
Fruiting from February to May.

Distribution From Zimbabwe in the north to the Western Cape in the south.

Habitat In montane forests, forest margins, in densely wooded kloofs and along streams.

Economic value The leaves are browsed by goats, cattle and game (kudu, klipspringer, grey and blue duiker). The ripe fruits are eagerly eaten by various bird species (bulbuls, starlings, barbets, pigeons, guineafowl and francolins).

The glossy leaves and the very decorative bright orange fruits together with the drooping habit of the green-barked branches make this an attractive specimen tree to be planted singly on the lawn. If a tree is preferred, the lower branches must be removed from an early stage. The root system is not aggressive, making it a good choice to plant close to buildings and paved areas. The lemon thorn is also a good species for filling an open spot in a shrubbery. The shiny leaves are decorative throughout the year. This tree is a must in any bird garden, birds seldom leaving the fruit to mature before gulping them down! It can also be grown successfully as a container plant, but it usually needs to be pruned quite often. A lemon thorn plant in a container and full in fruit makes quite a show! It makes a neat, interesting hedge if it is pruned often.

Other uses The ripe fruits are edible but do not always have an agreeable taste and flavour.

Cultivation Seeds germinate readily giving a germination of 70–80% if sown in pure river sand in seedling trays. Transplant the seedlings into nursery bags filled with river sand and compost (1:1) when they reach the 1-leaf stage. The growth rate is quite fast, up to 800 mm per year. The lemon thorn can tolerate an amazing amount of frost and drought. When the plant is under water stress, the leaves droop but recover quickly when watered. It can be grown either in shade or in the full sun.

MARULA

Description A deciduous tree up to 18 m tall with a round to spreading crown. **Bark** on young branches smooth and grey with prominent scars formed by the dropped leaves, but grey and flaking in patches on older branches and stems. **Leaves** unevenly compound with 7–13 pairs of leaflets plus a terminal one, crowded near the ends of branches, young leaves mostly toothed. **Flowers** in 50–80 mm long sprays, with sexes on separate trees, flowers yellow tinged red. **Fruit** fleshy, spherical and 30–35 mm in diameter, yellow when mature with a white clinging flesh and a large stone. **Wood** light reddish brown to whitish, with no definite heartwood, soft, light (air-dry 560 kg/m³), susceptible to borer attack if not treated.

Afrikaans	Maroela
Northern Sotho	morula
Zulu	umGanu
Botanical name	*Sclerocarya birrea* subsp. *caffra*
Family	Mango Family (Anacardiaceae)
National tree list no.	360

Name derivation *sclerocarya* = hard nut, *birrea* = 'birr', the common name for the tree in Senegal, and *caffra* = from Kaffraria (Eastern Cape)

Seed	52.51%
Edible flesh	6.47%
Vitamin C	67.9 mg/100 g
Calcium	6.2 mg/100 g
Magnesium	10.5 mg/100 g
Phosphorus	8.7 mg/100 g
Potassium	54.8 mg/100 g
Fructose	0.97 g/100 ml
Glucose	0.75 g/100 ml
Sucrose	5.95 g/100 ml

Diagnostic features Deciduous; roundish canopy; flaking bark; unevenly compound leaves with 7–13 leaflets and a terminal leaflet, crowded near the ends of branches; male and female flowers separate; fruit fleshy, yellow.

Flowering from September to November.
Fruiting from January to March.

Distribution From Ethiopia in the north to KwaZulu-Natal in the south.

Habitat Grows in various types of woodland on sand to sandy loam.

Economic value Cattle and game (elephant, giraffe, eland, kudu, waterbuck and warthog) utilize the fruit, leaves on the tree as well as on the ground and even the bark. Meyer's parrots feed on the kernels of green fruit. The wood is used for furniture and to a lesser extent, panelling. A popular wood for carvings and household articles. The fruit is popular with humans and with many bird and animal species. It is rich in vitamin C, with up to 2 mg/cc recorded.

Fruit analysis (after Quinn, 1959 & Wehmeyer, 1967):

Average mass	17.99 g
Skin	41%

Jelly (3 kg fruit to make 1 kg jelly) and jam can be made from the fruit. It produces a good-quality semi-sweet and sweet wine, port, beer (± 200 fruit produce 1 litre), juice and nectar. Each seed contains two or three edible nuts. Oil (56.2%) can be pressed from these and used as a preservative. These nuts can be eaten raw or roasted and are rich in oil and protein (28%).

The marula can be used most successfully as a shade tree in the garden or park and as a street tree. The improved strains of the marula can be planted in an orchard format for the commercial production of fruit. Drought-resistant but young trees are frost-sensitive. Plant young plants or truncheons in scattered groups of 5–10 individuals in a suitable habitat in camps. The marula tree can serve as shelter, browsing and food source.

Other uses A decoction of the bark is taken to treat dysentery and diarrhoea and prophyllactically for malaria. A brandy tincture of the bark is taken in small doses as a prophylactic against malaria. Bark contains 20.5% tannin and some alkaloids. The moist inner bark shows an antihistaminic action against insect bites and the burns of hairy caterpillars. The skin of the fruit can be boiled in water to make a drink; it is also burnt and used either as a substitute for coffee or as a snuff. Burns and abscesses are treated with an essence made from the leaves. A relatively good-quality rope can be made from the inner bark.

Cultivation Easily raised from seed. Plant seed directly into black nursery bags filled with river sand and keep in the shade until seedlings appear. Truncheons of 100–150 mm in diameter and 2 m long can be planted in early spring. One of the fastest growing trees in South Africa with a growth rate of up to 1.5 m per year.

MATUMI

Description An evergreen tree up to 40 m tall with a dense, straight and narrow crown. **Bark** on young stems smooth and green but grey-brown and rough with longitudinal cracks and ridges on older stems. **Leaves** simple, usually in whorls of four and crowded towards ends of branches, tapering to both ends, leathery and glossy with yellowish venation and a smooth margin. Leaf stalk up to 20 mm long. **Flowers** in round heads up to 40 mm in diameter and on long stalks with conspicuous bracts slightly above the middle of the stalk, borne in the leaf axils, flowers green to pale mauve, sweetly scented, with yellow exserted stamens. **Fruit** a small 2-lobed capsule. **Wood** with no distinct difference between sapwood and heartwood, yellowish with brown markings, with an oily smell, very hard, fine-grained and heavy (air-dry 1 026 kg/m³).

Diagnostic features Evergreen; leaves in whorls of 4, glossy green with yellow venation; flowers in round heads up to 40 mm in diameter, conspicuous bracts slightly above middle of stalk, stamens exserted; fruit a small 2-lobed capsule.

Flowering from December to March.
Fruiting June to August.

Distribution From Tanzania in the north to KwaZulu-Natal in the south.

Habitat Along banks of permanent streams. Sometimes with the roots in the water.

Economic value Used for parquet floors, for turning and boat-building. One of the best indigenous woods for making dining room tables and chairs, but also used for benches, side tables and trays. It makes excellent bread and meatboards for the kitchen. The oils in the wood prevent it from cracking when washed. One of the best woods to use for beams, the long trunks rendering long unjointed beams. It was very popular for railway sleepers up to 1960, with most of the tall matumi trees in the Transvaal Lowveld cut for this purpose. A popular wood for making dugout canoes in the countries north of Zimbabwe.

Afrikaans	Mingerhout
Northern Sotho	mohlomê
Zulu	umHlume
Botanical name	*Breonadia salicina*
Family	Gardenia Family (Rubiaceae)
National tree list no.	684

Name derivation *salicina* = with leaves like a willow.

The matumi makes a splendid street tree, with the narrow crown, evergreen glossy foliage and moderate to fast growth rate. In warmer areas it makes a fine shade tree – taking only a few years to reach maturity. A single matumi or a group planted on the lawn make fine specimen trees. It has rather an aggressive root system and should be planted away from buildings, paved areas and swimming pools. A very neat tree to plant in a park. Popular for making bonsai specimens.

Farmers in the warm, high rainfall areas can plant matumi trees in plantation form as a long-term project for harvesting hardwood later.

Other uses An extract of the bark is used for stomach complaints.

Cultivation Sow fresh seeds on the surface of river sand, cover them lightly with sand and keep moist. Germination is usually between 60–80%. Transplant the seedlings into nursery bags filled with a mixture of river sand and compost (5:1) when they reach the 3-leaf stage. Seedlings transplant well. The matumi grows in most soil types, provided that it receives enough water. It can grow with its roots in flowing water, but will not thrive in a waterlogged soil. The leaves are quick to show a lack of water and then take on a wilted appearance. It is frost-sensitive but can withstand some cold. The matumi has a fast growth rate, up to 1 m per year in warm, high rainfall areas, growing somewhat slower in a cooler climate.

The matumi is a protected tree in South Africa.

MITZEERI

Description A semi-deciduous to deciduous tree up to 20 m tall with a dense rounded crown and a tall bare stem. **Bark** on young branches grey-brown and smooth, but dark brown and rough cracking into squares on older branches and stems. **Leaves** alternate, simple, dark glossy green above and lighter below, with a neat herringbone venation ending at the margins and prominent on the lower surface, margin entire and slightly wavy. Autumn leaves a beautiful yellow, red and purple, young leaves coppery red. **Flowers** borne in clusters in axils of leaves, cream-coloured to light yellow, male flowers on short stalks and female flowers sessile. **Fruit** up to 8 mm long, glossy black and fleshy. **Wood** with a yellowish sapwood and a reddish brown to dark brown, hard and moderately heavy (air-dry 670 kg/m^3) heartwood.

Afrikaans	Mitserie
Northern Sotho	motsêrê
Zulu	umShonge
Botanical name	*Bridelia micrantha*
Family	Spurge Family (Euphorbiaceae)
National tree list no.	324

Name derivation *Bridelia* = named after Prof. S.E. de Bridel (1761–1828), and *micrantha* = small-flowered.

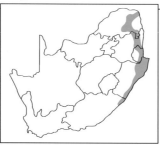

Diagnostic features Semi-deciduous to deciduous; leaves with herringbone venation ending at the margin, prominent on the lower surface; autumn leaves colourful; flowers in clusters, male and female flowers separate on same tree, female flowers sessile; fruit black and fleshy.

Flowering from September to December.
Fruiting from January to April.

Distribution From the Sudan in the north to the Eastern Cape in the south.

Habitat In swamp forest, along forest edges and streams. Also in open woodland.

Economic value The only animal recorded eating the leaves and the bark is the black rhino, and animals eating the leaves only are nyala, bushbuck and grey duiker. The ripe fruits are very popular with many of the fruit-eating birds (African green pigeons, Cape glossy starlings, purple-crested and grey louries, pied, black-collared and crested barbets, mousebirds and bulbuls), making the mitzeeri a must for the bird garden! Poles of mitzeeri are used for building huts and are sometimes cut for beams. The wood can be used for parquet floors, furniture and panelling. The oiled wood resembles black stinkwood. The termite-resist-ant wood makes good fence posts. Larvae of the giant charaxes (*Charaxes castor flavifasciatus*) and the Morant's orange (*Parasmodes morantii*) butterflies live on this tree.

Mitzeeri makes an excellent shade tree not only in the garden but also on the farm, forming a neatly shaped crown after only three years. These trees can be planted in areas that are flooded for short periods during the rainy season. The roots of the mitzeeri are extensive and bind soil effectively and it can therefore be used along eroded drainage lines and also along streams where the natural vegetation has been removed. The fast growing mitzeeri trees form a canopy under which various other plants germinate and grow, establishing new riverine vegetation. Farmers in the warm, high-rainfall areas can consider planting mitzeeri trees in a plantation as a long-term project for harvesting hardwood. Trees can be cut when they are 30 years old. The mitzeeri can be effectively used as a background plant in the garden adding a splash of colour in autumn with its yellow, orange and purple leaves. It has an aggressive root system and cannot be planted fairly close to buildings and paved areas.

Other uses The ripe fruit is edible, with a slight currant-like taste. The root is used as a purgative and an infusion made from the root is taken orally for coughs. The powdered bark is applied to burns to speed up healing. Leaf sap is used as an application for sore eyes.

Cultivation Use only fresh seed. The fruit pulp contains a growth inhibitor and must be removed from the seeds. Sow the seeds in seedling mix obtainable from the local nursery or garden centre or in a mixture of river sand and compost (2:1) and keep moist. The seedlings can be transplanted into nursery bags when they reach the 2-leaf stage. Seedlings and young plants transplant easily. One of the fastest growing indigenous trees in South Africa, with a growth rate of up to 2 m per year. Can withstand light frost but is not really drought-resistant.

A protected tree in South Africa.

MOBOLA PLUM

Description An evergreen tree up to 20 m tall with a single bare stem and dense roundish to mushroom-shaped crown. **Bark** on young stems covered with yellowish brown woolly hairs. **Leaves** alternate, simple, leathery to brittle, dark green above, with dense white to yellowish matted hairs below, venation conspicuous on both surfaces, finely parallel and raised on lower surface, margin smooth, leaf stalk hairy and 5–10 mm long. **Flowers** in branched heads borne in the leaf axils and covered with dense yellowish hairs, individual flowers with sepals hairy, petals white and sweetly scented, 7 or more stamens joined at the base into a short ring. **Fruit** oval to round and 30–50 mm long, greyish scaly and pitted becoming orange-yellow when ripe. **Wood** light brown, hard and moderately heavy (air-dry 720 kg/m³).

Afrikaans	Grysappel
Northern Sotho	mmola
Botanical name	*Parinari curatellifolia*
Family	Mobola Plum Family (Chrysobalanaceae)
National tree list no.	146

Name derivation *Parinari* = vernacular name for a Brazilian species, and *curatellifolia* = with leaves like the genus *Curatella*.

Diagnostic features Evergreen with rough bark; leaves hard and leathery, glossy dark green above and covered with dense white matted hairs below, veins all finely parallel; inflorescences covered with reddish brown hairs, fruit oval and pitted.

Flowering from July to October.
Fruiting from October to January.

Distribution From Senegal and Kenya in the north to Swaziland in the south.

Habitat Open woodland in low-lying areas or in wooded grassland, in areas of poor drainage. It often grows in sandy soil underlaid by poorly drained soil. The mobola plum is an indicator of a high water table and poor drainage.

Economic value Leaves are eaten by elephant, kudu and impala, the fruits by elephant, kudu, bushbuck, grey duiker, steenbok, bushpigs, baboons, vervet monkeys and porcupines. The wood is used for beams, poles and benches. The silica crystals in the wood make it difficult to work with. The trees produce abundant nectar and pollen thus making it popular with honey farmers. The larvae of the striped policeman butterfly (*Coeliades forestan*) use this as a food plant.

The mobola plum is a very neat, compact shade tree for the average garden. It does not have an invasive root system. Young plants planted in the veld in groups of 10 or more, as occur in nature, must be watered until they have established.

Other uses The fruits are edible, with a pleasant quince-like taste and eaten fresh or made into a porridge. Fruit can be boiled to make a very nutritious syrup. The seeds contain a large amount of oil and are eaten raw as a nut. The fruit is pounded with water and the resulting liquid is thickened with flour to make a gruel or thin porridge.

Cultivation Seed lying on the ground is nearly always parasitised; so collect fresh seed from the trees. Clean the flesh away and dry the seeds in the shade. Sow the seeds in river sand in flat seedling trays. Press seeds down until they are level with the soil surface and cover with a thin layer of sand. Be very careful when transplanting the seedlings for the taproot damages easily. Transplant seedlings into nursery bags when they are in the 3-leaf stage. Transplant these into the veld or garden only after two years. Plants grow quite fast. Very sensitive to frost and cold wind.

A protected tree in South Africa.

MONKEY THORN

Description A large, semi-deciduous tree up to 36 m tall with a spreading roundish crown and fluted trunk in old specimens. **Bark** on young branches corky and yellowish but, on older branches yellowish to brown, corky, rough and longitudinally fissured, often with scattered thorns on the trunk and branches. **Thorns** recurved to nearly straight, 8–12 mm long, dark brown and in pairs below the nodes. **Leaves** twice compound, glabrous, with a large gland just below the first leaflets, up to 160 mm long, with 7–14 pairs of pinnae with 12–40 pairs of leaflets. **Flowers** in 60–110 mm long spikes on short side shoots, with sessile flowers which are reddish to purplish before opening giving a reddish colour to the tree before the flowers are fully open, honey-scented. **Fruit** a pod, straight, 100–200 mm long, reddish to purplish brown, splitting, brittle. **Wood** with a pale brown sapwood and a hard, heavy (air-dry 980 kg/m³), coarse-grained, dark brown heartwood.

Afrikaans	Apiesdoring
Northern Sotho	mologa
Botanical name	*Acacia galpinii*
Family	Pod-bearing Family (Fabaceae)
National tree list no.	166

Name derivation *Acacia* = from the word 'akis' meaning a point or a barb, and *galpinii* = named after E.E. Galpin (1854–1941), banker and plant collector.

Diagnostic features Bark corky; scattered thorns on branches, thorns recurved and in pairs, dark brown; leaves with 7–14 pairs of pinnae and 12–40 pairs of leaflets per pinna; flowers in spikes, calyx purplish; pods brittle.

Flowering from September to January.
Fruiting from December to March.

Distribution From Zambia in the north to the Northwest Province in the south.

Habitat Occurs on river banks, in open wooded grassland and open woodland.

Economic value This tree is an indicator of sweetveld that stays palatable during the dry winter months. A valuable tree to provide shade for stock and game during the hot summer months. The heartwood was used for furniture, especially at the turn of the century when many chairs and *riempie* benches were made from this wood. The leaves and flowers are eaten by giraffe, with kudu eating the pods while they are still on the tree; later in the season they also eat the fallen pods.

Plant groups of 5–20 trees in suitable spots in camps on the farm to provide shade for labourers and animals during the hot summer months. One of the best indigenous trees to plant around the house to shelter it from wind but more so for the shade. When planted on the lawn it makes a good shade and specimen tree with the characteristic and attractive peeling bark. Keep the monkey thorn a fair distance away from buildings or paving as it does have an aggressive root system.

Other uses The bark provides a reasonably good-quality rope.

Cultivation Seed must be immersed in hot water, left to soak overnight and the swollen seeds planted the next morning. Sow seed in deep, flat seedling trays filled with river sand. Cover the seed lightly with sand and keep moist. Seeds usually germinate after 7–14 days, with a 80–90% germination. A species with a fast growth rate, up to 1 m per year. It can withstand light frost but young plants must be protected from frost for the first two seasons. Fairly drought-resistant. Plants thrive in a deep well-drained soil.

MOPANE

Description A semi-deci-duous tree with an erect narrow crown, growing up to 18 m in South Africa but up to 30 m in the Caprivi and further north. **Bark** dark grey or brown, on older branches and stems. **Leaves** leathery and shiny, young leaves a reddish coppery colour, leaflets asymmetric. **Flowers** in a slender raceme or panicle, individual flowers greenish yellow. **Fruit** a kidney-shaped pod, covered in oil glands. **Wood** with a thin yellow to light brown sapwood and dark red heartwood, very hard, heavy (air-dry 1 250 kg/m^3), durable and termite-resistant.

Afrikaans	Mopanie
Northern Sotho	mopane
Botanical name	*Colophospermum mopane*
Family	Pod-bearing Family (Fabaceae)
National tree list no.	198

Name derivation *Colophospermum* = from the Greek meaning oily seed, and *mopane* = derived from the local name for the tree.

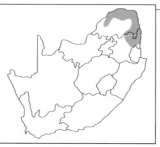

by elephant, the green and fallen leaves by giraffe, buffalo, eland, kudu, Lichtenstein's hartebeest, nyala, impala, grey duiker and steenbok. Mant successful game/cattle farms are situated in the mopane veld areas. Poles are valued as fencing posts for their hardness and durability. An excellent fuel source. In the past mopane was often used for railway sleepers and parquet blocks. The wood is somewhat difficult to work with, but produces high-quality furniture and is often used for inlay work in more light-coloured woods. Mopane poles are a most important building material and are used in building huts and cattle enclosures. Larvae of the foxy charaxes (*Charaxes jasius saturnus*) butterfly and mopane worm (*Gonimbrasia belina*) feed on the leaves. Mopane worms are 50–80 mm long and are eaten roasted or dried by various tribes. They have a very high protein content and are a highly nutritious food.

Diagnostic features Bark dark brown with deep longitudinal grooves; leaves with a single pair of triangular leaflets with 7–12 prominent veins from the base; flowers without petals; fruit a kidney-shaped flat non-splitting pod with numerous scattered oil glands; seed flat and very wrinkled with large reddish resinous oil glands.

Flowering from October to March.
Fruiting from March to June.

Distribution From Malawi and Zambia in the north to the Northern Province in the south.

Habitat Dry lowland woodland. It forms a distinctive vegetation type known as 'Mopane woodland'. Mopane is regarded as an indicator of shallow, poorly drained, often alkaline soils. Mopane trees growing in sandveld indicate a shallow layer of sand overlaying poorly drained soil.

Economic value When cattle and small stock have become accustomed to the aromatic odour, they readily browse the leaves, either fresh or in the dry state on the ground. The palatable young leaves produce more crude protein and nitrogen and have a lower percentage of tannin than the older leaves and they are therefore more readily eaten. The mature leaves are mostly eaten during summer and autumn. The crude protein content is in the order of 12–15% during summer and autumn and around 9% during winter and spring. Green leaves and young branches are eaten

Plant young mopane plants in groups of up to 50 in suitable areas in camps. The red, brown and orange autumn colours add attractive colour to the garden. It has a non-aggressive root system.

Other uses An extract from the bark is used in tanning leather which takes on a light brown colour. The inner bark can be used for making a very strong rope. A decoction made from the wood is used for inflammation of the eyes.

Cultivation Seed can be sown while still in the pod. However, removing the pod speeds up the process. Take care not to damage the seed when easing it out of the pod. Fill flat seed trays with river sand and place the seed on top of the sand and keep it moist. As soon as the seeds germinate, reduce the amount of water or else the seedlings will damp-off. Seedlings are initially slow-growing but the growth speeds up considerably when the plants reach a height of 200 mm. Transplant seedlings into black nursery bags filled with a mixture of compost, sand and loamy soil (1:2:7). Take care not to damage the roots while transplanting. The trees are sensitive to frost and it is therefore primarily a plant for frost-free areas.

MOUNTAIN HARD PEAR

Description An evergreen tree up to 20 m tall with a dense roundish crown. **Bark** on the young, square branches smooth and creamy white, but on older branches and stems creamy white to grey, flaking to reveal orange areas giving it a mottled appearance. **Leaves** opposite, simple, dark green and glossy above but lighter below, margins smooth, tip roundish with a prominent notch, base tapering. Leaf stalk very short and reddish. **Flowers** in compact many-flowered branched sprays, pink with a faint sweet scent, calyx tubular and minutely 5-lobed, petals 5, inserted in calyx tube, stamens inserted on inner rim of calyx tube below scales. **Fruit** a round, dark pink to reddish drupe up to 10 mm in diameter with a small grooved ring at the tip, in dense clusters between the leaves. **Wood** whitish to light brown, hard and heavy.

Afrikaans	Berghardepeer
Northern Sotho	mmasephaletsi
Zulu	uQudu
Botanical name	*Olinia emarginata*
Family	Hard Pear Family (Oliniaceae)
National tree list no.	514

Name derivation *Olinia* = named after J.H. Olin (1769–1824), a Swedish botanist, and *emarginata* = with a notch at the tip (of the leaf).

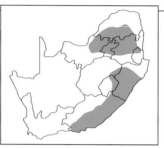

Diagnostic features Evergreen; bark mottled, young branches square and whitish; leaf tip notched, leaf stalk short and reddish; flowers pink, calyx tubular and minutely 5-lobed, stamens inserted on inner rim of calyx tube below scales; fruit reddish with a small grooved ring.

Flowering from October to January.
Fruiting from March to July.

Distribution From Zimbabwe in the north to the Eastern Cape in the south.

Habitat The mountain hard pear sually grows in the shade on mountain slopes, in evergreen forest patches and along wooded stream banks.

Economic value The ripe fruits are eaten by many species of fruit-eating birds (Rameron and African green pigeons, Knysna and purple-crested louries, bush black-caps, bulbuls and crested barbets). The dense crown of small leaves makes this an effective screening plant and windbreak. It can also be grown as an ornamental and makes a very neat container plant, with dense, small and glossy leaves, but for the best effect it must be kept in full sun and watered often. When in flower and fruit, the mountain hard pear makes a superb accent plant on the lawn. The neat growth habit makes it an ideal street tree. This is one of the best tree species for the small garden. The roots are not agressive and the tree is attractive with or without the flowers and fruit. The mountain hard pear makes a neat bonsai, resulting in a plant that resembles the adult tree in a relatively short period.

Cultivation It is difficult to propagate this tree from either seed or cuttings. Sow the seed in a seedling tray filled with seedling mix obtainable from the local nursery or in a mixture of river sand and compost (1:1) and keep moist. Take special care that the mixture does not dry out! Germination is erratic and usually takes up to 9 months. Transplant the seedlings into nursery bags when they reach the 2-leaf stage. Young plants must be watered well after transplanting. The growth rate is moderately fast, 500–700 mm per year. The mountain hard pear can withstand several degrees of frost but no drought.

MOUNTAIN KAREE

Description An evergreen tree with drooping branches, up to 8 m tall, with a dense crown. **Bark** on young branches reddish brown, but dark brown and rough on older branches and stems. **Leaves** with three dull green sessile leaflets, the middle leaflet the longest, up to 95 x 25 mm, midrib prominent above and below, margin mostly toothed. Leaf stalk up to 50 mm long. **Flowers** in many-branched sprays at tips of branches, flowers small and light yellow, male and female flowers on separate trees. **Fruit** flattened, glossy, light yellowish brown, up to 6 mm in diameter. **Wood** reddish brown, hard and heavy (air-dry 1 010 kg/m³).

Afrikaans	Bergkaree
Northern Sotho	mohlwehlwe
Botanical name	*Rhus leptodictya*
Family	Mango Family (Anacardiaceae)
National tree list no.	387

Name derivation *Rhus* = the classical Greek name for *Rhus coriaria*, and *leptodictya* = with a fine network, referring to venation of the leaf.

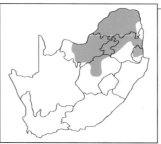

Diagnostic features Branches drooping; bark rough and dark brown, with reddish brown young branches; leaves with three leaflets, leaf margin mostly toothed, leaf stalk up to 50 mm long; flowers in sprays at tips of branches; male and female trees; fruit flattened.

Flowering from December to April.
Fruiting from March to June.

Distribution From Angola and Malawi in the north to the Free State in the south.

Habitat Occupies most habitat types but shows a preference for rocky slopes.

Economic value A valuable fodder tree during drought conditions. In some areas this is one of only a few evergreen tree species in the veld. It forms part of the primary and secondary diets of various game species (giraffe, eland, kudu, impala, grey duiker and steenbok). Popular with fruit-eating birds, especially barbets and bulbuls. Game birds such as guineafowl and francolin relish the fruit that drop to the ground.

Leaves of the mountain karee do not taint milk to the same extent as those of the karee (*Rhus lancea*). The leaves are readily eaten by domestic stock. The wood is suitable for the manufacture of small pieces of furniture. It becomes a dark glowing reddish brown after a few years of oiling.

This plant grows easily in shallow rocky soil and can be planted in groups of 10 or more scattered throughout cattle camps. Use this tree for shade by planting it near water points and salt licks, but protect it for the first one or two years from animals browsing the leaves. It is a popular garden plant with a dense roundish crown and contrasting dark brown stem that can be planted along a fence to form an effective hedge or windbreak. It becomes a fine shade tree after about five or more years. It also makes a beautiful specimen tree if planted alone. The mountain karee makes a most successful street tree (it has a non-aggressive root system) and is planted for this purpose in many towns in southern Africa. No bird garden should be without it!

Other uses Fruit edible, with a sourish taste. A strong beer can be made from the fermented fruit.

Cultivation Sow seed during December to March in seedling trays filled with river sand. Soak the seed overnight in water for the best results. Cover the seed only slightly with sand and keep moist. Germination is relatively quick, 6–8 days with a 80–100% success. Seedlings can be transplanted into nursery bags when they reach the 2-leaf stage. The mountain karee is frost- (up to -7°C) and drought-resistant and grows in any type of soil. It grows best in full sun but also does well in light shade. The growth rate is fast, up to 1 m per year. Young plants should be pruned to form a single-stemmed tree.

MOUNTAIN MAHOGANY

Description A semi-deciduous to deciduous tree up to 30 m tall, with a rounded crown and a straight clean trunk. **Bark** on young branches smooth and pale grey-brown covered with light brown hairs, on older stems and branches thick, grey-brown flaking in 100–120 mm large round patches producing a mottled appearance. **Leaves** up to 250 mm long, evenly compound with 6–7 pairs of mostly opposite pairs of leaflets, leaflets tapering into long thin tips, base of leaflets very asymmetric, they are dark green above and lighter below with margins smooth, leaves turning yellow during autumn. **Flowers** together with the new leaves, in furry sprays, individual flowers pale green and hairy outside, stamens forming a staminal tube 3–4 mm long. **Fruit** a woody, banana-like capsule up to 250 x 50 mm, splitting into five sections which curl back from the thick 5-angled central column marked with the impressions of the seeds; seeds with large papery wings. **Wood** scented, sapwood pale red and heartwood dark reddish brown, hard and moderately heavy (air-dry 740 kg/m³).

Afrikaans	Bergmahonie
Northern Sotho	mopumena
Botanical name	*Entandrophragma caudatum*
Family	Mahogany Family (Meliaceae)
National tree list no.	293

Name derivation *Entandrophragma* = Greek for 'in compartments', referring to the fruit, and *caudatum* = Latin word for 'tailed', referring to the tips of the leaflets.

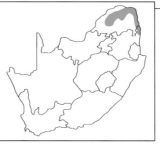

Diagnostic features Bark on older stems flake in large pieces giving a mottled appearance; leaves evenly compound, tips of leaflets long and thin, bases asymmetric; fruit banana-like with 5 valves curling back from the 5-angled central column resembling a half-peeled banana; seeds with a large papery wing.

Flowering from October to December.

Fruiting from April to June.

Distribution From Zambia in the north to Mpumalanga in the south.

Habitat The mountain mahogany ccurs in sandy and loam soils on rocky ridges and on mountain slopes.

Economic value The wood works easily, produces a very fine finish and is used for furniture and sometimes for cabinet-making. The bark as well as the red sap that oozes from between the wood and the bark is used for dyeing and tanning. Green fruits are eaten by elephants and the seeds by kudu and grey duiker. The wooden banana, as it is also known, can be planted as a plantation in suitable areas for the production of hardwood for furniture manufacturing. The medium growth rate of the tree makes this a long-term project. During the hot summer months, the wooden banana provides much needed dense shade for animals and birds. On the farm it can be planted in groups of up to 10 for its shade, but in the garden one tree is sufficient. The dry fruits that resemble half-peeled bananas are highly sought after by florists all over South Africa and abroad. They are rather fragile and should be handled carefully!

The mountain mahogany makes a splendid garden subject for the large garden and park with the yellow autumn leaves and the banana-like fruits. The young plant, with its swollen stem and simple leaves (compound leaves develop only 2–3 years later), makes an interesting container plant and a fascinating bonsai specimen. Although it is a rather large tree, it has a non-aggressive root system.

Cultivation Seeds must preferably be collected from the fruit just before it opens. Insects usually parasitize the seeds after the fruit has opened while still on the tree. Sow seeds in deep seedling trays in a mixture of river sand and compost (2:1). They should start to germinate after 14 days. Germination in this species is very erratic, seeds still germinating after three months. If planted in frost-free areas, it is a fairly fast grower, up to 800 mm per year. It is drought-tolerant but frost-sensitive.

A protected tree in South Africa.

MOUNTAIN SYRINGA

Description A deciduous tree up to 18 m tall, with a roundish to spreading crown. **Bark** on young branches initially smooth and glossy green with conspicuous leaf scars, but grey and smooth on older branches and stems. **Leaves** crowded at tips of branches, alternate, 100–200 mm long, unevenly compound with 20–40 pairs of shiny, grey-green, coarsely toothed, opposite and pointed leaflets with an odd leaflet at the tip, leaf stalk 30–40 mm long; leaves developing attractive yellow, red and purple autumn colours. **Flowers** in much branched compact heads, greenish white. **Fruit** a small light brown four-valved capsule. **Wood** greyish white, with no heartwood, medium hard, coarse-grained and light (air-dry 576 kg/m^3).

Afrikaans	Bergsering
Northern Sotho	modumela
Botanical name	*Kirkia wilmsii*
Family	Quassia Family (Simaroubaceae)
National tree list no.	269

Name derivation *Kirkia* = named in honour of of Sir John Kirk (1832–1922), explorer and naturalist, and *wilmsii* = named in honour of Dr F. Wilms (1848–1919), chemist and botanical collector from Lydenburg.

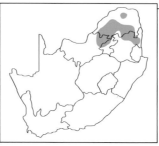

The wood is used for making household utensils. A strong rope can be made from the inner bark.

Groups of the mountain syringa can be planted in camps to provide the necessary shade for stock and game. A worthy addition to a garden – with its attractive autumn colours and contrasting grey branches. The mountain syringa does not have an aggressive root system and is often used as a street tree.

Other uses The mountain syringa is one of the best trees to tap the roots for water. A ± 80 mm in diameter shallow root is needed. Cut the root at a length of ± 1 m first at the end closest to the tree and then the other end and turn it upside down so that the end nearest to the tree, is at the bottom. Remove the bark at this end for ± 50 mm. After a short while water will start dripping out of the root. This water is clean and refreshing. Hunters, something to remember! The powdered root is sometimes used for toothache.

Diagnostic features Young branches with conspicuous leaf scars; bark grey and smooth; leaves crowded at tips of branches, compound with 20–40 pairs of thinly textured, grey-green leaflets; inflorescence has much-branched heads; flowers greenish white; fruit a four-sided capsule.

Flowering from October to December.
Fruiting from January to April and onwards.

Distribution Scattered throughout the four northern provinces of South Africa.

Habitat Occurs on rocky hillslopes in dry woodland. Always on clayey loam associated with dolomite outcrops and occasionally on granite hills.

Economic value The leaves of this tree form part of the diet of kudu, grey duiker and klipspringer, with impala eating the fallen leaves. Domestic stock also browse the leaves, especially those on the ground. It provides much needed shade for domestic stock and game in the hills and mountains during the hot summer months. Can be planted as a fence, especially for small stock. It is an indicator of dolomite.

Cultivation Easily propagated from seed, ± 940 000 seeds making up one kilogram. The quickest way to propagate this tree is from cuttings or truncheons. Seed should be sown during September in flat seedling trays filled with river sand. First mix the fine seed with fine river sand to ensure even distribution when sowing. Keep moist. Seedlings can be planted out into black nursery bags when they reach the 2-leaf stage. For the best results, keep the young trees until they are one year old before transplanting them into the veld. Protect the young trees for the first two seasons against frost, after which they should be able to survive heavy frost. Cuttings of 100–150 mm long can be made from last year's growth. Truncheons of up to 150 mm in diameter can be planted. Make sure to put some sand at the bottom of the truncheon hole. This will prevent fungi from growing on the cut end. This tree has a moderate to fast growth rate, up to 1 m per year. It is extremely drought- and frost-resistant. A splendid tree for the garden. It prefers loamy soil but will tolerate turf soil.

NATAL CAMWOOD

Description An evergreen tree up to 10 m tall with a dense roundish crown. **Bark** on young branches smooth and grey but brown and rough on older branches and stems. **Leaves** alternate, simple, tip and base tapering, leaf blade dark green and smooth, with a wavy margin. Leaf stalk with a thickening at base and tip. **Flowers** in large hanging sprays up to 100 mm long, resembling those of a pea, white, standard petal with a yellow spot at base, strongly violet-scented. **Fruit** a flat, brown, splitting pod up to 120 mm long, with a beaked tip. **Wood** yellowish.

Afrikaans	Natalse kamhout
Zulu	isiFithi
Botanical name	*Baphia racemosa*
Family	Pod-bearing Family (Fabaceae)
National tree list no.	224

Name derivation *Baphia* = dye, referring to the red dye from the heartwood of a tropical African species, and *racemosa* = referring to the racemes of flowers.

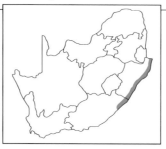

men tree with its bunches of white flowers and beaked pods. A group of these trees planted on the lawn makes a beautiful display and is eye-catching when in flower. This small tree is ideal for the small garden. It can be successfully used as a street tree in coastal areas. Larvae of the blue-spotted charaxes (*Charaxes cithaeron cithaeron*), brown playboy (*Deudorix antalus*) and the orange-barred play-boy butterfly *(Deudorix diocles)* feed on the leaves. Parrots favour the young seeds and destroy many pods in the process.

Diagnostic features Leaves simple, with a sharp tip, tip and base of leaf stalk swollen; flowers white with a yellow spot at base of standard petal, flower with strong violet scent.

Flowering from August to December.
Fruiting from January to June.

Distribution From Mozambique in the north to the Eastern Cape in the south.

Habitat In riverine and evergreen forest near the coast.

Economic value It makes a very decorative speci-

Other uses The stems can be used for implement handles.

Cultivation Collect the pods as soon as they turn brown and before they split open. Remove the seeds and soak overnight in hot water and sow the next morning in a container filled with river sand. Seeds germinate quickly, 5–8 days after sowing. Transplant the seedlings into bags filled with a mixture of river sand, loam and compost (2:2:1) when they reach the 1-leaf stage. Young plants transplant well but take care not to damage the taproot. It has a moderate growth rate of 500–600 mm per year. Natal camwood is a frost-sensitive species but can withstand some drought.

NATAL MAHOGANY

Description An evergreen tree up to 20 m tall with a round, widespreading crown. **Bark** on young branches smooth and grey-brown but smooth and dark grey-brown on older branches and stems. **Leaves** up to 500 mm long, unevenly compound with 3–5 pairs of leaflets plus a terminal one, dark green and glossy above, covered with short brownish hairs below, margins entire, veins prominent on lower surface. Leaf stalk 70–120 mm long, covered with velvety hairs. **Flowers** in dense short branched heads, creamy green and fragrant, up to 15 mm long. **Fruit** a pear-shaped capsule with a distinct neck up to 30 mm long, splitting into three valves to reveal the glossy black seeds enveloped in an orange-red aril. **Wood** with no real distinction between sapwood and heartwood, usually a pinkish colour and light (air-dry 560–597 kg/m³), but not resistant to borers and should be treated accordingly.

Afrikaans	Rooi-essenhout
Northern Sotho	mmaba
Zulu	umKhuhlu
Botanical name	*Trichilia emetica*
Family	Mahogany Family (Meliaceae)
National tree list no.	301

Name derivation *Trichilia* = Greek for 'in three parts', referring to the 3-lobed fruit, and *emetica* = with emetic properties.

grey and purple-crested louries, hornbills and barbets relish. Sunbirds visit the nectar rich flowers. Giraffe, kudu and nyala browse the leaves and young shoots, with baboon, vervet monkeys and nyala eating the fruit. Seeds used to be exported from Mozambique under the name Mafura or Mafurreira nuts. The larvae of the whitebarred charaxes (*Charaxes brutus natalensis*) butterfly feed on the leaves of this tree.

An excellent shade tree for the garden and with its fast growth rate this tree is recommended for planting where shade is needed. Plant groups of these trees in suitable habitats near water or watering points in camps where shade is needed for animals. It makes a neat and interesting street tree, never growing too high. Ideal for a parking area with its evergreen spreading crown. It has a non-aggressive root system.

Diagnostic features Evergreen tree with a roundish crown; bark smooth and dark grey-brown; leaves compound ending in a leaflet, dark glossy green above; flowers creamy green and fragrant; fruit a pear-shaped capsule splitting into three valves; seed glossy black with an orange-red aril.

Flowering from August to November.
Fruiting from December to April.

Distribution Occurs from the Sudan in the north to KwaZulu-Natal in the south.

Habitat Coastal, riverine and gallery forest on rich alluvial or sandy soils.

Economic value The wood produces beautiful furniture which darkens with the application of furniture oil. It also makes a good-quality wood for shelving. Popular for making carvings, musical instruments and various household articles. A worthwhile tree to provide shade and protection for livestock and game. It is regarded as an indicator of areas with palatable grass species. Birds are attracted to these trees for the dense shade (protection) and the seed which starlings,

Other uses Pieces of bark or powdered bark are soaked in warm water and used as an emetic or as an enema. A bitter tasting medicinal oil is obtained by boiling the ground seed in water, with the oil collected on the surface of the water and taken orally to relieve rheumatism. A good-quality soap can be made from the oil and it can also be used for preserving foodstuffs. A sweet, milky liquid is extracted from the arils which is edible. The skinned seeds are edible and eaten as such or soaked in water and ground, the resultant liquid mixed with spinach dishes. Trees with long straight stems are cut and used for dugout canoes.

Cultivation Seeds are perishable, so fresh seed must be used. There are ± 200 seeds per kilogram. Fresh seed germinates within 10–20 days after sowing. The tree is also easily cultivated by means of cuttings. Make the cuttings from layered branches or from one-year old coppice shoots. The Natal mahogany is a fast-growing species, with a growth rate of up to 1 m per year in colder areas and up to 2 m in warmer areas. It can be planted in either shade or full sun. Not resistant to frost and is therefore more suited to warmer areas. It can cope with long periods of drought.

A protected tree in South Africa.

NATAL WILD BANANA

Description An evergreen tree up to 12 m tall with large spreading banana-like leaves growing mostly in dense clumps at the tips of the stems. **Bark** light to dark grey, smooth but marked with prominent leaf scars. **Leaves** simple, opposite and sheathing the stem, leaf blade up to 2 m long, dark green, sometimes glossy, with leaf stalk deeply channelled, veins at right angles to midrib. **Flowers** in a typical crane-flower type inflorescence up to 500 mm long, individual flowers with white sepals and blue petals enclosed in a purplish blue sheath opening so that the flowers can emerge, up to 5 spathes arising one out of the other. **Fruit** a splitting 3-lobed woody capsule enclosing glossy black round seeds with prominent orange woolly arils. **Wood** white and very fibrous, soft and light.

Afrikaans	Natalse wildepiesang
Zulu	isiGude
Botanical name	*Strelitzia nicolai*
Family	Crane-flower Family (Strelitziaceae)
National tree list no.	34

Name derivation *Strelitzia* = named after Charlotte of Mecklenberg-Strelitz, wife of George III of England, and *nicolai* = named after Emperor Nicholas of Russia.

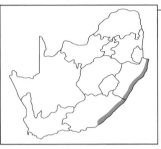

Diagnostic features Leaves banana-like, leaf stalk channelled; flowers in a typical crane-flower inflorescence, sepals white and petals blue; black seeds with bright orange woolly arils.

Flowering and fruiting throughout the year, but mostly from March to July.

Distribution From Mozambique in the north to the Eastern Cape in the south.

Habitat Mostly in coastal bush where it grows on vegetated sand dunes and in inland evergreen forests, but never very far from the sea where it grows in humus-rich sandy to loamy soil. Grows either in the full sun or in the shade of forest trees.

Economic value Blue duiker eat the flowers on the ground when dropped by monkeys. Birds (grey sunbirds, olive sunbirds and other sunbird species) visit the inflorescences for the copious nectar flowing out of the flowers. Samango and vervet monkeys and birds eat the orange aril of the seed. Indian mynahs are very partial to the seeds. Larvae of the strelitzia nightfighter butterfly (*Moltena fiara*) feed on the leaves. The seeds are sometimes eaten by people in KwaZulu-Natal but they are most popular with various barbets and starling species.

This is one of the best accent plants to use on the lawn and it makes a superb foliage plant when combined with other shrubs in a shrubbery. It is ideal as a background plant and for giving height in a planting. When used next to a swimming pool in combination with palms, a tropical atmosphere is created. It is, however, also suitable for planting next to a stream, pond or other water feature. Ideally suited for filling large gaps in the garden. It thrives in full sun but also in light shade. Prefers full sun in the colder areas. The root system is aggressive and easily breaks paving and walls. However, it makes a good container plant for a few years and can be planted out into the garden when too large for the container.

Other uses Rope made from the leaf stalks is used as a binding material. The floors of damp corn pits are lined with the leaves.

Cultivation Grows easily from seed and forms suckers from the base, so keep this in mind when planting it out into the garden. Removal of the suckers is the fastest way of propagating the Natal wild banana. Collect the seed and remove the orange arils. Sow the seeds in seedling trays filled with a 1:1 mixture of river sand and compost. Cover the seeds with a thin layer of fine compost and keep moist. Seedlings can be transplanted into nursery bags when the second leaf starts to unroll. Keep in the shade for at least the first season and harden them off slowly until they can withstand the full sun. Plants withstand strong salt spray at the coast. They are frost-tender but, if planted in a protected spot in areas that receive frost, they will grow and flower. Give water throughout the summer and a little less during the dry winter months. The growth rate is fast, up to 1 m per year.

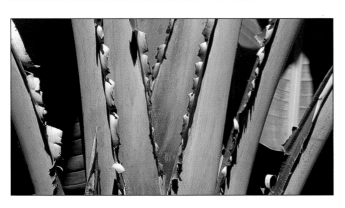

OUTENIQUA YELLOWWOOD

Description An evergreen tree up to 46 m in nature but quite smaller if planted in the garden or on the farm. Male and female trees. **Bark** on young branches smooth and ridged, but on older branches peeling off in curled, circular or rectangular flakes. **Leaves** spirally arranged, with parallel veins and smooth margins, tip sharply pointed. **Male cones** at tips of branches and mostly in groups of 2–4, ± 10 x 3 mm, brownish. **Female cones** consisting of minute fleshy scales, up to 27 x 2.5 mm, solitary. **Fruit** fleshy and spherical, up to 17 mm in diameter. **Wood** with no distinct difference between sapwood and heartwood, usually of a uniform light yellowish colour, annual rings resulting in darker lines, light (air-dry 620 kg/m³), moderately soft with a fine and smooth texture.

Afrikaans	Outeniekwageelhout
Northern Sotho	mogôbagôba
Zulu	umSonti
Botanical name	*Podocarpus falcatus*
Family	Yellowwood Family
	(Podocarpaceae)
National tree list no.	16

Name derivation *Podos* = Greek word for foot, referring to the swollen aril (foot), *carpus* = fruit, and *falcatus* = sickle-shaped, referring to the shape of the leaves.

This tree can be successfully planted in a plantation format. An experiment done in an area next to the Magoebaskloof Hotel near Haenertsburg in the Northern Province showed that the growth and survival rate of this yellowwood is in fact close to that of pine. Yellowwood trees 17–18 years old show the wood to be of excellent quality, with an increase in cubic metres when cut 2 years later, at 20 years of age. In the higher rainfall areas it can be planted as a windbreak around homesteads and crops. These trees can later be harvested for the wood. It makes an attractive specimen plant on a lawn, standing out in early spring with the new flush of blueish grey leaves contrasting with the dark green mature leaves. Excellent as a container plant for the patio, but remember to water it often. These container plants can be used as Christmas trees instead of pine or fir trees.

Diagnostic features Male and female trees; trunks straight; bark flaking in circular to rectangular pieces; leaves with parallel veins, margins parallel; male and female cones; fruit fleshy, round, berry-like and yellow.

Flowering from September to May.
Fruiting mostly throughout the year peaking from December to January.

Distribution From southern Mozambique in the north to the Western Cape forests in the south.

Habitat Mostly a member of evergreen montane forests, but also found in coastal swamp forest and montane wooded grassland. Mainly on humus-rich sandy soils.

Economic value The bark contains 3–6% tannin and is used for tanning leather. Ripe fruits are eaten by bats, bushpigs and fruit-eating birds (Cape parrots, purple-crested, Knysna and Ross's louries, Rameron, African green and Delagorgue's pigeons). The large, dense crown is a favourite roosting and nesting site for various bird species. The wood has been and still is extensively used for furniture, roof beams, floorboards, parquet blocks, door and window frames. One of the best woods for boat-building.

Other uses The ripe fruit is edible but very resinous. The sap is used as a remedy for chest complaints.

Cultivation Collect fresh cones (they look like large berries), from the tree or from the ground beneath the trees. It is important to remove the fleshy part of the fruit as it contains an inhibitor that supresses germination. The best time to sow seed is from September to November. Sow directly into black nursery bags filled with a mixture of sand and compost (1:1). Care must be taken to keep the mixture moist at all times. Germination is usually erratic and sometimes takes up to six months. When transplanting the seedlings into the open ground, care must be taken not to damage the tap root. Damage to the taproot will result in a long period, sometimes up to a year, during which the tree will show no growth. The growth rate is high under natural conditions in high rainfall areas and very fast under garden conditions. All myths about the yellowwood being a slow grower should be dispelled immediately! A tree in the authors' garden reached a height of over 5 m in 5 years, with a trunk increment of 13 mm per year. This yellowwood can tolerate moderate frost but not drought. A protected tree in southern Africa.

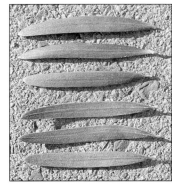

PAPERBARK FALSE-THORN

Description A deciduous tree up to 12 m tall with an open and spreading to flat crown. **Bark** on young branches smooth and greenish cream but peeling in large, thin, orange to reddish brown flakes flapping in the wind on trunk and older branches, with a thick layer of cream to yellowish powder on underbark. **Leaves** evenly twice-compound with 5–13 pairs of light green leaflets with tips blunt to slightly pointed, base prominently asymmetrical, margin smooth, with a prominant gland near base of leaf stalk just above swollen foot of leaf, young leaves reddish brown. **Flowers** creamy-white, sweetly scented, borne in half-spherical heads, with stamens many times longer than sepals and appearing before leaves. **Fruit** a splitting, broad, flat, reddish brown to dark brown pod up to 300 mm long, without thickened margins. **Wood** with no distinction between sapwood and heartwood, white, soft and light (air-dry 460 kg/m³).

Afrikaans	Papierbasvalsdoring
Botanical name	*Albizia tanganyicensis* subsp. *tanganyicensis*
Family	Pod-bearing Family (Fabaceae)
National tree list no.	157

Name derivation *Albizia* = named after an Italian nobleman from the Albizzi family of Florence, and *tanganyicensis* = from Tanzania formerly (Tanganyika).

Diagnostic features Bark consisting of thin smooth papery-peeling pieces; leaves evenly twice-compound, with prominent gland at base of leaf stalk; flowers in half-spherical heads; pods without thickened margins.

Flowering from August to November.
Fruiting from September to December.

Distribution From Tanzania in the north to the North-West Province in the south.

Habitat It grows on rocky ridges and mountain slopes in granitic and quartzitic sandy soil.

Economic value The leaves and young branches are eaten by elephant and the leaves and flowers by kudu and impala. The pods cause albiziosis, a disease in cattle which usually occurs in late winter or early spring when cattle eat the pods off the ground. The young pods are more toxic than the old, dry ones. Poisoned animals are hypersensitive, stagger while walking, fall down with convulsions and excessive kicking before dying of heart failure. The critical months are from August to November and cattle should then be grazed in camps where these trees are not present. Larvae of the satyr charaxes butterfly (*Charaxes ethalion*) feed on the leaves of this tree. Brown-headed parrots eat the green seeds, sometimes destroying the whole seedcrop in a population.

This tree with its contrasting bark is eye-catching and very effective as a specimen tree in a rock garden or on a lawn planted singly or in groups. It makes a very unusual container plant that remains attractive with its peeling bark and later the light green drooping leaves. It has a rather aggressive root system and should not be planted in small gardens or close to paved areas or buildings.

Other uses A decoction made from the bark is taken for coughs.

Cultivation Collect fresh seed and leave in a container with hot water overnight. Sow the swollen seeds the next morning in seedling trays filled with river sand. Cover them with a 5 mm thick layer of sand and keep moist in a sunny position. Seeds usually germinate after 4–10 days and give a 80–95% germination. Transplant the seedlings when they reach the 1-leaf stage but take care not to damage the taproot whilst transplanting. Try and plant the young plants into open ground as soon as possible. In areas that experience frost it must be protected for at least the first three years. This tree can also be grown from truncheons. Cut the truncheons as thick as your forearm and at least 1 m long. Place some sand at the bottom of the hole to prevent rotting and to stimulate root formation. The paperbark false-thorn can withstand cold but no frost and is extremely drought-hardy. Plants grow fast, 700–900 mm per year.

A protected plant in southern Africa.

PEAWOOD

Description An evergreen tree up to 15 m tall with a roundish dense crown. **Bark** on young stems covered with dense reddish brown velvety hairs but silvery and slightly flaky on older branches and stems. **Leaves** unevenly compound with 2–5 pairs of leaflets that are alternately arranged, leaf ending in a leaflet, leaflets leathery, glossy dark green, widest in lower half, with rounded base and pointed drip tip, margins smooth, main vein prominent below, with prominent venation on upper surface. Leaf and leaflet stalks covered with brown hairs and with a characteristic swelling at foot of leaf stalk, leaflet stalks wrinkled. **Flowers** borne in bunches at tips of branches, flowers white and very fragrant, up to 20 mm long. **Fruit** a splitting, smooth, brown, flat, slightly curved (boat-shaped) pod up to 65 mm long.

Afrikaans	Ertjiehout
Zulu	umBambalwenyoka
Botanical name	*Craibia zimmermannii*
Family	Pod-bearing Family (Fabaceae)
National tree list no.	229

Name derivation *Craibia* = named after W.G. Craib, Professor of Botany at Aberdeen, and *zimmermannii* = named after Prof. A. Zimmermann from Amani in Tanzania.

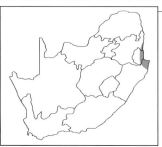

Diagnostic features Young stems covered with dense reddish brown velvety hairs; leaves unevenly compound, with leaflets alternately arranged, leaflets widest in lower half, venation prominent, leaflet stalks wrinkled; flowers resembling those of a pea, white and very fragrant.

Flowering from September to November.
Fruiting from March to September.

Distribution From Tanzania in the north to KwaZulu-Natal in the south.

Habitat The peawood grows in forests, forest margins and in sandveld forest in Zululand and Mozambique. It sometimes occurs in thick homogenous stands in sandveld forest.

Economic value Larvae of the blue-spotted charaxes butterfly (*Charaxes cithaeron*) feed on the leaves. The branches are used for construction purposes, especially for grain stores.

With its neat, dark green, roundish crown it makes a perfect shade and specimen tree for the lawn. It is ideal as a shade tree in a small or townhouse garden. Within the distribution range of the blue-spotted charaxes which stretches all along the coast from the Eastern Cape to Mozambique, the peawood can be planted to attract these beautiful blue and black butterflies to the garden. In the warmer areas this tree can be effectively used as a shade tree in parking lots. It does not have an aggressive root system.

Cultivation Pods must be collected on the tree just before they are about to split open. Seeds treated with hot water overnight tend to germinate faster than untreated seed. Sow seeds in seedling trays filled with river sand. Place the seeds flat on the sand surface and cover with a thin layer of sand as thick as the seed and keep moist. Seeds usually germinate after 7–16 days. Transplant the seedlings into nursery bags filled with a 1:1 mixture of river sand and compost when the first leaf is fully formed. The peawood has a moderate growth rate of 500–600 mm per year in warm areas, but is slightly slower in the colder areas. It will grow in a wide variety of soils but will do best in sandy soils with compost. Plants can withstand moderate frost and lengthy periods of drought. Protect young plants from frost and especially cold winds for the first two seasons.

This is a protected tree in South Africa.

PEPPERBARK TREE

Description An evergreen aromatic tree up to 20 m tall with a dense, erect canopy. **Bark** smooth and grey on young branches but brown and slightly rough with prominent yellowish corky lenticels on older branches and stems, inner bark reddish, with a peppery smell. **Leaves** alternate, simple, densely gland-dotted, with a strong peppery smell and taste when crushed, upper surface very glossy with young leaves lighter and blueish green, margins smooth, midrib prominent below. **Flowers** solitary or in 3-flowered cymes in axils of leaves, green, with 3 sepals and 10 petals, inner 5 petals smaller, thinner in texture and yellower than outer 5, filaments fused to form a prominent staminal tube. **Fruit** an oval berry with a smooth leathery skin, 20–40 mm in diameter, turning purple when mature, covered with glands. **Wood** with a light yellow sapwood and a dark yellowish brown heartwood.

Afrikaans	Peperbasboom
Northern Sotho	molaka
Zulu	isiBaha
Botanical name	*Warburgia salutaris*
Family	Wild Cinnamon Family (Canellaceae)
National tree list no.	488

Name derivation *Warburgia* = named after Dr Otto Warburg (1859–1938), botanist from Berlin, and *salutaris* = 'healthy' and refers to its medicinal properties.

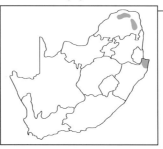

Diagnostic features All parts of the tree are highly aromatic, with a peppery smell and taste; bark with prominent corky lenticels; leaves very glossy; sepals 3 and petals in two rows of 5.

Flowering from April to May.
Fruiting from October to January.

Distribution From Zimbabwe in the north to KwaZulu-Natal in the south.

Habitat Evergreen montane forest to evergreen sandveld forest along the coast.

Economic value The pepperbark tree is one of the most popular medicinal trees having been used in Africa for centuries. The constant demand for the bark, especially the root bark, has led to large-scale destruction of natural populations to such an extent that many populations have been wiped out. Either fresh or dried leaves can be used in various dishes to add a pleasant aromatic peppery taste. Delicious when used with meatballs. A pleasant-tasting pepper tea can be made from dried leaves. Leaves can be collected, dried and sold for this purpose. This tree can be planted along fence lines, in scattered groups or preferably in a small plantation. The bark can be selectively harvested from the stems and branches and sold to the 'muti' trade. It is hoped that this would help to save natural populations from destruction. The pepperbark tree makes a dense and attractive hedge. It is a worthwhile garden subject with a very neat shape and glossy dark green leaves. It has a non-aggressive root system. When used as greenery in flower arrangements, small branches last up to 3 weeks in water. The pepperbark is one of the most successful indigenous trees grown in a container on the patio. If kept in light shade the plant takes on a neat shape and the leaves become very glossy.

Other uses Abdominal pains are treated with a decoction of powdered bark taken in porridge. The bark is smoked as a remedy for the common cold and small pieces or ground bark are placed on embers and the resultant smoke is inhaled. Bark is also dried, ground and used as a snuff to treat sinus problems and headaches. It is also used as an emetic to clear patches on the lungs. Bark from the stem and root is boiled in water and used to treat malaria. The bark contains tannin and mannitol, with the peppery taste due to the amorphous resinous substances.

Cultivation It can be grown from seed but these are invariably infested with insects. An easier and more successful method is to grow it from root suckers or, better still, from stem and tip cuttings. Make the cutting 100 mm long and remove most of the leaves leaving only the top 2 or 3. Dip the bottom part into a root-stimulating hormone powder (e.g. Seradix), place in river sand and keep moist. Best results are obtained under a mist spray with bottom heating. When sufficient roots are formed, transplant into nursery bags filled with a mixture of river sand and compost (3:1). Keep in these bags for a year before planting out. The growth rate in warm frost-free areas can be as high as 900 mm per year. It is not drought-resistant and is also not suitable for frost areas.

A protected tree in South Africa.

POD MAHOGANY

Description A deciduous tree up to 20 m (35 m in tropical Africa) high with a dense wide and spreading crown. **Bark** creamy brown and flaking in irregular thin sections on main stem and older branches. **Leaves** drooping, evenly compound with up to 7 pairs of opposite glossy green leaflets with smooth wavy margins, young leaves very glossy and copper-coloured. **Flowers** in erect clusters, with a strong sweet scent. **Fruit** a thick, hard, dark brown, splitting, woody pod containing up to 10 black seeds. **Wood** with sapwood pale brown and heartwood dark reddish brown with paler blotches, hard and heavy (air-dry 890 kg/m³).

Afrkaans	Peulmahonie
Zulu	iNkehli
Botanical name	*Afzelia quanzensis*
Family	Pod-bearing Family (Fabaceae)
National tree list no.	207

Name derivation *Afzelia* = named after Adam Afzelius of Upsala who lived in Sierra Leone, and *quanzensis* = named after the Cuanza River in Angola.

(*Eurytela dryope angulata*) butterflies feed on the leaves of the pod mahogany. The wood is known as Chamfuti in the building trade and is still exported under this name. It makes very strong, durable beams and is often used in the building trade for this purpose. For the past 50 years Chamfuti has been used extensively for the manufacture of plywood, panelling, parquet floors and for making the most exquisite furniture – notably dining-room tables and chairs. The tuning knobs of musical instruments are made mostly of this wood. The wood is termite- and borer-resistant and can therefore be used for corner poles for fences. Necklaces are made from the black seeds with the bright red arils and sold as curios. Sadly, most of the largest specimens of this species in South Africa have been felled and cut up for railway sleepers.

Diagnostic features Leaves drooping, glossy, leaflets with wavy margins; flowers in erect inflorescences, green with a single reddish petal; pod hard and woody; seeds black with reddish arils.

Flowering from October to December.
Fruiting from April to August.

Distribution From Somalia in the north to KwaZulu-Natal in the south.

Habitat Prefers well drained sandy soils in low-lying woodland and dry deciduous or sandveld forest. Sometimes the dominant species in areas with deep sandy soils.

Economic value The bark and leaves are eaten by elephants and the leaves browsed by eland and grey duiker. The sweet smelling flowers attract a myriad of insects and they in turn various insect-eating birds. The dropped flowers are eagerly eaten by game. The seeds are popular with rodents. Hornbills open the freshly split pods to eat the red arils and in the process discard the seeds which drop to the ground where they either germinate or are eaten by rodents or other animals. Larvae of the flame-bordered charaxes (*Charaxes protoclea azota*), foxy charaxes (*Charaxes jasius saturnus*), giant charaxes (*Charaxes castor flavifasciatus*), large blue charaxes (*Charaxes bohemani*), blue-spotted charaxes (*Charaxes cithaeron*), violet-spotted charaxes (*Charaxes violetta*), scarce forest charaxes (*Charaxes etesipe tavetensis*) and golden piper

The pod mahogany can be planted for hardwood in sandy to loamy soils in frost-free areas (i.e. Maputaland and Venda). One of the best indigenous trees to use for making a bonsai specimen. A tree with a good shape can be obtained in about 7 years, with an attractive thick stem and spreading crown.

Other uses In certain countries dugout canoes are made from the trunks. An infusion made from the roots provides a remedy for bilharzia and is also used for eye complaints. A small piece of bark is applied to an aching tooth.

Cultivation Fill flat seedling trays with a 5:1 mixture of river sand and compost. Press the seeds into the mixture until they are flush with the surface and keep moist. Seeds germinate easily, usually with a germination of up to 80% and they may take 2–3 weeks to germinate. Ten-year old seed may still germinate but the viability will then have decreased to at least 30%. Germination is surprisingly even. Transplant seedlings when they reach the 2-leaf stage. Frost-sensitive and slow growing in colder areas. Seedlings must be protected against cold wind for the first two seasons. Very drought-resistant. Growth rate ± 500–600 mm per year. A protected tree in South Africa.

POMPON TREE

Description A semi-deciduous to evergreen tree up to 13 m tall with a dense rounded crown. **Bark** on young branches grey-brown with prominent corky dots (lenticels) but grey with shallow brownish grooves on old branches and stems, very tough and can be removed in long strips. **Leaves** simple, in opposite pairs and crowded near tips of branchlets, midrib conspicuous, venation pale green and prominent below, margin smooth. Leaf stalk up to 5 mm long. **Flowers** in dense spherical terminal heads up to 50 mm in diameter, with 2–6 shield-like bracts at the base of each head, flowers pink to mauve, with a hairy tubular corolla up to 30 mm long, the calyx forming the petal-like lobes, with 10 stamens of different lengths inserted in tube. **Fruit** a brown to blackish nutlet at the base of the persistent calyx.

Afrikaans	Kannabas
Zulu	inTozane-emnyama
Botanical name	*Dais cotinifolia*
Family	Mezereum Family (Thymelaeaceae)
National tree list no.	521

Name derivation *Dais* = resembles a torch about to be lit, and *cotinifolia* = leaves resembling those of the genus *Cotinus*.

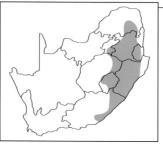

Diagnostic features Bark grey and tearing in long strips (family character); leaves in opposite pairs crowded near ends of branchlets; flowers in dense spherical heads, 2–6 shield-like bracts at base, lacking corolla but calyx forming the flower tube, pink to mauve, stamens 10 and of different lengths inside the corolla tube; fruit a nutlet at base of persistent calyx.

Flowering from November to February.
Fruiting from January to April.

Distribution From Zimbabwe in the north to the Eastern Cape in the south.

Habitat Evergreen, riverine and scrub forest and on rocky mountain slopes.

Economic value The pompon tree is possibly one of the most successful and attractive of all indigenous trees for the garden. The position of the pompon tree in the garden is immaterial – when in flower it will always be the focal point! Cut flowering stems keep well in water. It makes the ideal container plant for a patio. The pompon tree has been cultivated in Europe since 1757 and is grown worldwide. Every garden should have at least one pompon tree. It reacts well to pruning and can be trained into a standard. The non-aggressive root system of the pompon tree permits planting close to buildings and paved areas.

Other uses The bark is extremely tough and makes an excellent rope. Most of the large pompon trees close to human habitation are destroyed by people removing the bark to make ropes for tying up bundles of firewood.

Cultivation The pompon tree grows readily from fresh seed. Fresh seed can be collected and sown into seedling trays filled with seedling soil. Take care not to sow the seed too deep. The pompon tree can also be propagated from side shoots. These can be dug out and replanted. Stem cuttings can also be used for propagation. Make the cuttings 40–60 mm long and 5–10 mm in diameter. Treat them with a root-stimulating hormone powder and place them in river sand which drains well. The pompon tree has a fast growth rate, 0.8–1 m per year. Trees flower in their second year. It can withstand moderate frost but needs a fair amount of moisture.

PRIDE OF DE KAAP

Description An evergreen tree up to 5 m tall, occasionally rambling. **Bark** on young branches covered with brown hairs but older branches and stems light brown. **Leaves** simple, alternate, 2-lobed, the blade usually wider than long and up to 50 x 70 mm, prominently notched, veins conspicuous on undersurface, margin smooth. **Flowers** in branched sprays at tips of branches, flower 60–80 mm in diameter, petals brick-red to orange, 30–40 mm long, the lobe abruptly widened above from a conspicuous claw which is almost as long as the widened portion of the lobe, wavy-edged, with 3 fertile stamens and 7 stami-nodes (infertile stamens).

Fruit a flat, pointed, woody pod splitting into 2 valves while still on the bush, hairy when young but smooth when mature, seeds distributed by the explosive action of the opening fruit. **Wood** with no distinction between sapwood and heartwood, whitish brown, pliable and fine-grained.

Diagnostic features Evergreen; rambling habit; leaves notched and 2-lobed, venation prominent on undersurface; flowers mostly orange to brick-red, lobe abruptly widened above from a conspicuous claw which is almost as long as the widened portion of the lobe, wavy-edged, 3 fertile stamens and 7 staminodes (infertile stamens); fruit a pointed, flat, woody pod.

Flowering from September to March.
Fruiting from March to August.

Distribution From Zambia in the north to KwaZulu-Natal in the south.

Economic value A splendid garden subject flowering for 4–7 months of the year. It can be used in the garden as a specimen plant or to fill an opening in a shrubbery. This is a very successful plant to use as a hedge or screen between lands or camps. Because of its tolerance for extreme temperatures it has been used successfully on the centre islands on motorways. The

Afrikaans	Trots van De Kaap
Northern Sotho	motshwiriri
Zulu	umVangatane
Botanical name	*Bauhinia galpinii*
Family	Pod-bearing Family (Fabaceae)
National tree list no.	208.2

Name derivation *Bauhinia* = honouring two 16th century herbalist brothers, John and Caspar Bauhin, and *galpinii* = named after E.E. Galpin, a botanical collector of the late 19th century.

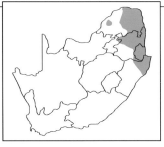

long flowering period produces a stunning display of colour. Its root system is non-invasive, but the shrub tends to scramble and become wild if not kept in check and pruned back regularly. It should be allowed a fair amount of space to achieve its true form and splendour! Leaves are eaten by game (black rhino, kudu, bushbuck and grey duiker). The grey and purple-crested louries eat the flower buds and the green seeds. Larvae of the brown playboy (*Deudorix antalus*) and the orange barred playboy (*Deudorix diocles*) butterflies breed in the pods, eating the young seeds. The foxy charaxes (*Charaxes jasius saturnus*), protea charaxes (*Charaxes pelias*) and bushveld charaxes (*Charaxes achaemenes*) butterflies feed on the leaves only.

Other uses The pliable branches are used for making baskets. The flexible stems are used in the construction of roofs in rural areas.

Cultivation To speed up germination, seed can be soaked in warm water and left overnight or for a couple of hours in boiling water. The seeds swell and are then ready for germination. Sow in a seed tray filled with ready-made seedling mix available from nurseries and garden centres or in river sand. The seed should be pressed into the seedling mix/sand, to a depth of 1.5 times the width of the seed. Cover with either seedling mix or fine sand. Germination is usually erratic and may take up to 2 weeks. Once the seedlings have reached the 2-leaf stage they must be planted out, as they form long tap roots which may be damaged if left longer. Pride of De Kaap can be grown from cuttings planted in river sand during spring or summer. Protect young plants from frost for the first year. They flower best in full sun, but are able to tolerate light shade. It usually flowers in its second year if planted as a seedling. They are drought-resistant and tolerates mild frost. Plants must be pruned if a tree shape is required.

PUZZLE BUSH

Description A deciduous tree up to 9 m tall with a much branched crown with somewhat drooping intertwined branches, the forest form having a small tangled crown. **Bark** on young branches smooth and grey but grey to dark grey and rough on older branches and stems. **Leaves** alternate, simple and borne close together at tips of short branches, smooth or covered with stiff hairs which are rough to the touch, tips rounded and base tapering, margin smooth. Leaf stalk up to 2 mm long. **Flowers** in dense clusters on the bare branches, lilac to mauve but turning whitish with age, up to 7 mm in diameter and sweetly scented. **Fruit** a round, orange to red fleshy berry. **Wood** whitish to light brown, tough and flexible.

Afrikaans	Deurmekaarbos
Northern Sotho	morôbê
Zulu	umHlele
Botanical name	*Ehretia rigida*
Family	Forget-me-not Family (Boraginaceae)
National tree list no.	657

Name derivation *Ehretia* = named after G.D. Ehret an 18th century botanical artist, and *rigida* = stiff or rigid referring to the rigid branches.

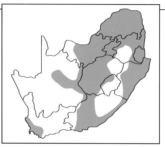

and later the bunches of orange to red berries make it an interesting and decorative tree to have in the garden. Puzzle bushes can be planted close together to form a hedge which can be pruned into a neat shape. A hedge like this is alive with birds and insects when in flower and fruit. It is hardy and very drought-resistant – ideal for the dry garden. It makes a very attractive and hardy container plant (it has a non-aggressive root system) but must be kept in the full sun.

Diagnostic features Deciduous; branches arching; bark grey; leaves close together at tips of short branches, leaf stalk short; flowers in dense clusters, lilac to mauve; fruit a fleshy orange to red berry.

Flowering from July to November.
Fruiting from October to January.

Distribution From Zambia in the north to the Western Cape in the south.

Habitat Ecologically widely adapted. Occurs in nearly all habitat types except aquatic.

Economic value Eagerly browsed by domestic stock and game (kudu, nyala, bushbuck, impala and grey duiker). Ripe fruits are eaten by birds (crested francolin, helmeted and crested guineafowl, brown-headed, and Meyer's parrots, grey louries, yellowbilled hornbill, crested barbets, black-eyed bulbuls and starlings).

The puzzle bush is a must for the garden to attract birds and insects. It is best to prune the tree to give it a neat shape. The clusters of lilac to mauve flowers

Other uses The ripe fruit is edible with an agreeable sweetish taste. The fruit analysis is as follows –

Moisture	85.6 g/100 g
Protein	1.7 g/100 g
Carbohydrate	10.4 g/100 g
Calcium	30.5 mg/100 g
Magnesium	27.8 mg/100 g
Sodium	2.5 mg/100 g
Potassium	547 mg/100 g
Vitamin C	7 mg/100 g

Some plants tend to have either sourish or bitter fruit. The root is sometimes used as a remedy for gall sickness in cattle. The pliable branches are still being used for making bows in Botswana. These branches are also sometimes used for making fishing baskets. It is popular with people making fire-by-friction using a branch of the puzzle bush for the upper or turning stick.

Cultivation Easily grown from seed or from cuttings. Seed can be sown in a seedling tray filled with river sand or a mixture of river sand and compost (5:1) and covered with a thin layer of sand. Take care not to sow the seed too deep. The seeds usually take 10–20 days to germinate. Transplant the seedlings into nursery bags when they reach the 2-leaf stage. Keep the plants in the bags until the next season before planting them out into open ground. The growth rate is moderately fast, 600–700 mm per year. It is very drought- and frost-resistant.

QUININE TREE

Description Evergreen tree up to 30 m tall with a roundish crown. All parts of the tree exude a toxic white milky latex. **Bark** on young branches smooth, green and glossy with prominent leaf scars but yellowish brown, corky and cracked into small squares on older branches and stems. **Leaves** in whorls of 3–5, thinly leathery, tapering to both ends, glossy, midrib channelled above, side veins translucent, margin smooth. Leaf stalk up to 30 mm long. **Flowers** in branched heads at tips of branches, flowers small and white, waxy and sweetly scented, with dense hairs at mouth of flower tube. **Fruit** in large clusters, glossy black, up to 15 mm in diameter. **Wood** yellowish white, with a small heartwood, soft and light (air-dry 540 kg/m³).

Afrikaans	Kinaboom
Northern Sotho	monadi
Zulu	umHlambamanzi
Botanical name	*Rauvolfia caffra*
Family	Oleander Family (Apocynaceae)
National tree list no.	647

Name derivation *Rauvolfia* = named after Leonhart Rauwolf a 16th century medical doctor from Augsberg, a collector of drug plants, and *caffra* = from Kaffraria (Eastern Cape).

Diagnostic features Evergreen; bark corky and yellowish brown; leaves in whorls of 3–5; flowers very small, white, with hairs in mouth of flower tube; fruit a black fleshy drupe.

Flowering from May to October.
Fruiting from October to March.

Distribution From Tanzania in the north to the Eastern Cape in the south.

Habitat Along rivers and streams. When growing away from rivers and streams it is always associated with available ground water. Regarded as an indicator of water.

Economic value Leaves browsed by nyala and the leaves, flowers and fruit eaten by vervet monkeys. The ripe fruits are eaten by birds (hornbills, barbets, pigeons and bulbuls) and bushbabies. Flowers attract many butterflies and other insects and they in turn many insect-eating birds. The wood is suitable for general timber work on the farm and takes nails well. An excellent wood for making fruit boxes. Ideal for kitchen furniture and shelving. Household utensils are sometimes carved from the wood.

A very decorative tree for the larger garden and park, also making a neat shade tree. The lush, tropical foliage lends a cool atmosphere to the garden. A must in the garden to attract birds and butterflies. Unfortunately its large size and invasive root system make it unsuitable for the smaller garden.

Other uses The latex is sometimes used to treat diarrhoea and other stomach ailments. The bark is used as a dressing for wounds. Pieces of bark are chewed to treat coughs. An infusion of the bark is used for killing maggots in wounds.

Cultivation The quinine tree grows easily from seed, cuttings or truncheons. Collect fruit and make sure that the pulp is removed, wash with water and sow in seedling trays filled with seedling mix obtainable from the local nursery or in a mixture of river sand and compost (1:1). Press the seeds into the mixture until they are flush with the surface. A thin layer of sand over the seeds is optional. Transplant the seedlings into nursery bags when they reach the 3-leaf stage. Seedlings and young plants transplant well. Give them sufficient water for the first three months until they are established. The quinine tree needs a lot of water. It has a fast growth rate, up to 1.5 m per year. Frost-tender.

A protected tree in South Africa.

RED BEECH

Description An evergreen tree up to 25 m tall with a dense rounded crown and dense foliage. **Bark** smooth and reddish brown on young branches but dark brown and rough on older branches and stems, a milky juice exuding from wounds. **Leaves** simple, opposite to sub-opposite, up to 150 mm long (the specific name refers to this), leathery but smooth, dark green above, paler below, bluntly pointed, midrib prominent underneath with side veins fine and parallel, forking near thickened wavy leaf margin, young leaves copper-coloured but a few bright red leaves always present on the tree. Leaf stalk up to 25 mm long. **Flowers** borne in dense sprays at tips of branches, greenish white to pinkish, male and female flowers on separate trees. **Fruit** a fleshy oval berry up to 13 mm in diameter turning purple to mauve with whitish lines when ripe. **Wood** with sapwood greyish pink and heartwood dark brown, fairly hard and fine-grained.

Diagnostic features Evergreen, exuding a milky juice; leaf blade long (up to 150 mm), with a roundish tip, midrib prominent below, side veins fine and parallel, branching at tips, leaf margin thickened, young leaves coppery red; separate male and female trees; fruit fleshy and purplish with whitish lines when ripe.

Flowering from July to October.
Fruiting from September to December.

Distribution Endemic to South Africa, from the Northern Province in the north to the Eastern Cape in the south.

Habitat Grows in well drained, composted areas in evergreen forests, forest margins, kloofs and in riverine vegetation.

Economic value The bark and leaves are eaten by

Afrikaans	Rooiboekenhout
Zulu	isiFice
Botanical name	*Protorhus longifolia*
Family	Mango Family (Anacardiaceae)
National tree list no.	364

Name derivation *Proto* = the first (or before), *rhus* = another genus in the same family, and *longifolia* = long leaves.

black rhino and the ripe fruits by birds (pigeons, parrots, louries, mousebirds, barbets, bulbuls and starlings) and other animals (bushpigs, red duiker, samango and vervet monkeys). In the past the wood was utilized for making beams used in the building trade for it is easy to obtain long, straight logs. It can be cut into planks for making shelves and furniture, especially tables. The light-coloured wood turns an attractive deep brown after many years of oiling.

The red beech makes a stunning specimen tree if planted singly on a lawn where it attracts the attention with its dense foliage and some bright red leaves that are always present – and then of course the drooping bunches of pink fruit turning purple. It makes a very neat, dense shade tree if the lower branches are trimmed from an early age. The red beech is a must for the bird garden as it attracts many fruit-eating birds. Young trees tend to have the branches down to the ground and this makes them ideal to use as screen plants or as a windbreak. The root system is not aggressive.

Other uses The bark yields 10–18% tanning material and 7% tannin giving a distinct colour to skins being tanned. Powdered bark is poisonous.

Cultivation It is best to collect seeds from the trees just before they drop, for those on the ground are quickly parasitised. It is important to clean the flesh around the seeds before drying them in the shade. Sow the seeds in trays filled with a 1:1 mixture of river sand and compost. Cover them with a layer of sand or fine compost as thick as the seed and keep moist. Germination is usually erratic but speeds up later on. Transplant the seedlings into the same mixture as in the seed trays and keep in the shade. These trees do well in deep shade or full sun. The growth rate is moderately fast, up to 800 mm per year. The red beech can tolerate very mild frost and is drought-hardy.

RED BUSHWILLOW

Description A semi-deciduous to deciduous tree up to 9 m tall. **Bark** on young twigs sticky, young branches covered with reddish brown fibrous bark but grey to light brown and smooth and scaly in old specimens. **Leaves** on current growth up to 130 x 80 mm and light green, young leaves sticky and glossy, tip of leaf blade ending abruptly in a slender point, margins smooth and sometimes wavy. Leaf stalk up to 100 mm long. **Flowers** greenish yellow to yellow and heavily scented, borne in single spikes up to 70 x 20 mm. **Fruit** with four wings and up to 30 x 25 mm, glossy and reddish brown. **Wood** with the sapwood yellowish and the heart wood dark reddish brown to dark brown, hard and heavy (air-dry 1 230 kg/m³).

Afrikaans	Rooibos
Northern Sotho	mohwelere
Zulu	umBondwe
Botanical name	*Combretum apiculatum*
	subsp. *apiculatum*
Family	Combretum Family
	(Combretaceae)
National tree list no.	532

Name derivation *Combretum* = a name used by Pliny for a climbing plant, and *apiculatum* = ending abruptly in a short point, referring to the leaf tip.

posts as it is resistant to termites and borers. It makes an excellent firewood and it is the best wood for a braai. Larvae of the striped policeman butterfly (*Coeliades forestan*) live on the leaves. Red bushwillow veld is regarded as an indicator of mixed veld that is good for spring and summer grazing. Where these trees occur, they usually form the dominant tree species and that is why this type of veld is called red bushwillow/rooibos veld.

These trees can be planted in scattered groups of up to 15 in a suitable habitat. It is advisable to water the young plants for at least six months after planting out into the veld. Protect the young plants against herbivores until they are at least 1 m tall. The red bushwillow makes a splendid specimen plant for the dry garden, with its interesting profile and sparse foliage. Displays beautiful autumn colours ranging from light green, yellow, red and sometimes purple. It has a non-aggressive root system and will not lift paving or buildings.

Diagnostic features Tree semi-deciduous; leaves ending in a slender point, young leaves sticky; petals small and inconspicuous, heavily scented; fruit with four wings.

Flowering from September to February.
Fruiting from January to May.

Distribution From Kenya in the north to KwaZulu-Natal in the south.

Habitat On sandy to rocky soil in dry open woodland in areas of low rainfall to semi-arid conditions. Prefers areas with less than 600 mm of rain per year.

Economic value An excellent fodder tree for domestic stock and game. Leaves are eaten from the tree and dropped leaves are picked from the ground. The leaves are eaten by elephant, giraffe, eland, kudu, bushbuck, impala, klipspringer and steenbok. Brown-headed parrots relish the mature fruit. The flowers attract many insects and they in turn various species of insect-eating birds. The wood be used successfully as fencing

Other uses A decoction of the leaves is used as an enema to relieve stomach disorders. The dark red soluble gum is edible but not very tasty and can be stored for some months before use.

Cultivation Seed should be removed from the encapsulation and soaked in water for 5–10 hours before sowing. Place the seed on top of river sand and cover with a thin layer of sand. Seeds planted too deep will take much longer to germinate. Seedlings usually appear 8–16 days after sowing. Germination is usually 60–80%. Transplant the seedlings when the first true leaf appears. Plants should be kept moist but never wet. Not a plant for areas with frost but it can withstand cold. If planted in cold areas it must be protected until at least 1 m tall. The growth rate is moderate to slow, 3 m in four years.

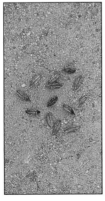

RED CURRANT

Description A semi-deciduous to deciduous tree up to 20 m tall with an open rounded crown. **Bark** smooth with spinous stems on older branches and sometimes on young branches. **Leaves** compound, 3-foliolate (with three leaflets), up to 130 mm long, leaflets with very short petiolules, membranous and glabrous, dark green turning red before falling, young leaves reddish, margin entire and usually undulate, with a pinkish midrib impressed above and prominent below, leaf tip sharply tapering. Leaf stalk 50–70 mm long, pinkish red. **Flowers** borne in panicles, male and female flowers on separate trees, male flowers in long sprays at tips of branches, female flowers in shorter sprays in leaf axils, flowers small and cream-coloured. **Fruit** a round, shiny, dark reddish brown drupe, up to 6 mm in diameter. **Wood** with sapwood yellowish and heartwood hard, heavy and rich reddish brown.

Afrikaans	Bostaaibos
Northern Sotho	monoatlou
Zulu	umHlabamvubu
Botanical name	*Rhus chirindensis*
Family	Mango Family (Anacardiaceae)
National tree list no.	380

Name derivation *Rhus* = the classical Greek name for *Rhus coriaria*, and *chirindensis* = named after the Chirinda Forest in Zimbabwe.

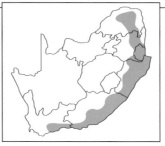

purple-crested louries, black-eyed bulbuls, pied and crested barbets, Cape white-eyes, and Cape parrots) and monkeys (vervet and samango monkeys). The wood is still used for making the most attractive furniture, the red colour of the wood giving it a special character.

One of the most successful indigenous trees for the garden where it can either be used as a specimen plant on a lawn or as a background plant in a shrubbery. It does not have an aggressive root system. A firm favourite with the birds – they relish the fruits! Red currant trees must be pruned from an early stage to ensure a single-stemmed tree for use on a lawn; if left unpruned it will grow into a multistemmed shrub. The beautiful autumn colours compensate for the fallen leaves on the lawn. When fruiting heavily it makes a beautiful show. The ripe red fruits are edible, with a sweetish sour taste.

Diagnostic features Spinous stems on older branches; leaves with 3 leaflets, leaflets membranous, with an undulate margin, midrib pinkish and impressed above and prominent below, leaf stalk 50–70 mm long, pinkish; separate male and female plants; male flowers in long panicles at tips of branches, female flowers in shorter much branched panicles in leaf axils.

Flowering from August to March.
Fruiting from December to March.

Distribution From Tanzania in the north to the Western Cape in the south.

Habitat In forests, forest margins, riverine bush and wooded grassland.

Economic value Bark and leaves are browsed by black rhino and the leaves by kudu, nyala, bushbuck and red duiker. The ripe fruits of the red currant are eaten by many birds (African green pigeons, Knysna and

Other uses The sap tapped from the stems is used for treating heart complaints.

Cultivation The red currant is easily grown from truncheons. Cut the truncheons so that they are ± 100 mm in diameter and 2 m long. Remember to place some river sand at the bottom of the hole to prevent fungal growth and speed up root growth. Semi-hardwood cuttings must be planted in river sand after treating with a root-stimulating hormone powder and kept moist. It is important that the sand never dries out. Sow seed in a seedling tray filled with a mixture of river sand and compost (1:1), cover lightly with sand and keep moist. Fresh seed germinates after 5–8 weeks with the germination as high as 80%, dropping to 30–40% when the seed is older than six months. This tree can withstand light frost and it is drought-resistant. It can be grown in either full sun or in light shade and prefers well drained soil. The growth rate is fast, up to 1 m per year.

RED IVORY

Description An evergreen to semi-deciduous tree up to 15 m tall with a dense and much branched roundish crown. **Bark** on young branches grey and smooth with light grey corky dots (lenticels) but grey-brown and rough breaking up into segments on older branches and stems. **Leaves** opposite, simple, green with a blueish green bloom, tip round to bluntly tapering, side veins in a herring-bone pattern terminating in the wavy margin giving the leaf a scalloped appearance, venation prominent on lower surface and sunken on upper surface, sometimes tinged purple on lower surface. Leaf stalk up to 4 mm long. **Flowers** yellowish green and star-shaped, borne in sparse clusters in the leaf axils on stalks up to 10 mm long. **Fruit** a fleshy reddish to purple drupe. **Wood** with a yellowish sapwood and a very hard, pinkish to red, very heavy (air-dry 1 083 kg/m³) heartwood.

Afrikaans	Rooi-ivoor
Northern Sotho	monee
Zulu	umNeyi
Botanical name	*Berchemia zeyheri*
Family	Dogwood Family (Rhamnaceae)
National tree list no.	450

Name derivation *Berchemia* = named after M. Berchem, a French botanist, and *zeyheri* = named after C.L.P. Zeyher (1799–1858), a famous German plant collector.

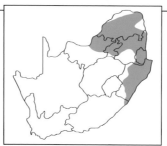

Diagnostic features Young bark grey, with lenticels; leaves opposite and thinly textured, side veins terminate in the margin giving it a scalloped appearance, midrib and veins sunken on upper surface and prominent below; flowers on long stalks up to 10 mm long; fruit fleshy and reddish to purple when ripe.

Flowering from September to January.
Fruiting from November to April.

Distribution From Zimbabwe in the north to the Eastern Cape in the south.

Habitat Open woodland and rocky hillsides, rocky ridges and along drainage lines.

Economic value The bark is eaten by porcupine and the leaves are browsed by giraffe, eland, kudu, nyala, bluewildebeest, bushbuck and impala. The ripe fruit is a favourite with most fruit-eating birds (Rameron and African green pigeons, Meyer's parrots, grey and purple-crested louries, mousebirds, crested, black-collared and pied barbets, black-eyed bulbuls and redwinged starlings), baboons and vervet monkeys. A good furniture wood, giving a very smooth finish but darkening after a few years of oiling. Wood is used for carvings, wooden bowls and walking sticks which are sold as curios. The wood is termite-resistant and used as fence poles.

The red ivory makes an attractive specimen plant and is one of the best trees to plant in the garden to attract birds. An ideal tree for the small garden, with its non-invasive root system, where it can be used as an accent plant. With little attention, it makes a very neat and compact container plant requiring little pruning to maintain its neat shape.

Other uses Fruit edible, with a most agreeable sweet taste. An excellent syrup can be made from the ripe fruits. Ripe fruits can be stored in containers where they form a brown sweet mass to be used at a later stage. Red ivory fruit can be bought on several markets during the fruiting season. The bark is used as a dye for fibre and woven material, giving it a purplish colour. Powdered roots are smoked as a cure for headaches or sometimes used as an enema. An extract made from the bark is used to relieve backache.

Cultivation The red ivory grows easily from seed. Collect ripe fruit from the tree and eat the flesh; plant the seeds in seedling trays filled with river sand or a mixture of river sand and compost (1:1). Cover the seed lightly with sand and keep moist. Seeds germinate fast, 5–9 days after sowing. Germination of fresh seed is usually 80–90%. Transplant seedlings into nursery bags when they reach the 2-leaf stage. Seedlings usually seem to make little progress for a few weeks after being planted out, but after this period the growth is rapid. It is drought-resistant and can take light frost.

A protected tree in South Africa.

RED-LEAVED ROCK FIG

Description A semi-deciduous tree up to 25 m tall with a deeply grooved stem and low spreading crown. It can grow as a rocksplitter or as a strangler on other trees. All parts exude a white milky latex. **Bark** on young branches smooth and green but smooth, grey and peeling off in small thin flakes on older branches and stems. **Stipules** covering the growth tip like a hood but falling at an early stage. **Leaves** coppery-red when young, simple, smooth and glossy green, with a thin but brittle texture, up to 150 x 100 mm, heart-shaped at the base. Margins smooth, venation prominent on lower surface. Leaf stalk 10–35 mm long. **Figs** borne singly or paired in leaf axils, 10–15 mm in diameter, green turning purplish red when ripe. **Wood** off-white with no heartwood and light (air-dry 570 kg/m³).

Afrikaans	Rooiblaarrotsvy
Northern Sotho	monokane
Zulu	umDende-obomvu
Botanical name	*Ficus ingens* var. *ingens*
Family	Fig Family (Moraceae)
National tree list no.	55

Name derivation *Ficus* = the classical name for the cultivated fig, and *ingens* = 'huge'.

The red-leaved rock fig can be planted in camps to provide necessary shade during the hot summer months and shelter during the winter. The best tree to plant in a large garden for the red to coppery spring foliage. Remember to keep the tree dry during early spring to enhance the red colour of the new leaves. In colder areas it can be planted next to a large boulder. In time the stems will climb all over the rock in a flat plane. In this way the plant maximises its exposure to the sun. Never plant any wild fig tree near buildings, paved areas, swimming pools or near drains as it has an aggressive root system. The red-leaved rock fig makes a great container plant and looks stunning in spring with the red new leaves. A popular plant for making bonsai.

Diagnostic features Bark smooth and grey; milky latex in all parts; stipules cover growth tip; new leaves coppery-red, base of leaves heart-shaped, petioles 10–350 mm long; figs 10–15 mm in diameter.

Fruiting and flowering from June to December.

Distribution From Ethiopia in the north to the Eastern Cape in the south.

Habitat Rocky outcrops or hills in woodland or forest.

Economic value Domestic stock seldom utilise this tree for browsing, but the young leaves turning green are eaten in large quantities by kudu, nyala and grey duiker. Ripe fruits are eaten by monkeys, baboons, squirrels, dassies, bushbabies and the ones that drop to the ground are eagerly eaten by bushpig, warthog, nyala, grey duiker and suni. Many fruit-eating birds relish the ripe figs (Rameron and African green pigeons, Cape, brown-headed and Meyer's parrots, Knysna, purple-crested and grey louries, bulbuls, starlings and barbets). The light yet strong wood can be used for general timber on the farm. The wood is sometimes used for making drums and mortars.

Other uses The ripe figs are edible, with a sweetish taste, but they are nearly always full of small insects. A decoction of the bark is used as a remedy for anaemia and the milky latex is used as a disinfectant.

Cultivation Collect fruit before it drops. The seed is very fine and should first be mixed with very fine river sand before sowing to ensure even distribution. Sow the sand/seed mixture in seedling trays filled with a mixture of river sand and compost (1:1) and keep moist by placing the seed tray into a container of water - when the surface is moist, enough water has been drawn up. Seed germinates within 15–30 days. Germination is always erratic in wild figs. It is easier and faster to grow from cuttings or truncheons. Cuttings can be made from either soft or hardwood and usually root easily. Truncheons must be left in the shade for a few days prior to planting. Branches with a in diameter of 50–150 mm in diameter are best to use for truncheons. Remember to place some river sand at the bottom of the hole before planting the truncheon. It promotes the formation of roots and prevents fungi from attacking the tip of the truncheon. The red-leaved rock fig is a fast grower and can withstand cold. Plant in a warm, sunny area in regions that receive frost and protect for the first two years.

RHODESIAN TEAK

Description A semi-deciduous tree up to 20 m tall with a dense, spreading, much branched crown. **Bark** on young branches grey and densely covered with hairs but grey-brown and vertically fissured and cracked on older branches and stems. **Leaves** evenly compound, alternate and up to 100 mm long with 4 or 5 opposite pairs of leaflets, sparingly hairy especially on undersurface and midrib, tips rounded. **Flowers** in axillary upright racemes up to 350 mm long, the buds densely covered with brown hairs, the 4 sepals leathery and also covered with dense brown hairs, the 5 petals pale pink, mauve or magenta and up to 30 x 25 mm, with crisped edges and with hairs along the midrib, the 10 stamens pink and up to 30 mm long. **Fruit** a flattened woody pod up to 140 mm long, with a prominent beak and broadest near the tip, tapering to the base and covered with dark brown velvety hairs, splitting explosively, the valves spiralling and scattering the seeds in the process. **Wood** with a hard, fine-grained dark reddish brown heartwood.

Afrikaans	Rhodesiese kiaat
Botanical name	*Baikiaea plurijuga*
Family	Pod-bearing Family (Fabaceae)
National tree list no.	206
Zimbabwe tree list no.	257

Name derivation *Baikiaea* = named after W.B. Baikie, commander of the Niger Expedition in 1858, and *plurijuga* = many-paired.

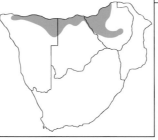

Diagnostic features Bark on young branches covered with dense hairs; leaves evenly compound with 4 or 5 opposite pairs of leaflets with rounded tips; inflorescence erect, buds and sepals densely covered with brown hairs, petals pink to mauve with crisped edges, up to 30 mm long, stamens pink, up to 30 mm long; pod beaked, with widest part near tip and tapering to bottom, covered with dark brown velvety hairs.

Flowering from December to March.
Fruiting from June to September.

Distribution From Tanzania in the north to Zimbabwe in the south.

Habitat Deciduous woodland. It is often the dominant tree species. Restricted to Kalahari sands.

Economic value One of the most important and most-exported timbers in southern Africa. It is systematically cut on a sustained yield basis in Botswana, Caprivi, Zimbabwe and Zambia. It is used as a general timber for bridge construction and in the building trade for beams, window and door frames and for doors. The most popular wood for parquet floors here and abroad. Rhodesian teak makes beautiful, heavy furniture with a smooth finish. Popular for tables and arm chairs. Many of the railway sleepers in South Africa were cut from Rhodesian teak and sleepers are still cut from this wood in certain areas. Popular for making dug-out canoes along the Zambezi in the Caprivi and Zambia. Termite and borer-resistant and used in certain areas as fencing posts. It makes a good fuel, producing very hot coals.

Rhodesian teak is a tree for the larger garden and ideal for a park. The grey stems, dark green leaves, pinkish flowers and dark brown pods make this a very decorative tree. Unfortunately it is not commonly cultivated here and not easy to obtain from our nurseries. It has a non-aggressive root system. The sandveld areas of Maputaland and Tongaland are ideal for planting this tree in a plantation for the production of hardwood.

Other uses The bark is used for tanning leather, giving it a reddish colour.

Cultivation Seed must be soaked in hot water and left overnight and the swollen seed planted the next morning in a mixture of river sand and compost (2:1). Cover with a thin layer of sand and keep moist, ensuring that the medium never dries out. Seeds usually take 7–25 days to germinate. When the seedlings reach the 2-leaf stage they must be transplanted into nursery bags into a mixture of river sand and compost (5:1). Take care not to damage the taproot while transplanting. Rhodesian teak is frost-sensitive but can withstand some drought. It has a moderate growth rate, 500–700 mm per year.

RIVER BUSHWILLOW

Description Deciduous to semi-deciduous tree up to 20 m tall with a dense roundish crown. **Bark** smooth and grey on young branches turning darker grey on older branches and stems, flaking in pieces to reveal biscuit-coloured patches. **Leaves** sub-opposite, sometimes in whorls of three and up to 130 x 50 mm, venation on upper surface sunken but very conspicuous and yellowish on undersurface, young leaves light green to yellowish and sticky, slightly hairy above, with entire margin. Leaves with brilliant yellow and red autumn colours. Leaf stalk 2–4 mm long. **Flowers** on dense, roundish spikes in axils of leaves on new side shoots, greenish white to pale yellow, with a faint sweet scent. **Fruit** 4-winged and 10–15 mm in diameter, light brown when dry, old fruits usually remaining on the tree until the next flowering season. **Wood** with no real distinction between sapwood and heartwood, yellow, tough and moderately heavy (air-dry 670 kg/m³).

Afrikaans	Vaderlandswilg
Northern Sotho	modibo
Zulu	umBondwe
Botanical name	*Combretum erythrophyllum*
Family	Combretum Family (Combretaceae)
National tree list no.	536

Name derivation *Combretum* = name used by Pliny for a climbing plant, and *erythrophyllum* = red leaves (during autumn).

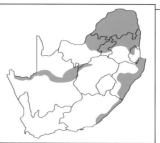

Diagnostic features Bark smooth and grey, flakes on old branches; young leaves somewhat sticky, venation sunken on upper surface, prominent and yellowish on lower surface, yellow and red autumn colours; flowers in dense roundish spikes; fruit 4-winged and light brown; common along streams.

Flowering from September to November.
Fruiting from January to October.

Distribution From Zimbabwe in the north to the Eastern Cape in the south.

Habitat Mostly along rivers and streams. Sometimes away from rivers in wooded grassland where the water table is high enough. Not restricted to any specific type of soil.

Economic value Leaves are eaten by elephant, giraffe, nyala and bushbuck and the young twigs and flowers by giraffe. The seed of unripe fruit is extracted and eaten by pied barbets. The wood is a favourite for general timber on the farm, with very durable beams made from it. The gum that exudes from the stem is used for tanning.

The river bushwillow has been successfully used as street trees in various towns throughout South Africa. It makes a good shade tree in the larger garden. The spectacular autumn colours add a splash of red and purple to an otherwise dull winter garden. This tree can be planted along streams and springs to provide shade and protection of the water source and breeding and foraging areas for aquatic birds and fish. Herons and cormorants prefer to breed in the river bushwillow. A good species to plant along driveways as it does not have an invasive root system.

Other uses The root is used as a purgative but an overdose can cause the patient's death. The gum has a slight antibiotic activity and can be dried, powdered and applied to sores. The wood is popular for making household articles, especially wooden spoons.

Cultivation Seed must be removed from the winged fruit and soaked overnight in water. Sow the swollen seed the following morning in flat seedling trays filled with a mixture of river sand and compost (5:1). Press the seeds into the soil until level with the soil surface and cover lightly with a thin layer of sand. Seeds should germinate within 7–16 days, giving a germination of between 70–90%. Transplant seedlings into black nursery bags when they reach the 2-leaf stage. Grow them on until they reach 300–500 mm before planting them out. They grow best in deep well-drained soil with an ample supply of water. Growth rate is usually fast, 0.7–1.2 m per year. It can withstand drought and frost but must be protected for the first 2–3 winters.

ROUND-LEAVED KIAAT

Description A deciduous tree up to 20 m tall with an open roundish crown, branching from reasonably low down. **Bark** on young branches velvety and grey but brownish grey, rough and longitudinally fissured on older branches and stems. **Leaves** compound, with 1–3 opposite or sub-opposite pairs of leaflets and a terminal leaflet, 80–250 mm long, glossy and pale green, with velvety hairs underneath, veins conspicuously parallel, margin smooth but sometimes wavy. Leaf stalk 30–50 mm long and covered with velvety hairs. **Flowers** yellow, borne in large terminal inflorescences up to 150 mm long, scented, with crinkly petals. Flowering is stimulated by rain. **Fruit** flat non-splitting pods, with a thickened dark central portion surrounded by a thinnish light brown wing and hanging in clusters. **Wood** with no specific distinction between heartwood and sapwood, yellow with pale brown markings, moderately heavy (air-dry 848 kg/m³).

Afrikaans	Dopperkiaat
Northern Sotho	mokwatapa
Zulu	iNdlandlovu
Botanical name	*Pterocarpus rotundifolius* subsp. *rotundifolius*
Family	Pod-bearing Family (Fabaceae)
National tree list no.	237

Name derivation *Pterocarpus* = winged fruit, and *rotundifolius* = round or circular leaflets.

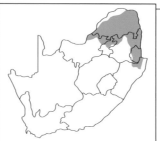

be used for shelving, kitchen furniture and picture frames. As it is so floriferous with a good source of nectar and pollen for honeybees, it is a favourite with bee farmers. When plants are exposed to fire each year, most of the above-ground parts burn away, stimulating coppicing. Overgrazing by cattle and game can also cause coppicing. This is one of the major causes of the pure stands of round-leaved kiaat in certain areas of Swaziland and in the Mpumalanga Lowveld.

Plant groups of 10–20 individuals in suitable habitats in camps, especially along fence lines and at the bottom of hills. They will provide shelter for animals and nesting sites for birds as well as browsing for cattle and game. A very worthwhile subject for the garden which can be used as a background plant or a shade tree during the hot summer months. Its root system is non-aggressive. Relatively quick-growing, up to 1 m per year.

Diagnostic features Leaves compound, with 1–3 pairs of circular leaflets and a terminal leaflet, glossy, veins conspicuously parallel; flowers in terminal inflorescences, yellow, scented, with crinkly petals; pods winged.

Flowering from October to February.
Fruiting from November to July.

Distribution From Malawi and Zambia in the north to KwaZulu-Natal in the south.

Habitat Open woodland and wooded grassland, sometimes on rocky hillsides. More common on sandy soils but also on loamy and clay soils.

Economic value A valuable tree species on the farm as the young branches and leaves are browsed by cattle, small stock and game (elephant, giraffe, kudu and impala). In certain areas it is more heavily browsed by cattle than in others. Larvae of the bushveld charaxes butterfly (*Charaxes achaemenes achaemenes*) live on the leaves. The wood is used as a general purpose timber on the farm. Pieces large enough can

Other uses An infusion made from the leaves is dropped into sore eyes.

Cultivation From seed, cuttings or truncheons. Sound seeds are very rare as insects infest them whilst still immature. Remove seeds from the pods, soak in hot water and leave overnight. Sow them the next morning in flat seedling trays filled with river sand. Transplant into black nursery bags filled with a mixture of sand, loam and compost (7:2:1) when they reach the 1-leaf stage. Take care not to damage the long taproot while transplanting. The easiest way to cultivate the round-leaved kiaat is by truncheons planted in spring when the sap starts to rise. Truncheons should ideally be as thick as one's forearm and 2–3 m long. Before planting, place sand in the bottom of the hole. This will speed up root formation and prevent fungal growth. Young plants flower when still relatively young. When in flower, trees are literally covered in a mass of yellow flowers. It is a drought-hardy plant which withstands some cold, but it is mainly a tree for frost-free areas. When young plants are planted in colder areas, they must be protected against cold winds for at least the first two years.

RUSSET BUSHWILLOW

Description A semi-deciduous to deciduous tree up to 10 m tall with a dense irregular crown. **Bark** on young branches peeling in strips but dark grey, rough and longitudinally fissured on older branches and stems. **Leaves** opposite to sub-opposite, simple, elliptic to oval, up to 50 x 35 mm, dark green above, underside covered in long rusty brown hairs, veins prominent, margin smooth, leaftip mostly rounded. Leaf stalk 3–5 mm long. **Flowers** emerging before appearance of the leaves, borne in dense spikes 20–40 mm long bearing cream-coloured to yellow, sweetly scented flowers. **Fruit** with four prominent wings and up to 20 x 20 mm, rich dark reddish brown. **Wood** without a prominent sapwood but brown on the outside to reddish brown on the inside, hard and heavy (900 kg/m³).

Afrikaans	Kierieklapper
Northern Sotho	mokata
Zulu	umHlalavane
Botanical name	*Combretum hereroense*
Family	Combretum Family (Combretaceae)
National tree list no.	538

Name derivation *Combretum* = the name used by Pliny for a climbing plant, and *hereroense* = from Hereroland.

Diagnostic features Leaves small, shorter than 40 mm, covered with long rusty brown hairs on underside; flowers appearing before the flush of young leaves and borne in short dense spikes; fruit four-winged and rusty brown.

Flowering from September to November.
Fruiting from January to June.

Distribution From Uganda and Kenya in the north to KwaZulu-Natal in the south.

Habitat Various woodland types and in wooded grassland. It prefers sandy to loamy soils.

Economic value A useful fodder tree, the leaves being browsed by cattle and game (elephant, giraffe, kudu, nyala, impala and steenbok). These trees usually show a prominent browse line. Meyer's parrots relish the seed of the young to semi-dry fruit. The wood is termite and borer-proof and stems can be used for fence posts if they are long enough. The flowers attract a myriad of insect species, especially butterflies and wasps which in turn attract a wide variety of insect-eating birds.

The russet bushwillow is best planted in dense groups of 10–15 in a suitable habitat. This will provide fodder and protection for smaller animals and birds. It makes a very decorative tree for the medium to small garden as it does not have an invasive root system. They grow well in containers and with a little pruning it can be neatly shaped. One of the best species to train as a bonsai, taking on the shape of an adult plant after only three years.

Other uses A good-quality tea that resembles ordinary tea in appearance and taste is made from the boiled fruit. Take care not to boil the fruit too long – a bitter taste will result. An infusion of the roots is used for stomach troubles. The dry wood produces a high-quality fuel, the coals long-lasting. Furniture of a high quality can be made from the wood, especially chairs and side tables.

Cultivation Seeds are easily infested by insects, so cultivate the russet bushwillow from fresh seed. Remove the seed from its winged covering and soak in water overnight. Sow the seed the next morning in flat seedling trays in a mixture of river sand and compost (5:1). Seeds usually germinate within 1–2 weeks, with a germination rate of 60%. Transplant into black plastic bags when the seedlings reach the 3-leaf stage. Plants are relatively fast growing for the first 3–4 years (300–500 mm per year), but slow down considerably later on. It can reach 4 m in 12 years. Protect seedlings and young plants from severe cold and frost until they are at least 1 m tall. The russet bushwillow is very drought-resistant and can take some cold, but is mostly suited to warm areas.

SAFSAF WILLOW

Description A semi-deciduous to evergreen tree up to 15 m tall with an open crown and drooping branches. **Bark** on young branches smooth and greenish red but dark brown and fissured on older branches and stems. **Leaves** simple, alternate, dark green above and much lighter below, tapering towards both ends, margins finely serrate. Leaf stalk reddish and short. **Flowers** in short male and female spikes, male dense and up to 50 mm long, female shorter and thicker. **Fruit** a splitting capsule releasing seeds covered in long white wool. **Wood** with no clear distinction between sapwood and heartwood, pale mauve with a fine grain.

Afrikaans	Safsafwilger
Northern Sotho	mogokare
Zulu	umNyezane
Botanical name	*Salix mucronata*
Family	Willow Family (Salicaceae)
National tree list no.	36

Name derivation *Salix* = the Latin name for willow, and *mucronata* = from the word 'mucronate', with a sharp straight point.

Plant near or in water or springs to protect the water source against trampling by animals. Groups of these trees planted next to dams will attract many bird species that will use them for breeding, especially herons, darters and cormorants. This tree certainly has a place alongside ponds in larger gardens and gives the effect of a marshy area. The root system makes it unsuitable for the small garden. It can be used successfully to stabilise and revegetate eroded streambanks if truncheons are planted close to one another in lines across the streambank.

Diagnostic features Branches somewhat drooping; bark deeply fissured on old stems; leaves dark green above and lighter below, leaf stalk reddish; flowers in male and female spikes; fruit a splitting capsule; seed woolly.

Flowering from August to September and March to April.

Fruiting from January to April and June to July.

Distribution From Syria in the north to KwaZulu-Natal in the south.

Habitat Mainly along river and stream banks.

Economic value Leaves browsed by domestic stock and game (hippo, kudu, nyala, bushbuck and grey duiker). The larvae of the African leopard butterfly (*Phalanta phalantha*) feed on the leaves. Various types of baskets are made from the tough young branches. Household articles are made from the dense, strong wood. Popular for carving small figures.

Other uses An infusion made from the root is given for burning stomach pains and a decoction made from the roots is used as a treatment for headaches and fever. Powdered bark is sprinkled on burns. A tea is made from the leaves and taken as a remedy for rheumatism and can also be used as a mild laxative.

Cultivation The safsaf willow can be grown from seed sown in flat seedling trays filled with river sand. Cover the seeds lightly with a thin layer of sand and keep moist. Transplant seedlings into black nursery bags filled with a mixture of compost, river sand and topsoil (1:2:1) when they reach the 2-leaf stage. The best and fastest way to propagate the safsaf willow is by cuttings or truncheons. Cuttings strike easily if treated with a root-stimulating hormone powder and planted in pure river sand. Ideally cuttings should be 120 mm long. Truncheons placed in a well drained medium during early summer usually start rooting within 14 days. Wait for the first branches to form before planting them out into the open ground. The growth rate is medium to fast, 0.7–1 m per year. It can withstand a surprising amount of frost and drought, and it is therefore not necessary to plant it next to streams or dams.

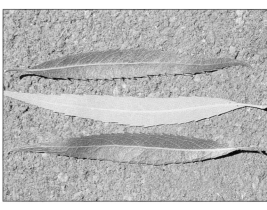

SAGEWOOD

Description A semi-deciduous to evergreen tree up to 8 m tall with a dense, roundish crown with drooping branches. **Bark** on the 4-angled young branches covered with dense woolly hairs but greyish brown and stringy on older branches and stems. **Leaves** simple, opposite, aromatic, dark to grey-green and wrinkled above, with rusty to whitish hairs underneath, venation raised and conspicuous beneath, base of the leaves deeply lobed, margin with fine rounded and thickened teeth. Leaf stalk very short to absent, interpetiolar stipule well developed. **Flowers** in large terminal pyramidal heads up to 120 mm long, individual flowers tubular, white to purple, up to 10 mm long, scented. **Fruit** an ovoid capsule 4–5 mm long, protruding from the persistent calyx. **Wood** with a cream-coloured sapwood and a close-grained, hard and heavy, brown heartwood.

Afrikaans	Saliehout
Northern Sotho	molalatau
Zulu	iLoshane
Botanical name	*Buddleja salviifolia*
Family	Wild Elder Family (Loganiaceae)
National tree list no.	637

Name derivation *Buddleja* = named in honour of the Rev. Adam Buddle, English botanist of the 17th century, and *salviifolia* = leaves like a salvia.

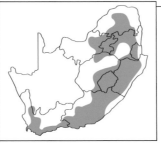

Diagnostic features Young branches 4-angled and covered with dense woolly hairs; leaves opposite, aromatic, with roundish teeth, surfaces wrinkled, venation prominent underneath, leaf stalk very short to absent; flowers tubular; fruit a capsule protruding from the persistent calyx.

Flowering from August to October.
Fruiting from October to December.

Distribution From Tanzania in the north to the Western Cape in the south.

Habitat Growing in forest margins, on rocky outcrops and along drainage lines, especially those with permanent water.

Economic value This is possibly one of the best plants to attract a wide variety of insect species and therefore a number of insect-eating birds. Insects and birds find the tree irresistible! The flowers produce a fair amount of pollen and nectar, making it a popular tree with bee farmers.

The leaves are browsed by game (eland, kudu, bushbuck, impala and grey duiker). Young plants must be protected for at least the first season against game damaging the soft young branches. At least 15 species of butterflies visit these bushes when in flower, but it is the host plant for only one species, the African leopard butterfly (*Phalanta phalantha aethiopica*).

Sagewood is a valuable tree for stabilizing embankments along dams, furrows, streams and rivers. The fine but strong roots which are able to grow even in flowing water, together with the habit of sending out strong shoots after a veld fire and its adaptability to soil and climatic conditions, make this an ideal plant for this purpose. A fountain that is in the process of drying up can often be saved if the correct type of vegetation is planted in and around the sponge area or eye of the fountain. Clumps of sagewood are ideal for this purpose. If pruned often, sagewood can be used as a hedge – which is particularly attractive when in full flower. It forms a perfect background plant in a shrubbery and makes a neat and colourful container plant. Sagewood is a good garden subject, but must be pruned if a tree is required or else it will remain a tall shrub. It has an aggressive root system.

Other uses A decoction of the root is used as a remedy for coughs and colic and an infusion of the leaves is applied as an eye lotion. Fresh or dried leaves can be boiled and used as a tea. Drink it without milk but with a bit of honey.

Cultivation Easily grown from seed or cuttings, the latter being the best way of propagating sagewood. Make the cuttings from hardwood and treat with a root-stimulating hormone powder. Plant the cuttings in river sand and keep moist. They usually strike after 2–3 weeks. Transplant the rooted cuttings into black nursery bags filled with a mixture of river sand and compost (5:1). Sagewood trees are hardy plants resistant to frost and drought. Adult trees can be successfully transplanted. Sagewood flourishes in shade and/or full sun. The growth rate is fast, 600–800 mm per year.

SAUSAGE TREE

Description A semi-deciduous to deciduous much branched tree up to 25 m tall with a dense rounded crown. **Bark** grey and smooth, flaking somewhat in old specimens. **Leaves** crowded near tips of branches, opposite, sometimes in whorls of 3 on young branches, leaf scars prominent on thick branchlets, compound with 3–5 opposite and one terminal leaflet, leaflets stiff, with obliquely rounded bases and short petiolules, venation prominent on underside of leaves, margin sometimes toothed but nearly always wavy, the lowest pair of leaflets are the smallest and the top pair the largest, young leaves browny red. **Flowers** in long, loose pendulous sprays of 5–12 flowers, calyx tubular and with 2–5 ribbed lobes, petals united and deep velvety red with yellow veining on outside, stamens 4. **Fruit** pendulous on a long fruit stalk up to 1 m long, fruit cylindrical to sausage-shaped, grey and rounded at apex, up to 1 m long and 200 mm in diameter. **Wood** whitish to yellowish or pale brown, soft, with no distinction between sapwood and heartwood, moderately heavy (air-dry 720 kg/m³).

Afrikaans	Worsboom
Northern Sotho	modukguhlu
Zulu	umBongothi
Botanical name	*Kigelia africana*
Family	Jacaranda Family (Bignoniaceae)
National tree list no.	678

Name derivation *Kigelia* = based on an African name, and *africana* = from Africa.

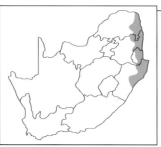

Diagnostic features Leaves opposite or in whorls of 3 on young branches, compound with 3–5 opposite and 1 terminal leaflet, stiff, leaf scars prominent; flowers in long loose sprays, calyx tubular, petals united forming a deep cup, velvety red with yellow veining on outside, stamens 4; fruit sausage-shaped.

Flowering from August to October.
Fruiting from December to June.

Distribution From Tanzania in the north to KwaZulu-Natal in the south.

Habitat Open woodland and along riverbanks. Common on alluvial soils.

Economic value The flowers of the sausage tree are eagerly eaten by domestic stock and game. The leaves are eaten by elephant and kudu. Flowers on the ground are eagerly picked up and eaten by kudu, nyala, impala and grey duiker. Bushpigs will sometimes eat the fruit. The wood is easy to work with and produces a good-quality timber for general use on the farm, fruit boxes and shelving. Inhabitants of the areas along larger rivers, especially the Chobe and Zambezi, make their dugout canoes from this tree.

The sausage tree makes a good shade tree, casting dense shade. Depending on the climate, it reaches shade tree proportions in 4–5 years. It is not advisable to park a vehicle, or to put up a tent underneath a sausage tree during the fruiting period. The 'sausages' that drop every so often can weigh anything up to 12 kg and can cause considerable damage! With its fast growth rate, spreading canopy and interesting flowers and fruit, it makes a good street tree and is popular for this purpose in various towns in the countries north of South Africa and also in Australia. The sausage tree makes an interesting specimen tree in a park in the warmer areas. It should be borne in mind that it has a fairly invasive root system. It can be used successfully for bonsai, the thick stem making an attractive feature.

Other uses Seeds from ripe fruits are edible if roasted in warm ash. Powdered fruit is applied as a dressing in the treatment of wounds, abscesses and ulcers. The green fruit is used as a poultice for syphilis and rheumatism and a poultice made from leaves is used to treat backache. An infusion is made from the ground bark and fruits to treat stomach problems in children, with an infusion from the bark and root taken orally to cure pneumonia. A decoction made from the bark is gargled to relieve toothache. The head is washed with an infusion made from the bark to treat epilepsy.

Cultivation Sow fresh seed in September for the best results. Place the seeds in seedling trays filled with pure river sand. Press the seed into the sand until the tip is level with the sand and cover lightly with a thin layer of sand or pure compost and keep moist. Seeds usually germinate after 10–25 days. The sausage tree is not frost-resistant but if young plants are protected for the first 2–3 years from cold winds in the colder areas, they will survive. The growth rate is at least 1 m per year but it is slower in colder areas.

A protected tree in South Africa.

SCENTED THORN

Description A semi-deciduous tree up to 10 m tall. **Bark** rough and deeply fissured on older branches and stems. **Leaves** twice-compound, hairy, up to 50 x 25 mm, with 4–11 pairs of pinnae and 7–36 pairs of leaflets. **Flowers** only on new growth, 10–12 mm in diameter. **Fruit** with warty seed shields. Young fruits full of moisture, a strong, sweet, fruity scent developing as they mature. **Wood** with a light brown sapwood and a reddish, very hard, heavy (air-dry 1 100 kg/m³) heartwood showing a very fine texture.

Afrikaans	Lekkerruikpeul
Northern Sotho	moku
Zulu	umNqawe
Botanical name	*Acacia nilotica* subsp. *kraussiana*
Family	Pod-bearing Family (Fabaceae)
National tree list no.	179

Name derivation *Acacia* = from the Greek word 'akis' meaning a hook or a barb, *nilotica* = from the Nile, and *kraussiana* = named after Dr Ferdinand Krauss, Director of the Stuttgart Museum.

Diagnostic features Spines paired from a common base, slightly curved backwards; bark dark grey, rough and deeply fissured; leaves with some glands at base of upper pinnae pairs; flowers deep yellow and in round heads; fruit a non-splitting pod, scented, constricted between the seeds; seed shields warty.

Flowering from September to April.
Fruiting from March to September.

Distribution From Tanzania in the north to KwaZulu-Natal in the south.

Habitat Occurs in dry thornveld, river valley scrub, woodland and scrub. It frequently dominates thornveld.

Economic value Leaves are eaten by black rhino, giraffe, eland, kudu, gemsbok, nyala, impala and grey duiker. The pods are relished by cattle and various species of game. The scented thorn is regarded as an indicator of sweetveld and clay soils. If goats consume a large quantity of leaves, and especially ripe pods, abortion commonly occurs in the ewes. If the toxic levels are very high, the adult animal may also die. To date there are no reports of stock dying from prussic acid poisoning originating from the scented thorn. The bark and seed pod contain 14–45% tannin and are therefore used in tanning leather. The riper the pod, the darker the colour of the tanned leather. The gum is edible and yields 14.4% moisture and 2.4% ash – thus suitable for confectionary. The wood is durable, termite- and borer-resistant. It makes a good fuel resulting in hot coals. In certain areas it is preferred to the wood of other species for this purpose. A popular wood for fence posts, easily lasting up to 50 years. The wood is popular for cabinet-making and furniture in general. At the turn of the century, wood of this tree was popular for making *riempie* benches and small tables in the Springbok Flats area and in the Thabazimbi district, Northern Province.

The scented thorn should do well if planted as a fodder tree. Plant in groups of up to 20 in loamy or clay soil. It is advisable to protect the young trees against browsers for the first two years. A scented thorn is a must for any garden as it is always alive with insects, reptiles and birds. Flowering commences when the plant is at least three years old. This makes it a firm favourite for the garden and also for planting on the farm.

Other uses The inner bark is stripped and a useful rope can be made from it. The root and dried pods can be boiled and the resultant decoction used as ink. The root is used in the treatment of tuberculosis and the bark for loosening phlegm; a decoction of bark is applied topically to ulcerations of leprosy. It can also be taken for coughs. The fruit is used as a remedy for diarrhoea. Gum that exudes from the stem and branches is edible and is also used for relief of throat and chest complaints.

Cultivation Seeds are usually not infested by insects and dry pods can be collected from the tree or picked up underneath it. Make sure that the pods are dry or else it will be difficult to extract the seed from the fruit pulp. Place seed in hot water and leave overnight to soak. The next morning the slightly swollen seed can be sown in small black nursery bags filled with a mixture of loam and compost. The seedlings soon develop a long taproot; it will not survive if the taproot is damaged during transplanting. Seeds germinate within 7–15 days. Germination is usually erratic, 60–90% of the seeds germinating during this period. The scented thorn is drought- and frost-resistant and has a growth rate of up to 700 mm per year.

SEPTEMBER BUSH

Decription An evergreen small tree up to 4 m tall with a dense crown. **Bark** on young branches greenish grey and smooth but grey to brown and smooth on older branches and stems. **Leaves** simple and alternate, broad at the coast, much narrower inland, light green, soft, leaf tips rounded to nearly flat with a short point, margin smooth. **Flowers** up to 25 mm in diameter, flowers with 3 petals made up of 2 wings and 1 keel with a feathery crest, and varying in colour from pink, mauve to purple with purple veins, stamens 8 and joined to form a split tube. **Fruit** a small, oval, slightly winged and splitting capsule enclosed by the persistent sepals.

Afrikaans	Septemberbossie
Botanical name	*Polygala myrtifolia*
Family	Milkwort Family (Polygalaceae)
National tree list no.	302.1

Name derivation Greek words *poly* = many, *gala* = milk for promoting secretion of milk, and *myrtifolia* = myrtle-like leaves.

Diagnostic features Evergreen; leaves soft and light green with rounded tips ending in a sharp point, leaf stalk very short; flowers in short clusters at tips of branches, 3 petals made up of 2 wings and 1 keel with a feathery crest, stamens 8 forming a split tube. Fruit a slightly winged splitting capsule.

Flowering throughout the year with a peak from May to September.

Fruiting throughout the year.

Distribution From Zululand in the north to the Western Cape in the south.

Habitat Occurs in forests, scrubveld, wooded grassland, along streams and on dunes.

Economic value The flowers of the September bush attract masses of black and brightly coloured carpenter bees which pollinate them. The fruits are eaten by laughing doves.

The September bush makes a very neat and interesting hedge. It can be clipped more than once a year. If left unpruned it makes an effective screen plant. It gives the best display of shape and colour if planted next to a stream or pond. It can be planted in full sun or in light shade. A neat plant along a driveway giving shape, texture and colour the whole year round.

Other uses The leaves are made into a poultice for treating gout.

Cultivation Easily raised from seed sown in spring. Sow the seed in trays filled with a 1:1 mixture of sand and compost. Cover the seeds with a thin layer of river sand and keep moist. Can also be propagated by means of semi-hardwood cuttings. Dip the bottom ends of the cuttings into a root-stimulating hormone powder before planting in pure river sand. Young plants flower when they reach a height of 300 mm. It can be planted directly into the open ground or into nursery bags filled with a sandy or loamy mixture and then planted out the next season. September bushes tend to seed themselves, forming a small community in no time. The growth rate is fast, up to 1 m per year. The September bush is drought-resistant. It can withstand very mild frost.

SHEPHERD'S TREE

Description Evergreen to semi-deciduous tree up to 7 m tall. **Bark** smooth and whitish grey becoming dark grey and flaky in old specimens. **Leaves** spirally arranged and commonly in groups on side shoots, simple, side veins obscure, leaf margin entire. **Flowers** in dense bunches; individual flowers 4 mm in diameter, with no petals, greenish yellow, with a strong smell. **Fruit** yellow with a reddish flesh. **Wood** dull white to light yellowish brown, close-grained, tough, with prominant annual rings and pores, moderately heavy (air-dry 800 kg/m³).

Afrikaans	Witgat
Northern Sotho	mohlôpi
Zulu	umVithi
Botanical name	*Boscia albitrunca* var. *albitrunca*
Family	Caper Family (Capparaceae)
National tree list no.	122

Name derivation *Boscia* = named after the French professor of agriculture, Louis A.G. Bosc (1777–1850), *albi* = white, and *trunca* = trunk.

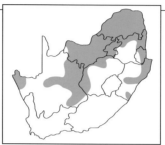

able porridge made from them. Sometimes the root is boiled in water to yield a syrup. Young flower buds make a good substitute for capers. The fruit is edible but has an unpleasant taste. Larvae of the zebra white (*Pinacopteryx eriphia*), brownveined white (*Belenois aurota*), queen purple tip (*Colotis regina*), speckled sulphur tip (*Colotis agoye*), banded gold tip (*Colotis eris*) and lemon traveller tip (*Colotis subfasciatus*) butterflies live on the leaves of the shepherd's tree.

In a garden the habit of this tree differs markedly from that in its natural habitat and it requires much pruning to produce a neat crown. The shepherd's tree can be successfully planted either near the house or in chosen spots in the veld. It is worthwhile to plant scattered groups of at least 20 individuals each in camps with natural grazing. It has a rather invasive root system.

Diagnostic features Tree with smooth, whitish stem and neat roundish crown; leaves brittle, with prominent midrib; flowers without petals, strongly scented; fruit round, 10–15 mm in diameter.

Flowering from August to November.
Fruiting from November to April.

Distribution From Zambia in the north to the Northern Cape in the south.

Habitat Grows in dry open woodland. Common on sandy to loamy soils and very common on calcrete soils.

Economic value One of the most valuable fodder trees for cattle and game (giraffe, gemsbok, kudu, nyala, impala, steenbok and Damara dik-dik) in bushveld areas. The leaves and young twigs have a crude protein content of about 14% and a high vitamin A content. This tree is regularly browsed, even though there may be an abundance of other edible material available. Animals sometimes eat the bark as an anthelmintic. Milk of cows browsing the leaves may be tainted. Branches can be cut for cattle during the dry winter months, but care must be taken not to cut them too low as the trees take years to recover. Many fruit-eating birds (doves, parrots, mousebirds, hornbills, barbets, bulbuls and starlings) visit these trees when they are in fruit. A must for the bird garden in the drier areas. Roots are cut up, dried, roasted and ground and used as a substitute for coffee. The taste is not always agreeable. Roots are also dried and beaten to remove the fibrous material, with an agree-

Other uses A decoction of the roots is used as a treatment for haemorrhoids. A cold infusion of the leaf is used as a lotion for inflamed eyes in cattle.

Cultivation Easily grown from seed or shoot and root cuttings. Seed must be collected from the trees when the fruits are ripe and then dried in a shady place. Be sure to remove all the flesh from the seed as it contains a growth inhibitor. Seed on the ground is usually parasitized. If trees are going to be planted in areas that experience some frost during winter, it is best to collect the seed from colder areas. Seed should be planted in seedling trays filled with river sand. Merely press the seed until it is below the soil level and cover lightly with sand. Keep under conditions conducive to germination. Seeds usually germinate after 7–14 days. Seedlings must be transplanted directly into open ground. If planted out into nursery bags, growth tends to stop. Young plants tend to bush, but they react well to pruning. The growth rate depends on the amount of moisture in the ground, and it is usually fast-growing during the first five years. This tree is well adapted to dry conditions and high summer temperatures and can withstand short periods of frost.

This is a protected tree in South Africa.

SICKLE BUSH

Description A semi-deciduous to deciduous tree up to 7 m tall with an open crown. **Bark** on young branches green and hairy but dark grey-brown and longitudinally fissured on older branches and stems, but smooth on spines formed from modified side-shoots. **Leaves** twice-compound ending in two leaflets with 20–27 pairs of leaflets each, glands prominent on leaf stalk and rachis. **Flowers** in pendulous, 40–50 mm long, two-coloured spikes, upper part pink and consisting of staminodes, lower part yellow, made up of fertile flowers. **Fruit** a cluster of non-splitting, contorted pods up to 100 x 15 mm. **Wood** with a yellowish sapwood and a deep red-brown, very dense, hard, closely grained and heavy (air-dry 960 kg/m³) heartwood.

Afrikaans	Sekelbos
Norhtern Sotho	morêtsê
Zulu	uGagane
Botanical name	*Dichrostachys cinerea* subsp. *africana*
Family	Pod-bearing Family (Fabaceae)
National tree list no.	190

Name derivation *dichrostachys* = two-coloured spike, and *cinerea* = refers to the greyish hairs of the typical subspecies which is confined to India.

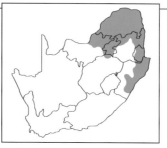

Larvae of the satyr charaxes butterfly (*Charaxes ethalion ethalion*) feed on the sickle bush. Fencing posts are durable and termite-resistant, easily lasting up to 50 years. It makes an excellent fuel, producing very hot coals that last for a long time and also a good-quality charcoal. An excellent wood for tool handles due to its strength and hardness.

Sickle bush trees can be planted as scattered single specimens in camps. By planting it in this way, it is easy to check regeneration. It is advisable to remove the lower branches to force the tree to form a single stem with a spreading crown. Once this shape is attained, cattle and game will keep the crown trimmed. Game prefer to utilise single sickle bush trees where they do not feel threatened. It is advisable for farmers not to eradicate all sickle bush plants when doing encroachment control, but to leave a few well-spaced individuals which can easily be controlled. The sickle bush can be planted in the garden as a specimen plant showing off the beautiful pink and yellow lantern flowers during early summer and the interesting branching pattern during winter. It attracts many insects and they in turn attract various insect-eating birds, making it a must for the dry garden. It does not have an aggressive root system. A favourite plant to train as a bonsai.

Diagnostic features Bark longitudinally fissured, modified side-shoots form spines; glands prominent on leaf stalk and rachis; flowers in pendulous, pink and yellow spikes; fruit in clusters of non-splitting contorted pods.

Flowering from October to February.
Fruiting from May to September.

Distribution From Ethiopia in the north to KwaZulu-Natal in the south.

Habitat Occupies a diverse range of habitats, including woodland at high and low altitudes, forest margins, scrub and grassland. It grows on all types of soil.

Economic value Cattle and game (giraffe, buffalo, kudu, Lichtenstein's hartebeest, nyala, impala, klipspringer, red duiker and Damara dik-dik) relish the palatable pods that drop to the ground. Even the young twigs and leaves are eaten by these animals. Pods and seed do not contain hydrocyanic acid, minimizing the chance of poisoning animals. Sicklebush encroaches rapidly on overgrazed, trampled ground and on old lands where the grass cover has been removed. It is difficult to eradicate as it shoots again from portions of roots. In certain situations mechanical or chemical control measures are the only way to control it.

Other uses The inner bark is very tough and used for making rope. It is also used as a remedy for toothache and stomach troubles. The powdered bark is used as a local application for all kinds of skin conditions. Chewed roots are placed on scorpion stings and snake bites.

Cultivation The sickle bush can easily be grown from seed or root cuttings. Seed can be soaked in hot water, left overnight and planted directly into black nursery bags the next morning. Seedlings soon develop a long taproot. Take care not to damage the taproot while transplanting the young plant into open ground. Make root cuttings 100 mm long and plant them in pure river sand and keep moist. It is a medium to slow grower, with a growth rate of 600–800 mm per year. Usually not frost-resistant but definitely drought-resistant.

SIMPLE-SPINED NUM-NUM

Description An evergreen tree or scrambler up to 6 m tall with a much branched dense canopy. All parts of the plant exude a white non-toxic milky latex. **Bark** on young branches green, smooth or covered with short hairs but light brown and corky with deep cracks on older branches and stems. Plant armed with rigid spines up to 70 mm long. **Leaves** simple and opposite, leathery, dark green above and paler below, midrib sunken, other veins obscure, leaf tip tapering into a bristle-like tip, leaf base shallowly lobed, margin smooth. Leaf stalk up to 5 mm long. **Flowers** in terminal heads up to 40 mm in diameter, white tinged pink to purple and up to 20 mm long and 20 mm in diameter, corolla lobes overlapping to the right, with a sweet jasmine-like scent. **Fruit** a roundish purple to black berry up to 25 mm in diameter.

Afrikaans	Enkeldoring-noemnoem
Northern Sotho	mothokolo
Botanical name	*Carissa edulis*
Family	Oleander Family (Apocynaceae)
National tree list no.	640.4

Name derivation *Carissa* = probably from the Sanskrit 'Corissa', and *edulis* = edible.

ing a pleasant sweet taste and being much sought after. The fruit can be fermented to make a refreshing pink wine or left longer to make vinegar. If planted close together, it can be grown as an effective hedge to keep intruders out; it takes heavy pruning quite well. Birds favour this tree for nest building, and fruit-eating birds (francolins, louries, hornbills, barbets and bulbuls) love the fruit.

Plant as hedges along fences. After a period of about eight years, the hedge will be so thick that no stock or game would be able to penetrate it. A delightful addition to any garden. It does not have an invasive root system and can be planted close to buildings. It makes a successful background plant with its scrambling habit and masses of fragrant whitish flowers.

Diagnostic features Evergreen; all parts exuding a white milky latex; rigid simple spines; leaves opposite; flowers in terminal heads up to 40 mm in diameter, individual flowers white tinged purple, up to 20 mm long, with a sweet jasmine-like scent; fruit a roundish fleshy purple to black berry.

Flowering from September to December.
Fruiting from November to January.

Distribution From Senegal in the north to Mpumalanga in the south, also growing in Asia from Yemen to India and Thailand, and on some Indian Ocean Islands.

Habitat Common in deciduous to evergreen woodland. Partial to granitic soils.

Economic value Leaves are eaten by eland, kudu, nyala, bushbuck, impala and grey duiker and the fruit eaten by kudu, grey duiker, baboons, vervet monkeys and bushpigs. Fruits edible, the milky red pulp hav-

Other uses The powdered root is used as a remedy for chest complaints; an infusion made from the root is drunk to ease stomach ache, as a cough remedy or dropped onto the eye for cataract problems. A decoction made from the root is administered as a mild purgative to children. A hot pack is made from the root and placed on abscesses to treat infection.

Cultivation Easily grown from fresh seed. Fill a flat tray with river sand and place the seed on the surface, press them into the sand until they are flush with the surface and cover with a layer of sand equal to the thickness of the seed. Keep moist and in a warm spot. Seeds usually germinate after 7–14 days. Seedlings can be transplanted into nursery bags filled with a mixture of soil and compost (2:1) when they reach the 2-leaf stage, or they can be planted out directly into open ground. Seedlings and young plants are frost-tender and should be covered by grass or shade cloth for the first two winters. After this they should be able to tolerate light frost conditions. The simple-spined num-num has a growth rate of 1–1.2 m per year. It is very drought-resistant.

SJAMBOK POD

Afrikaans	Sambokpeul
Northern Sotho	monêpênêpê
Botanical name	*Cassia abbreviata*
	subsp. *beareana*
Family	Pod-bearing Family (Fabaceae)
National tree no.	212

Name derivation *Cassia* = an ancient Hebrew name, *abbreviata* = shortened, and *beareana* = named after Dr O'Sullivan Beare who collected the tree in Tanzania.

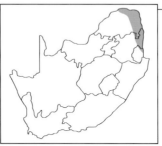

Description A deciduous tree up to 13 m tall with a neat roundish crown and drooping branches. **Bark** on young branches smooth and faintly ridged and furrowed but brownish grey and very rough on older branches and stems. **Leaves** drooping, evenly compound with 5–12 pairs of thinly textured dull green leaflets with rounded tips and smooth margins, leaf stalk up to 50 mm long. **Flowers** in large loose terminal sprays up to 200 mm long, appearing with or just after the leaves, flowers sweetly scented, yellow, becoming brown-veined with age, up to 45 mm in diameter, on thin flower stalks that are up to 70 mm long. **Fruit** a long cylindrical dark brown hanging pod up to 900 x 30 mm. **Wood** with a pale brown sapwood and a dark brown coarse-grained heartwood with paler blotches, heavy (air-dry 896 kg/m³).

Diagnostic features Crown roundish; leaves evenly compound with thinly textured leaflets with roundish tips; flowers yellow and in large loose terminal sprays; pod dark brown, cylindrical and up to 900 mm long and hanging.

Flowering from September to October.
Fruiting from December to April.

Distribution From Somalia in the north to Swaziland in the south.

Habitat Open woodland or in wooded grassland, common on termitaria in the arid lowveld.

Economic uses The young branches and leaves are eaten by elephant and leaves eaten by giraffe, kudu and nyala. The fruit pulp and seeds are very popular with brown-headed and Meyer's parrots, grey louries, barbets and various hornbill species.

This is one of the neatest indigenous trees for the garden and containers on a patio. In the warmer areas this tree can be planted along driveways, creating a bright yellow avenue during the flowering season. The sjambok pod makes an ideal specimen tree if planted on a lawn, singly or in groups. The prominent rough dark brown bark, drooping light-coloured leaves, bunches of bright yellow flowers and hanging pods make this a much sought-after tree for the garden. It has a taproot system which is not aggressive. Remember to give it a dry period during winter, which will result in masses of flowers during early spring. Over-watering results in a poor display of flowers. This is one of the most interesting trees to train as a bonsai – resulting in a plant resembling the adult tree after only three years.

Other uses The powdered root is taken for the relief of backache. An infusion made from the bark and roots is used for the relief of abdominal pains, constipation, diarrhoea and as a remedy for toothache. An extract of the bark is still used for treating blackwater fever. The smoke of burnt branches is inhaled to relieve headaches. Abscesses are treated with the powdered bark.

Propagation Seeds germinate easily. Always remove the green-coloured flesh surrounding the seed prior to sowing. Soak fresh seed in boiling water for 20 minutes or in warm water and leave overnight. Sow the swollen seeds the next day in a sand : compost mixture (1:1) and keep warm and moist. Seeds usually germinate 4–10 days after sowing. A very long taproot is produced early on and if the seed is sown into seedling trays, the seedlings should be planted out within a week or two. It is better to sow the seed directly into black nursery bags or into the ground. The growth rate is moderate, up to 700 mm per year. It is frost-tender, particularly when young; so, protect for the first few seasons. Very drought-resistant.

SMALL KNOBWOOD

Description A deciduous tree up to 15 m tall with an open to shapeless crown. **Bark** on young branches smooth with straight dark brown thorns and light to dark grey on older branches and stems with straight spines on scattered cone-shaped knobs. **Leaves** in clusters on short side branches, unevenly compound with 4–10 pairs of leaflets plus a terminal one, lower leaflets decreasing in size, glossy dark green with clear gland dots in scalloped margin, each leaflet with 2 lobes at base, midrib often spiny, leaf with a strong citrus smell when crushed. Leaf stalk deeply chanelled above. **Flowers** in terminal sprays, sweet-smelling and greenish white, with 4 sepals and 4 petals, separate male and female trees. **Fruit** a round splitting capsule up to 5 mm in diameter, covered with glands, green turning red when ripe, splitting later to reveal a single black oil-rich seed per capsule. **Wood** yellowish and fairly hard, heavy (air-dry 944 kg/m³), with a fine grain.

Afrikaans	Kleinperdepram
Northern Sotho	monokwane
Zulu	umNungumabele
Botanical name	*Zanthoxylum capense*
Family	Citrus Family (Rutaceae)
National tree list no.	253

Name derivation *Zanthoxylum* = the Greek for yellow wood, and *capense* = from the Cape.

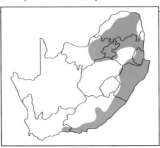

Diagnostic features All parts of the tree with a citrus-like smell; straight thorns on corky knobs on main stem; leaves with oil glands on margin; separate male and female trees; flowers with 4 sepals and 4 petals; fruit a capsule with a single glossy black seed.

Flowering from October to February.
Fruiting from November to July.

Distribution From Zimbabwe in the north to the Western Cape in the south.

Habitat Mostly in dry to evergreen woodland and on rocky hill slopes, but adapted to a wide range of ecological niches.

Economic value Leaves browsed by game (kudu, klipspringer and grey duiker). The ripe fruits are eaten by vervet monkeys and baboons. The seeds are eaten by various bird species. Larvae of the citrus swallowtail butterfly (*Papilio demodocus*), white-banded swallowtail (*Papilio echeroides*) and the emperor swallowtail (*Papilio ophidicephalus*) butterflies feed on the leaves of this tree. Popular for making walking sticks and spoons.

The small knobwood makes an excellent specimen tree with its glossy dark green foliage and glossy red fruits in summer and the decorative grey and knobbly stem in winter. This tree is a must to attract birds, a wide variety of bird species enjoying the seeds. It is most successful as a container plant either in the full sun or in light shade. Plant this tree in the rock garden for a stunning effect. The root system is not aggressive at all, giving it a wide range of applications.

Other uses The dried and powdered root and stem bark are used for treating sore throats, blood poisoning and related diseases. The ground roots are also used for treating toothache. Quick relief from stomach cramps is achieved with a tea made from the leaves. A decoction made from the roots and leaves is used against fever. The crushed seeds are used as perfume by some tribes. The fruit is sometimes used for colic. Gall-sickness in cattle is treated with a decoction made from the bark.

Cultivation Collect fresh seed, which should be soaked in a hydrochloric or sulphuric acid solution and then soaked overnight in hot water prior to sowing. Sow the seed in a 1:1 mixture of river sand and compost and keep moist in a shady spot. Germination is usually very erratic. Transplant the seedlings into nursery bags when they reach the 2-leaf stage. Seedlings found underneath trees in the veld transplant well and this is the best method of obtaining this tree. The growth rate is moderate to fast, 600–800 mm per year. Plants are well adapted to drought and frost.

This is a protected tree in South Africa.

SNEEZEWOOD

Description An evergreen to semi-deciduous tree up to 35 m tall. **Bark** dark grey with deep longitudinal and interlinked furrows on older branches and stems. **Leaves** with a slightly winged rachis bearing 3–8 opposite dark green leaflets, autumn foliage yellow to reddish. **Flowers** in short branched heads, flowers sweetly scented, 5–7 mm in diameter. **Fruit** an oblong capsule with the top part notched turning reddish brown when mature, splitting to release winged seeds. **Wood** fine-grained, the sapwood yellowish brown and the heartwood honey-brown, hard and heavy (air-dry 1 040 kg/m³), containing an aromatic oil with a slight peppery smell causing sneezing.

Afrikaans	Nieshout
Zulu	umThathe
Botanical name	*Ptaeroxylon obliquum*
Family	Sneezewood Family (Ptaeroxylaceae)
National tree list no.	292

Name derivation *Ptaeroxylon* = Greek words meaning 'sneezewood', and *obliquum* = refers to the oblique leaflets.

Diagnostic features Leaves opposite, evenly compound with distinct oblique leaflets; separate male and female trees; flowers with 4 petals and a fleshy disc; fruit a splitting 2-lobed capsule.

Flowering from August to December.
Fruiting from December to February.

Distribution From Tanzania in the north to the Eastern Cape in the south.

Habitat Grows in well-drained sandy to rocky soil in woodland, scrub forest and evergreen montane forest. Plants growing in the dry bushveld tend to be no higher than 3 m and those in forests usually higher than 10 m.

Economic value Widely used as a general purpose timber but makes very durable furniture. Around the turn of the century this was regarded as one of the best woods for making benches and chairs. Sneezewood is very much in demand for furniture nowadays. Beams of this wood are still in use after installation 200 years ago.

Earlier this century farmers, for the lack of metal bearings, used sneezewood bearings that lasted nearly as long as the metal ones. Sneezewood lasts nearly indefinitely in water and this makes it ideal for bridge and jetty construction. Wood was once cut by the tons for railway sleepers, and is nowadays incorrectly called 'Yellow Jarra' by furniture manufacturers. Still a popular wood with stock-farmers as they use it for almost indestructible fence poles. Dry wood makes an excellent fuel. Young shoots and leaves are eagerly browsed by giraffe, nyala, kudu, impala and duiker. This is the food plant for the larvae of the citrus swallowtail butterfly (*Princeps demodocus demodocus*). At certain times of the year masses of larvae defoliate the trees.

Farmers in high rainfall areas can plant a hectare or more with sneezewood as a long-term investment. These trees will be ready to harvest 30 years later. The wood is becoming progressively scarcer and plantings like these can later prove to be financially rewarding. The neat crown, dark and glossy green leaves turning yellow to reddish in autumn makes sneezewood a rewarding and worthwhile garden subject. The small, neat crown together with the non-invasive root system makes this tree ideal for the small garden.

Other uses Snuff made from the bark and wood is used to treat headaches and sinusitis. To remove warts in humans and cattle, resin collected from the heated wood is placed on the warts until they disappear. Pieces of wood are still placed in cupboards to repel moths and other insects. This insect-repelling property made it a popular wood for bedsteads. Popular for making fire-by-friction with the bottom piece from this tree. The inflammable oils ignite easily.

Cultivation Collect seed just before the fruits split. Dry fruits are usually heavily infested with insects. Sow seeds in a mixture of river sand and compost (1:1), covering the seed with a thin layer of sifted sand. Place a glass pane over the seedling trays to speed up germination. Transplant seedlings into nursery bags or directly into open soil when they reach the 3-leaf stage. Seedlings planted in open soil need much additional water to establish. A tree with a moderate to fast growth rate, 0.4–1 m per year, depending on the habitat; it will flower when about five years old. It can withstand moderate frost and is very drought-tolerant.

Sneezewood is protected in South Africa.

SNOT APPLE

Description An evergreen to semi-deciduous tree up to 10 m tall with a dense round-ish crown. **Bark** on young branches with shaggy hairs but grey to brown, rough and cracked lengthwise on older stems and branches. **Leaves** simple, upper surface furnished with rough star-shaped hairs, lower surface with soft hairs, leaf margin smooth. Leaf stalk hairy, 100–130 mm long. Young leaves velvety and reddish coloured. **Flowers** solitary in axils of leaves, up to 60 mm in diameter, with a conspicuous cup-like calyx and a fused epicalyx, petals crinkly, overlapping, hairy outside, stamens fused into a tube with a few free filaments at the tip. Flowers ageing to orange-red. **Fruit** 20–50 mm in diameter and densely covered with hairs. **Wood** deep brown and mottled.

Afrikaans	Snotappel
Northern Sotho	monatő
Botanical name	*Azanza garckeana*
Family	Hibiscus Family (Malvaceae)
National tree list no.	466

Name derivation *Azanza* = origin of the name obscure, and *garckeana* = named after Prof. August Garcke (1819–1904), a German botanist.

Diagnostic features Leaves 3–5-lobed, 3–7-veined from the base, longitudinal fissure on midrib; flowers yellow with brown to purple blotch at base of each petal; fruit a splitting, hairy, 5-lobed capsule.

Flowering from December to May.
Fruiting from February to September.

Distribution From Sudan in the north to Mpumalanga in the south.

Habitat Open woodland and wooded grassland, growing on a wide range of soils but more common on clay soil.

Economic value The adaptability of the snot apple to various climatic conditions and soil types makes it suitable for planting as a shade tree in most areas. The trees are evergreen in the warmer areas but semi-deciduous in colder regions. The wood is used for the manufacture of small pieces of furniture (side tables and chairs) and boxes, and when available in sufficient quantity it is used for shelving. The heartwood is still used as implement handles and in the area north of the Zambezi River, for knife sheaths. A good-quality rope can be made from the fibres of the inner bark.

Plant groups of up to 15 individuals in camps where shade is needed for cattle, small stock and game. It also makes an attractive shade tree for the average garden with its attractive foliage, yellow flowers and non-aggressive root system. This tree certainly deserves a spot in the garden, but it is unfortunately (like so many other species) not readily available. The snot apple makes a successful and interesting container plant but must be kept in full sun.

Other uses The hard outer covering of the fruit is peeled off and the sweet to slightly insipid glutinous pulp round the seeds eaten. A decoction is made from the roots and taken orally for painful menstruation and to treat coughs and chest pains. An infusion made from the roots and leaves is dropped into the ear to treat earache or taken orally as an antiemetic.

Cultivation Seeds germinate easily, usually taking 20–60 days. Fill a seedling tray with river sand and press the hairy seeds into the sand until they are flush with the surface and cover with a thin layer of sand. Guard against keeping it too moist. This is a common problem. The sand should be damp at all times, but not moist. Transplant the seedlings into nursery bags filled with a compost-rich loamy soil when they reach the 3-leaf stage. The growth rate is initially fast, so do not keep in bags for more than one season before planting out into open ground. Trees sucker freely and these can be planted with great success. If grown from truncheons, they must not be thinner than 80 mm in diameter. Place some sand into the bottom of the hole before planting the truncheon, to prevent fungal growth and speed up root formation. A strike percentage of 60% is regarded as very good. Reasonably slow-growing, up to 600 mm per year in the warmer areas and up to 400 mm in areas receiving some frost. The snot apple is drought-resistant but thrives with abundant water during the rainy season. Surprisingly enough, it can withstand mild frost. This tree is the host for the cotton stainer (*Dysdercus nigrofasciatus*) and should therefore not be planted in cotton-producing areas. These insects damage cotton plants directly from their feeding on the seed or indirectly through the transmission of a fungal infection that affects the maturation of the ball and the lint.

SPEKBOOM

Description An evergreen succulent tree up to 5 m tall with soft, fleshy stems and a dense crown. **Bark** on young branches smooth, glossy purple but smooth and reddish brown to grey on older branches and stems. **Leaves** simple and in opposite pairs, thick and succulent, obovate, with obscure venation and entire margins, leaf stalk very short. **Flowers** in dense sprays on short side branchlets, star-shaped, pink, with 2 sepals and 5 petals. **Fruit** a 3-winged papery capsule 3–5 mm long. **Wood** spongy and light.

Afrikaans	Spekboom
Zulu	isiDondwane
Botanical name	*Portulacaria afra*
Family	Purslane Family (Portulacaceae)
National tree list no.	104

Name derivation *Portulacaria* = based on the Latin word 'Portulaca', and *afra* = African.

Diagnostic features Evergreen; bark smooth; leaves succulent, leaf stalk very short; flowers pink, star-shaped, with 2 sepals; fruit 3-winged.

Flowering from June to November.
Fruiting from August to February.

Distribution From the Soutpansberg in the north to the Western Cape in the south.

Habitat Hot dry rocky hillsides and river valleys in succulent scrub and woodland.

Economic value Excellent fodder with a high moisture but low protein content. Most domestic animals and game (elephant, kudu, nyala, bushbuck, impala, klipspringer and grey duiker) browse on this plant. A real life-saver in the drier areas, especially during periods of drought. Although not invasive, the spekboom does have an extensive root system and this together with the fact that it grows very easily from stem cuttings, makes it a useful tool in combating soil erosion. Branches can be planted in and across drainage lines. The flowers produce copious nectar, making this tree a favourite with bee farmers.

A practical place to plant spekboom on the farm is along fence lines. Plant cuttings or young plants 5 m away from the fence so that fence patrols can still be done once the plants are 3 m tall or more. The effectiveness of the wire fence will be enhanced by the spekboom hedge. Once established, it forms a thick impenetrable hedge that can easily be clipped and trained. A hedge like this is very effective around vegetable gardens for keeping unwanted visitors out! The spekboom makes a very successful container plant and can be pruned into a neat shape. It flowers and readily produces fruit when grown as a container plant. A prostrate form growing no higher than 150 mm is available from certain nurseries and can be used as a groundcover in a flowerbed or on a rockery where the branches can trail. For hardiness, the spekboom is almost unrivalled. It is popular for bonsai – taking on the shape of the adult plant after only two years – and can be trained in various bonsai styles.

Other uses The leaves are eaten by women of certain tribes who have insufficient milk for their babies. Dried and ground leaves are used as a snuff.

Cultivation Easily grown from cuttings made from 1-year old shoots and planted during spring. Cuttings must be planted into the soil for $1/2$ to $2/3$ of their length. Another method is by layering. Branches on the ground will form roots after a while and can then be cut up into 300 mm long pieces which can then be planted. It can also be propagated from seed, but cuttings are faster and easier. Extremely drought-resistant and will survive a limited amount of frost. Grows well in all soil types, even in heavy black turf. If planted in the garden, choose a sunny place with ample space. Spekboom plants in the garden need to be pruned often. Many bird species utilize this plant as a nesting site. The growth rate is moderately fast, 0.7–1 m per year.

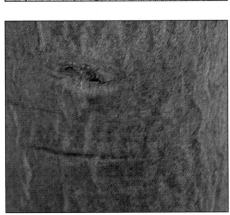

SUMACH-BEAN

Description A deciduous tree up to 6 m tall with a dense roundish to elongated crown. **Bark** on young branches smooth and grey-green but dark brown to blackish brown and very rough on older branches and stem. **Leaves** evenly twice-compound, up to 250 mm long, with 4–8 pairs of pinnae each with 12–23 pairs of leaflets. Leaf stalk 25–65 mm long. **Flowers** fragrant, cream-coloured, in 50–100 mm long spikes borne in axils of leaves. **Fruit** a flat brown to reddish brown pod up to 300 x 40 mm, with rims of pods remaining and valves curling up between them.

Afrikaans	Basboontjie
Northern Sotho	mositsane
Botanical name	*Elephantorrhiza burkei*
Family	Pod-bearing Family (Fabaceae)
National tree list no.	193

Name derivation *Elephantorrhiza* = elephant root, and *burkei* = named after Joseph Burke (1812–1873), a botanical and zoological collector in the 19th century.

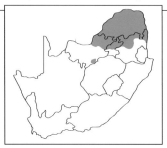

leather, giving it a characteristic reddish colour. This plant is popular with bee farmers, producing honey with a very delicate but characteristic taste.

The sumach-bean is spectacular when in flower. It can be grown as a specimen tree on a rocky ridge or on a rockery, giving colour and texture. It grows well as a container plant but then does not react well to pruning and must always be in full sun. It does not have an aggressive root system. It is also striking if planted in a group on the lawn, with its grey-green leaves and dark bark, cream coloured flowers and long pods remaining on the plant after the leaves have dropped. The flowers attract a myriad of insects and they in turn insect-eating birds.

Diagnostic features Bark dark brown and rough on the stems; leaves grey-green and evenly twice-compound with 4–8 pairs of pinnae; flowers cream-coloured, in dense 50–100 mm long spikes; pod flat with rims of pods remaining and valves curling between them.

Flowering from October to November.
Fruiting from February to May.

Distribution From Zambia in the north to the North-West Province in the south.

Habitat Occurs on rocky ridges and slopes in woodland, grassland and scrub veld.

Economic value It is extensively used for tanning leather. The root and especially the root bark is chopped into pieces and left in water for the tannin compounds to mix with the water. This is then used for tanning

Other uses An infusion made from the roots is used for constipation and as an anti-emetic drug.

Cultivation Collect fresh seed from pods turning brown and dry in the shade. If left too late, worms quickly ruin the seed. Place the seeds in a container, pour boiling water over them and leave until the next morning when they must be planted in seedling trays filled with a 1:1 mixture of river sand and compost. Cover the seeds lightly with a 5 mm thick layer of sand and keep moist. The seeds usually germinate after 10 days but germination is very erratic. Transplant the seedlings into nursery bags when they reach the 2-leaf stage. Take care not to damage the taproot whilst transplanting. The growth rate is somewhat slow, up to 500 mm per year under very good conditions. It can withstand some frost and is very drought-resistant.

SWEET THORN

Description An evergreen tree up to 20 m. **Bark** rough and fissured on older branches and stems. **Thorns** elongated and abundant on young trees, 30–250 mm long. **Leaves** in axils of thorns, twice-compound with 2–6 pairs of pinnae each with 5–27 pairs of leaflets. **Flowers** sweetly-scented, 10–13 mm in diameter. **Fruit** a brown sickle-shaped splitting pod up to 160 x 10 mm. **Wood** with a light brown to yellowish sapwood with prominent annual rings and a reddish brown hard and moderately heavy (air-dry 800 kg/m³) heartwood.

Afrikaans	Soetdoring
Northern Sotho	mookana
Zulu	umuNga
Botanical name	*Acacia karroo*
Family	Pod-bearing Family (Fabaceae)
National tree list no.	172

Name derivation *Acacia* = from the word 'akis' meaning a point or a barb, and *karroo* = from the Karoo.

colour. An infusion of the bark is given to cattle with *Homeria* (tulp) poisoning. An excellent source of pollen and nectar – ideal for the bee farmers. The wood is susceptible to borer attack but this can be prevented if the wood seasoned in water for six months.

The sweet thorn with its adaptability to a wide range of soil types and climatic conditions has secured a place on the farm and in the towns. In areas with very little or no trees, the sweet thorn can be planted as a windbreak around buildings, holding pens for livestock and around croplands. With its dark brown bark, dense foliage and golden yellow inflorescences, it makes a stunning specimen tree regardless of where it is used. Its invasive root system makes it unsuitable for use in paving or near buildings. The flowers attract masses of insects and they in turn a wide variety of insect-eating birds, making it a must for the bird garden.

Diagnostic features Young branches reddish brown; thorns in pairs and straight; gland on leaf stalk large; flowers deep yellow and in round inflorescences grouped towards tips of branches; splitting sickle-shaped pod.

Flowering from October to February.
Fruiting from January to May.

Distribution From Zambia and Angola in the north to the Western Cape in the south.

Habitat Occupy most habitat types. Adapted to various climatic and moisture regimes. Most frequently in wooded grassland and on the margins of marshy areas. Not restricted to any specific soil type.

Economic value An excellent fodder tree with palatable leaves, flowers and pods, with no danger of hydrocyanic acid poisoning. The young leaves are relished in spring by game (black rhino, giraffe, eland, kudu, nyala, sable, gemsbok, impala and springbok) and livestock. Larvae of the club-tailed charaxes (*Charaxes zoolina zoolina*), silver spotted grey (*Crudaria leroma*), black-striped hairtail (*Anthene amarah amarah*), common hairtail (*Anthene definita*), otacilia hairtail (*Anthene otacilia*), talbot's hairtail (*Anthene talboti*), black heart (*Uranothauma nubifer*), topaz-spotted blue (*Azanus jesous*), thorn-tree blue (*Azanus moriqua*), Natal spotted blue (*Azanus natalensis*) and the velvet spotted blue (*Azanus ubaldus*) butterflies are dependent on the young shoots and thorns of the sweet thorn for survival. The bark contains 19% tannin and is used for tanning leather, giving it a reddish

Other uses The gum (arabinose-galactose type) is edible, with a pleasant, slightly sour taste and is a favourite with children but it can also be used for both confectionery and as an adhesive. At one time it was exported as 'Gomme du Cap' (Cape Gum) for use in the confectionery trade. The inner bark is pliable when wet and used for making a very strong rope. Seed can be burnt and ground and used as a substitute for coffee, but most people find the taste unpleasant. A dilution of the gum is used as a mouthwash for thrush and sprue. An infusion of the bark is still used as a remedy for diarrhoea and dysentery.

Cultivation Grows easily from seed. Seed must be soaked in hot water, left overnight and then sown the next morning. Plant seed either directly into small black nursery bags or in flat seedling trays filled with seedling mix obtainable at any nursery. Cover the seed lightly with sand and keep moist. Seeds usually germinate 3–12 days after being sown. Transplant from the trays when the seedlings unfold their second leaves. In spite of the long taproot, seedlings transplant well. The sweet thorn is frost- and drought-resistant, with a fast growth rate, up to 1 m or more per year being normal. A protected tree in the Northern Cape and Free State.

SYCAMORE FIG

Description A semi-deciduous tree up to 35 m tall. **Bark** on young branches covered in long hairs, greenish yellow but pale brown to yellowish brown and flaking in papery pieces on older branches and stems, main trunk sometimes growing to more than 2 m in diameter. **Leaves** on new growth, simple, oval to elliptic and up to 170 x 150 mm, base lobed, veins raised on lower surface. The 20–30 mm long leaf stalks are hairy on young leaves but become glabrous in older leaves. **Fruit** in close-packed clusters on many-branched, fruit-bearing branchlets; the figs nearly round, 20–50 mm in diameter and yellowish red to red when ripe, with 25–35 mm long fruit stems. **Wood** soft, very light (air-dry 510 kg/m³), pale brown, without a noticable heartwood.

Afrikaans	Rivierwildevy
Northern Sotho	mogobôya
Zulu	umKhiwane
Botanical name	*Ficus sycomorus*
Family	Fig Family (Moraceae)
National tree list no.	66

Name derivation *Ficus* = the classical Latin name for the cultivated fig, and *sycomorus* = the Sycamore of the Bible.

or dams. A few of these trees around the perimeter of an earthen dam are not only aesthetically pleasing but also advantageous to the ecology of the area. A few trees can be planted next to lands to give shade for the labourers during the hot summer months. It makes a beautiful shade tree in the large garden and park. This tree is a must for the bird garden. It is constantly alive with small mammals, birds, bats, reptiles and insects. The fruits attract many insect-eating and fruit-eating birds. The rather invasive root system should be borne in mind when positioning this tree. It is a wild fig tree that really does well in a container if pruned once to twice a year. The yellowish bark shows at an early stage, contrasting well with the green leaves. A popular species to grow as a bonsai.

Diagnostic features Milky latex in all parts of the tree; bark yellowish and flaking in papery pieces; stipules covering the growth tip; leaves rough to the touch, leaf tip rounded; figs in clusters on much-branched fruit-bearing branchlets.

Flowering and fruiting throughout the year, with a peak from July to December.

Distribution From Israel in the north to KwaZulu-Natal in the south.

Habitat Along streams, rivers or dry stream beds.

Economic value A useful tree to have in the garden or in the veld for the ripe figs are relished by many fruit-eating birds (pigeons, doves, parrots, louries, mousebirds, hornbills, barbets, bulbuls and starlings), fruit-eating bats, game (elephant, giraffe, kudu, nyala, bushbuck, impala, grey duiker, bushpigs, warthogs, baboons, monkeys and bushbabies). A tree can bear several crops of fruit per year. To stimulate milk production, cows can be fed with the highly nutritious and easily digested leaves of this tree. The leaf is a valuable fodder in overstocked semi-arid areas where the trees occur naturally.

As it needs a substantial amount of water, it is best planted next to drainage lines, streams, rivers, springs

Further uses Various tribes throughout Africa use a piece of dry wood from this tree as the base block when making fire by means of the friction method. The soft wood carves easily and is used for making drums. The fruit is edible, with a pleasant flavour; however, they are nearly always full of insects, but these can be washed out. The fruit can be dried and stored for later use. A strong rope can be made from the inner bark. A decoction of the bark and the latex is used for chest conditions, coughing and scrofula. Inflamed areas are treated with the milky latex. Ringworm is treated with the bark and milky latex.

Cultivation As viable seed is difficult to obtain, it is preferable to cultivate this tree either from cuttings or truncheons. Truncheons must be left in the shade for a few days to dry before planting. Failing this, the tips of the truncheons will rot. Branches with a diameter of 50–150 mm are the best to use for truncheons. Make sure you remove most of the leaves before planting. Plant in a hole 1 m deep with some sand at the bottom. This prevents rotting of the truncheon and helps to stimulate root formation. Cuttings can be made from either hardwood or softwood. The sycamore fig is sensitive to frost but can withstand some cold and it is best to protect young plants until they reach a height of 1 m or more. This will also protect them from browsers defoliating the plant. The growth rate is fairly fast, 1–1.5 m per year in frost-free areas.

TAMBOTI

Description Semi-deciduous to deciduous tree up to 18 m tall. All parts exuding a toxic milky latex. **Bark** forming rectangular blocks arranged in longitudinal rows. **Leaves** alternate, simple and up to 70 x 35 mm, margin finely toothed. Leaf stalk 4–6 mm long. **Flowers** 15–30 mm long bearing both male and female florets, female florets borne at base of spike, bracts reddish brown and overlapping, petals absent, the 3 stamens forming a tube, ovary 3-locular, fused styles forming a thick cylindrical column. **Fruit** a splitting capsule 8–10 mm in diameter. **Wood** with a thin yellowish sapwood and a brown to dark brown heartwood with blackish stripes, hard and heavy (air-dry 960 kg/m³).

Afrikaans	Tambotie
Northern Sotho	morekuri
Zulu	umThombothi
Botanical name	*Spirostachys africana*
Family	Spurge Family (Euphorbiaceae)
National tree list no.	341

Name derivation *Spirostachys* = spirally arranged flower segments, and *africanus* = from Africa.

Diagnostic features Bark dark brown and cracked into rectangular blocks arranged in rows; young branches spiny; leaves turning yellow to red in autumn, two small glands at base of leaf blade, milky latex; flowers in catkin-like spikes; fruit woody and 3-lobed, pupae of a moth in the fruit causing it to jump.

Flowering from July to January.
Fruiting from October to February.

Distribution From Tanzania in the north to KwaZulu-Natal in the south.

Habitat Along drainage lines in all woodland types. Indicator of brackish areas, clay soils, poorly drained soils and underground water. Commonly forms dense homogeneous stands.

Economic value A well sought-after tree by game. Porcupines relish the bark during the winter months, ringbarking many trees which eventually die. The leaves are eaten fresh by elephant, black rhino, giraffe, eland, kudu, nyala, bushbuck, impala and the Damara dik-dik. Fallen leaves are eaten by nyala, impala and duiker. Dropped fruit is eagerly eaten by guineafowl, francolin and various dove species. One of the most sought-after furniture woods in the world. The sawdust is very harmful to the eyes and can even cause blindness. The wood finishes very smoothly and takes wood polish and oil readily. Furniture treated with oil over long periods tend to darken. The smell of the wood is characteristic and remains for years. A piece of wood a hundred years old will still give off a strong smell if scraped. Beautiful gun-stocks can be made from the wood.

Plant tamboti trees in dense groups along drainage lines in cattle camps. One of few tree species that can be planted on brackish soils. Tamboti trees can be planted for the timber in a plantation format. This is a long-term project of 18 years or more, but well worth the wait. A group of 3–5 trees planted on a lawn or next to large boulders will give a stunning display of autumn colours and contrast beautifully with the dark brown of the bark. It makes an interesting potplant for the patio, showing its branch architecture and autumn leaves to the full. It does not have an aggressive root system. One of the most popular choices for a bonsai specimen.

Other uses The milky latex is very toxic and can cause blisters on the skin and severe pain and/or damage to the eyes. Latex can be used to poison fish. The wood is unsuitable for fuel or for roasting meat. The milky latex is extremely toxic when heated, resulting in severe diarrhoea if meat roasted on coals from its wood is eaten. In severe cases death may result. Small quantities of bark are used as a purgative, but large dosages cause damage to the internal organs. A decoction is made from the bark to treat stomach pains, diarrhoea and dysentery. The milky latex is applied to boils to ease the infection and a few drops are taken by mouth in porridge for stomach pains.

Cultivation Collect fresh seed from the trees, as unparasitised seeds are rarely found if collected on the ground. Sow in containers filled with river sand. It is not necessary to cover the seed with sand, but they should be pushed into the sand until flush with the surface and kept moist. Initially seedlings grow slowly but growth speeds up after 9–12 months. Tamboti trees can withstand periods of drought and cold but not frost. A relatively slow grower, up to 500 mm per year if planted on the Highveld, but up to 1 m if planted in the garden where it receives more than its usual quota of water. A protected tree in South Africa.

TASSEL BERRY

Description An evergreen to semi-deciduous tree up to 15 m tall with a dense rounded crown with the tips of the branches drooping. **Bark** on young branches covered with reddish brown hairs but pale grey, shallowly grooved and flaking in long fibres on older branches and stems. **Leaves** alternate and simple, leathery, dark glossy green and covered with rusty hairs on lower surface, margins smooth, venation prominent on lower surface and looping along margin, tip rounded or bluntly pointed. Leaf stalk hairy and short, up to 6 mm long. **Flowers** of different sexes on different trees, male flowers in spikes up to 160 mm long and with blood-red anthers, female flowers reddish and in long racemes up to 80 mm long, strongly scented. **Fruit** a black, fleshy, 1-seeded drupe borne on long tassel-like bunches up to 120 mm long. **Wood** with a yellow sapwood and the heartwood light brown with a reddish tinge, hard and moderately heavy (air-dry 670 kg/m³).

Afrikaans	Voëlsitboom
Northern Sotho	modulane
Zulu	isiBangamlotha
Botanical name	*Antidesma venosum*
Family	Spurge Family (Euphorbiaceae)
National tree list no.	318

Name derivation *Antidesma* = Greek meaning 'for a band', the bark being used for rope, and *venosum* = Latin for conspicuously veined.

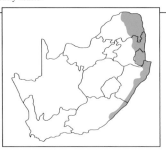

Diagnostic features Bark flaking in long strips; leaves with rusty hairs on lower surface and on the leaf stalk, venation prominent on lower surface; separate male and female trees; male flowers with red anthers, female flowers reddish; fruits from white to black in long tassels.

Flowering from October to January.
Fruiting from January to May.

Distribution From the Sudan in the north to the Eastern Cape in the south.

Habitat On the margins of evergreen forest, various types of woodland and wooded grassland. Prefers sandy and well-drained soils.

Economic value The leaves and young shoots are eaten by game (elephant, kudu, nyala and bushbuck) and the fruits by kudu, nyala, impala, baboons and vervet monkeys. Dropped fruits are eaten by guineafowl and francolins and those on the tree by greenspotted doves, tambourine doves, African green pigeons, louries, hornbills, barbets, bulbuls and mousebirds. The tassels have fruits ranging in colour from white, pink, red, purple to black – ensuring that birds keep visiting the tree over an extended period. The wood is popular as hut-building material. The dry wood is also collected for firewood.

One of the best trees to plant for attracting birds to the garden. Fruits are abundant, the whole tree covered in many-coloured tassels. If fruits are required, more than one tree must be planted as the male and female flowers are on separate trees. It makes an exceptionally attractive specimen tree, especially if planted in a group on a lawn. It can be used effectively as a screen plant in a shrubbery. It does not have an aggressive root system. The tassel berry is ideally suited to the bird and wildlife enthusiast's garden!

Other uses The ripe fruit is edible with, a slightly acid to sweet mulberry taste. An infusion made from the roots and leaves is taken for coughs.

Cultivation It grows easily from seed. Collect the black fruits from the tree, dry in the shade and sow in seedling mix obtainable from the local nursery, or in a mixture of river sand and compost (1:1). Cover the seeds with a thin layer of sand or compost and keep moist in a warm place. Seeds usually germinate from 10–20 days, with a germination rate of 70–80%. Once the seedlings have reached the 3-leaf stage, transplant them into nursery bags filled with sand and compost (1:1). The growth rate is quite fast, 800–900 mm per year. A tree for frost-free areas only.

TRANSVAAL BLUEBUSH

Description A deciduous tree up to 5 m tall with an open crown and drooping branches. **Bark** on young branches covered with long hairs but grey to brown and smooth on older branches and stems. **Leaves** simple, alternate, up to 50 x 20 mm, sparsely hairy above, venation prominent below and distinctly sunken above, tip of blade round or bluntly pointed, young leaves densely hairy. Leaf stalk short. **Flowers** male or female in axils of leaves, pendulous, calyx deeply divided and densely hairy on both sides, corolla cream-coloured, tube up to 8 mm long and with reflexed lobes, filaments short and broad, anthers densely hairy. **Fruit** nearly round and up to 10 mm in diameter, fleshy, red, with a translucent jelly-like flesh when ripe, persistent calyx with much enlarged lobes.

Afrikaans	Transvaalsebloubos
Northern Sotho	motloumana
Zulu	umBulwa
Botanical name	*Diospyros lycioides* subsp. *guerkei*
Family	Ebony Family (Ebenaceae)
National tree list no.	605.2

Name derivation *Diospyros* = Greek for 'divine pear', *lycioides* = resembling the genus *Lycium*, and *guerkei* = named after Dr Max Gürke (1854–1911), a famous German botanist.

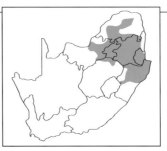

and grey duiker. Larvae of the Mooi River opal butterfly (*Poecilmitis lycegenes*) live on the leaves.

A very decorative tree for the garden, with the light green leaves, masses of cream-coloured flowers and the red fruits attracting masses of birds. It makes a great specimen tree and is a stunning sight when covered with the bright red fruit. The Transvaal bluebush is easily pruned into a tree with a neat crown. It can also be grown as a screen in a shrubbery. Very successful as a container plant and can be kept in either full sun or in shade. Remember that plants in containers dry out far more quickly than those in flowerbeds, and must be checked often. The Transvaal bluebush does not become very large and has a non-invasive root system, making it ideal for the smaller garden. A must for the bird garden, but remember to plant a few trees to make sure that you have both male and female trees. The excess male plants can be cut out at a later stage. An excellent plant for making bonsai.

Diagnostic features Bark smooth and grey; leaves with prominent venation below and distinctly sunken above, oblanceolate; flowers male or female, calyx deeply divided, corolla tube up to 8 mm long with reflexed lobes, anthers densely hairy; fruit red.

Flowering from September to December.
Fruiting from January to May.

Distribution From the Northern Province in the north to KwaZulu-Natal in the south.

Habitat Prefers rocky habitats and is often associated with quartzite outcrops. Prefers well drained soils.

Economic value The ripe fruits are eaten by dassies and are very popular with fruit-eating birds (purple-crested and grey louries, speckled and red-faced mousebirds, black-collared, pied and crested barbets, black-eyed bulbuls and redwinged starlings). Leaves browsed by nyala, bushbuck, impala, Sharpe's grysbok

Cultivation Put seeds in hot water to scarify them, leave to soak overnight and plant the next morning in flat seedling trays filled with seedling mix obtainable from the local nursery or in a mixture of river sand and compost (1:1). Press the seeds lightly into the soil and cover with a thin layer of sand and keep moist. The older the seeds, the more erratic the germination. Seeds usually start to germinate 7–20 days after sowing. Transplant the seedlings into containers when they reach the 2-leaf stage. The best growth medium at this stage is a well-drained compost-rich soil. Young plants transplant well but must be watered thoroughly. The growth rate is relatively fast, ± 600–700 mm per year. When it reaches 1 m or more, it should be both drought- and frost-resistant. It will grow in any type of soil, but struggles to attain a neat shape in clay soils.

TRANSVAAL GARDENIA

Afrikaans	Transvaalkatjiepiering
Northern Sotho	morala
Zulu	umGongwane
Botanical name	*Gardenia volkensii*
	subsp. *spatulifolia*
Family	Gardenia Family (Rubiaceae)
National tree list no.	691.1

Name derivation *Gardenia* = named after Alexander Garden, a medical doctor from South Carolina, *volkensii* = named in honour of G. Volkens who collected on Mt Kilimanjaro during 1892–1894, and *spatulifolia* = leaves spathe-shaped.

Description A semi-deciduous to evergreen tree, depending on the habitat, up to 8 m tall with a roundish much branched crown. **Bark** on young branches smooth and light grey, branchlets in whorls of 3 at right angles to the branches, flakes on older grooved stems leaving yellowish and green patches. **Leaves** in whorls of 3, crowded at tips of short stout branchlets, mostly spathe-shaped, glossy, with an entire margin, midrib and secondary veins conspicuous on upper surface, with hair-filled pockets in axils of veins on lower surface, base tapering into the leaf stalk. **Flowers** single, calyx ribbed with a short slit down one side, corolla white and fragrant, turning yellow with age, 100 mm in diameter, flower tube 30–80 mm long, stamens inserted 8–10 mm below mouth. **Fruit** ovoid to spherical, shallowly ribbed, up to 60 x 50 mm, greyish green and covered with grey warts, remaining on the tree for a long period. **Wood** white, fine-grained, hard and heavy (air-dry 880 kg/m³).

Diagnostic features Branchlets in threes and at right angles to the branch; leaves in whorls of 3 at tips of branchlets; flowers large, white, with a long flower tube, calyx with short slit down one side; fruit ridged and warty.

Flowering from July to December.
Fruiting from August to May.

Distribution From Angola in the north to KwaZulu-Natal in the south.

Habitat Grows in most woodlands and on any soil type but it appears to prefer well-drained soils. Often associated with termite mounds.

Economic value The leaves are browsed by livestock and game (elephant, giraffe, eland, kudu, impala and dassies). A valuable food tree for livestock during dry periods and in winter. Fruits are eaten by elephant, kudu (the alternative Afrikaans name *koedoeklapper* refers to this), nyala and vervet monkeys.

A worthwhile tree to have on any farm, especially a game farm. Plant groups of up to 10 trees scattered in the veld in suitable habitats. Water the young plants for the first growing season to ensure their survival. The interesting branching, large white flowers turning yellow and the warty fruits make this a worthy addition to every garden. A definite specimen plant. With its slow growth rate, small stature, non-aggressive root system and masses of large waxy white flowers, it is ideal for the small garden. It makes an interesting container plant for the patio, adapting well, flowering every season and delighting everyone with its waxy white fragrant flowers. Makes a fantastic bonsai specimen.

Other uses The wood is used mostly for household articles, small items and carvings. Roots are burnt and the ashes applied to the chest to treat pneumonia. Epilepsy is treated by taking a decoction orally. To treat headaches, an infusion is made and dropped into the eyes and also applied as a cold compress on the forehead. Earache is treated with an infusion dropped into the ear.

Cultivation Propagate from fresh seed. Sow seed in flat seedling trays filled with river sand and cover the seeds with a thin layer of sand and keep moist. Transplant seedlings into black nursery bags filled with a well-drained mixture when they reach the 3-leaf stage. The seedlings usually grow fast and soon need transplanting into bigger bags. This tree can also be propagated from cuttings. Treat the cuttings with root-stimulating hormone powder before planting. Truncheons are not always successful, but branches up to 80 mm in diameter will usually grow if planted with some river sand in the bottom of the hole. The Transvaal gardenia is quick-growing if given well-drained soil and a protected environment. It is drought-resistant but does not like frost or cold winds. Seedlings must be protected against cold wind and especially frost for the first two seasons. A tree planted under these conditions can attain 3 m in 4 years.

TRANSVAAL RED-MILKWOOD

Description An evergreen tree up to 15 m tall. **Bark** grey and smooth on young branches but dark brown and rough on older branches and stems. **Leaves** simple, alternate, lance-shaped to oblong and up to 110 x 50 mm, with a prominent midrib on lower surface, young leaves and growth tips covered in dense rusty hairs. Leaf stalk 10–30 mm long. **Flowers** borne in clusters, creamy white and strongly scented, 8–10 mm in diameter, on rusty brown recurved flower stalks 10–30 mm long. **Fruit** yellow to deep orange, oval, fleshy, up to 30 x 25 mm, containing 2–4 shiny brown seeds, fruit crowned by the persistent style. **Wood** with no clear distinction between sapwood and heartwood, reddish brown to biscuit-coloured and fairly hard and heavy (air-dry 850 kg/m^3).

Afrikaans	Moepel
Northern Sotho	mmupudu
Zulu	umPushane
Botanical name	*Mimusops zeyheri*
Family	Milkwood Family (Sapotaceae)
National tree list no.	585

Name derivation *Mimo* = from the Greek meaning ape, and *ops* = resembling, and *zeyheri* = honouring C.L.P. Zeyher (1799–1858), German botanist and plant collector.

Diagnostic features Evergreen with roundish crown; containing milky latex; all young parts with dense reddish brown hairs; leaves glossy dark green, leathery; flowers star-shaped, white, scented; fruit oval, fleshy, orange, with persistent style.

Flowering from October to March.
Fruiting from April to October.

Distribution From Tanzania in the north to KwaZulu-Natal in the south.

Habitat Usually grows in woodland on rocky hillsides, in mountain kloofs and in riverine vegetation.

Economic value A valuable tree to have on any game or cattle farm, providing dense shade during the hot summer months, and fodder and fruit to a wide variety of animals and birds. The young branches and leaves are browsed by various game species (elephant, eland, kudu, nyala and grey duiker). Fruit on the ground is relished by kudu, nyala, duiker and bushpigs. The ripe fruits on the trees are eaten by baboons, samango and vervet monkeys which, in the process, knock off many of the ripe fruits. A popular tree with fruit-eating birds (Rameron and African green pigeons, purple-crested and grey louries, red-collared and crested barbets and bulbuls) which relish the ripe fruit. Larvae of the pied false acraea butterfly (*Pseudacraea*

lucretia tarquinia) live on the leaves of this tree. The wood is a good general purpose timber, with selected planks making strong benches and chairs.

Plant groups of this tree in sheltered areas for additional browsing and where shade is needed during the hot summer months. Young trees will grow faster if watered for the first one to two years. The Transvaal red-milkwood, with its neat roundish crown, glossy dark green leaves, masses of white scented flowers and bunches of orange fruit, makes a good garden subject and if planted on a lawn, makes a fine specimen tree. It casts a dense shade, making it popular as a shade tree. The neat evergreen crown and medium growth rate make it ideal for use as a street tree requiring minimum care. The root growth is not aggressive, making it one of the few trees that can be planted near buildings, paths, patios and swimming pools. The Transvaal red milkwood makes a neat and attractive container plant for the patio with its dark green glossy leaves and dense growth. Another role for which it is ideally suited is that of a houseplant, as it is genetically adapted to grow under low light conditions as well as full sun. However, if used as a houseplant it must receive sufficient air flow. A favourite with bonsai growers – with a reduction in leaf size of more than 60%.

Other uses The fruit is edible, with a somewhat mealy and pleasantly sweet-flavoured pulp. It contains 50–80 mg/g vitamin C.

Cultivation Use only fresh seed and treat with a fungicide beforehand to prevent damping-off disease. Sow seed in flat seedling trays in a mixture of river sand and compost (1:1). Do not plant the seed deeper than 5 mm. Seeds usually germinate after 6–14 days, with a germination percentage of 60–80%. The first true leaf emerges after 6 weeks and this is the best time to transplant them into black nursery bags. They can be planted out into the open ground after they have reached a height of 250 mm. The Transvaal red-milkwood is drought-resistant and can take a certain amount of cold, but it is frost-tender. It grows well either in sun or shade. The growth rate is medium to fast, 800 mm per year.

TREE FUCHSIA

Description An evergreen tree up to 30 m tall in forests but up to 10 m in wooded grassland, with opposite branches and a dense roundish crown with somewhat drooping branches. **Bark** on young four-angled branches smooth and green but light brown, grooved and flaking in long strips on older branches and stems. **Leaves** opposite, simple, glossy green above and lighter below, margin finely toothed except at base, leaf blade tapering to a prominent tip. Leaf stalk up to 10 mm long. **Flowers** single or in clusters in axils of leaves but also on stems and even on main trunk, corolla funnel-shaped and up to 40 mm long, curved and orange to red, with 4 stamens. **Fruit** a fleshy berry up to 20 mm in diameter, with a long persistent style, black when mature. **Wood** yellow, tough and hard.

Afrikaans	Notsung
Northern Sotho	mothêbêrêbê
Zulu	iMinza
Botanical name	*Halleria lucida*
Family	Snapdragon Family (Scrophulariaceae)
National tree list no.	670

Name derivation *Halleria* = named in honour of Albrecht von Haller, a botanist at the University of Göttingen during the 18th century, and *lucida* = shining, referring to the shiny leaves.

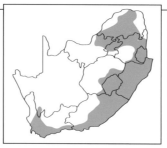

Very popular with sunbirds and bees which visit the nectar-rich flowers, also with fruit-eating birds (Rameron pigeons, Knysna louries, purple-crested louries, Cape parrots, Kurrichane thrushes, bulbuls, robins and white-eyes) which are attracted by the fleshy berries. Very well-suited to a shrubbery where it provides glossy, green foliage and colour! For the bird enthusiast – a definite inclusion in the garden. It has a non-aggressive root system. A most attractive yellow-flowering form is now available!

Other uses An infusion made from moistened dry leaves and roots is poured or dripped into the ear for the relief of earache. A straight, dry branchlet can be used as the turning stick when making fire-by-friction.

Diagnostic features Evergreen; branches opposite; bark peeling in strips; leaves opposite and glossy green, toothed except at base; flower tube orange to red and curved, flowers in clusters on old wood and in axils of leaves, stamens 4; fruit a fleshy black berry with persistent style.

Flowering from April to December.
Fruiting from June to February.

Distribution From Ethiopia in the north to the Western Cape in the south.

Habitat Mostly near water but also on rocky outcrops on grassy mountain slopes, wooded grassland and in evergreen forests.

Economic value Leaves browsed by stock and game (eland, kudu, nyala, bushbuck and grey duiker). The black fleshy fruits are edible, with a sweet taste and can be stored for a reasonably long period when ripe.

Cultivation The flesh of the fruit contains a chemical that retards germination. The seeds must therefore first be removed from the ripe fruits and dried in the shade. Sow the seeds in a flat seedling tray filled with a compost-rich soil or in a ready-made seedling mix from any nursery or garden centre. Cover the seeds with a thin layer of fine compost or sand and keep moist. Germination percentage is usually 85–90% and seeds take 4–8 weeks to germinate. The tree fuchsia layers naturally and these can be removed from the parent plant and transplanted. Cuttings must be made in early spring or summer. Make the cuttings about 100 mm long and remove most leaves, leaving only the two at the top. Dip the base of the cuttings into a root-stimulating hormone powder and plant in river sand. Make sure that the medium never dries out. Seedlings and young plants transplant well and are usually fast-growing, up to 1 m per year. If planted from seed, it will flower after two years. It can withstand light frost, and people living in cold areas should try and obtain seed of plants from their area, making it easy to grow and flower with no damage by frost.

TREE WISTERIA

Description A deciduous tree up to 18 m tall with a narrow crown and drooping branches. **Bark** on young branches smooth and grey but dark grey to blackish brown and deeply grooved on older branches and stems. **Leaves** spirally arranged and unevenly compound with 3–7 pairs of leaflets plus a terminal one, base of leaflet markedly asymmetric, glossy green above and duller below, venation not prominent. Leaf stalk up to 60 mm long. Dropped leaves leave prominent leaf scars. **Flowers** in long (up to 300 mm) drooping bunches, blueish mauve to violet, scented, resembling those of a pea. **Fruit** a narrow, thin, non-splitting, grey-brown pod up to 100 mm long, hanging in clusters. **Wood** with a thin, bright yellow sapwood and a pale to dark brown, hard and strong, heavy (air-dry 930 kg/m^3) heartwood.

Afrikaans	Vanwykshout
Northern Sotho	mogapa
Zulu	umHohlo
Botanical name	*Bolusanthus speciosus*
Family	Pod-bearing Family (Fabaceae)
National tree list no.	222

Name derivation *Bolusanthus* = named after Dr Harry Bolus (1834–1911), well known Cape botanist, and *speciosus* = beautiful.

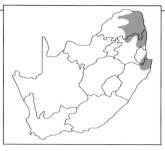

Diagnostic features Drooping branches; bark deeply grooved; glossy, dark green, unevenly compound leaves; flowers blue to violet and in bunches.

Flowering from August to January.
Fruiting from September to March.

Distribution From Zambia and Angola in the north to KwaZulu-Natal in the south.

Habitat Grows in woodland and wooded grassland. An indicator of clay soils.

Economic value Vervet monkeys eat the flower buds and grey duiker eat the pods and dropped leaves. Giraffe and gemsbok eat the leaves. Long, straight stems make good fence poles as they are termite- and borer-resistant and do not burn easily in a veld fire. The wood works to a fine finish and makes beautiful furniture. Popular for side tables and chairs. It is said that this tree is a good indicator of underground water.

One of the most beautiful indigenous trees when in flower. The tree wisteria retains its foliage during winter and drops the leaves for a short period in early spring, but trees in a well-watered garden are evergreen. It makes a very neat street tree with a stunning display when in flower, and requires very little maintenance. Ideal for use in the smaller garden. The tree wisteria makes a good container plant, especially when kept in full sun. It makes an interesting specimen tree if planted in a small group of up to five plants. The fissured bark, drooping glossy foliage and mauve flowers make this a focal point wherever it is planted. The tree wisteria does not have an aggressive root system. It is a popular species for making bonsai.

Other uses The roots are boiled together with beans and the decoction is taken orally for stomach problems. An infusion made from the root is used as an emetic. The dried inner bark is used to relieve abdominal pains.

Cultivation Easily grown from seed. Soak the seeds overnight in hot water and plant the next morning in seedling trays filled with river sand. Cover the seeds with a thin layer of sand and keep moist. Ensure that the sand never dries out. The first seedlings usually appear after 4–5 days, and the germination rate for fresh seed can be up to 95%. Transplant the seedlings into a mixture of sand, loam and compost (1:2:1) when they reach the 3-leaf stage. Take care not to overwater the seedlings. Young plants transplant easily. It tolerates moderate frost but protect young plants for the first two seasons against cold winds and frost. The tree wisteria can survive long periods of drought. The growth rate is fast, up to 800 mm per year.

A protected tree in South Africa.

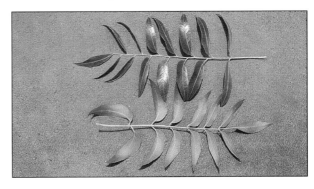

UMBRELLA THORN

Description A semi-deciduous tree up to 20 m tall. **Bark** on young branches grey to reddish brown and shortly hairy but grey to dark brown and fissured on older branches and stems. **Thorns** thin, in pairs, mostly with one straight and one hooked thorn. **Leaves** grouped at nodes, twice-compound with 4–10 pairs of pinnae and a petiolar gland just below lowest pinnae pair, with 6–22 pairs of leaflets per pinna. **Inflorescence** a cluster of round balls, 5–7 mm in diameter. **Fruit** a non-splitting spirally twisted pod, borne in bunches. **Wood** with a light brown sapwood showing conspicuous annual rings and large pores. The heartwood is reddish brown, very hard and heavy (air-dry 990 kg/m³).

Afrikaans	Haak-en-steek
Northern Sotho	mosu
Zulu	umSasane
Botanical name	*Acacia tortilis*
	subsp. *heteracantha*
Family	Pod-bearing Family (Fabaceae)
National tree list no.	188

Name derivation from the Greek word *akis* meaning a point or a barb, *tortilis* = twisted, referring to the shape of the pods, and *heteracantha* = different thorns (some thorns are straight and some are hooked).

to a certain extent to make furniture but has to be treated against borers. Treated wood is still in use on some farms as a general-purpose timber. It is a popular fuel in most parts of Africa.

It is well worth planting groves of umbrella thorn on cattle or game farms. The trees provide fodder and protection for animals and nesting sites for birds. They attract various types of wildlife ranging from insects to game and are a must for the bird garden. Young plants should be protected from browsers for at least the first season after planting. It can be used as a shade tree but has the nasty habit of dropping old thorns. Its dark stem and spreading to flat canopy make it a rather interesting specimen tree for the lawn – watch out for the thorns though! The umbrella thorn has an extensive root system and has been used most successfully in stabilising eroded areas. Keep it away from paved areas and buildings. Trees can be planted close to each other (1 m apart) and will quickly stabilise the soil; the dense branching pattern of the roots will help with catching silt. The umbrella thorn is a popular bonsai plant.

Diagnostic features Crown dense and mostly flat; combination of one hooked thorn and one straight thorn; inflorescence globose and cream-coloured; fruit non-splitting and spirally twisted, in bunches.

Flowering from October to January.
Fruiting from March to July.

Distribution From Angola in the north to the Northern Cape in the south.

Habitat Occurs in deciduous woodland, thornveld and bushveld. The umbrella thorn prefers red and black loamy soil but also grows in Kalahari sand underlain by clay. In certain areas it is restricted to black clay soil.

Economic value Regarded as an indicator of veld with palatable grasses during winter. The bark, leaves and pods make a nutritious fodder for both domestic and wild animals (elephant, giraffe, eland, waterbuck, kudu, gemsbok, nyala, springbok, bushbuck, impala and grey duiker). Most game species utilise the pods as a food source. Ripe pods and seed hold little danger of hydrocyanic acid poisoning. Pods normally contain about 18.83% protein, 2.44% fat, 46.25% carbohydrate, 5.1% minerals and 20.1% fibre. Pods are mostly eaten off the ground but cattle and especially game will take pods from the tree. The wood is used

Other uses Children eat the gum that forms where the stems are injured. Baboons, vervet monkeys and parrots (Meyer's and brown-headed parrots) relish the green seed. The inner bark can be used to make rope.

Cultivation A kilogram of seed contains roughly 32 000 seeds. This tree is easily grown from seed immersed in hot water, left to soak overnight and planted directly into black plastic nursery bags or in seedling trays the following morning. River sand is a good medium to use. Cover seed lightly with the same river sand and keep moist. This is one of the *Acacia* species of which the seedlings form a very long tap root and they must be planted out after the first leaf has formed. The umbrella thorn is frost- and drought-resistant. It has a medium growth rate, 500–600 mm per year, but it can be speeded up by cutting away the lower branches.

The umbrella thorn is a protected tree in the Northern Cape and Free State.

UMZIMBEET

Description A semi-deciduous tree up to 25 m tall with a spreading crown. **Bark** light to grey-brown and smooth on young branches but flaking on older branches and stems. **Leaves** compound with up to 7 pairs of opposite leaflets and a terminal leaflet, glossy dark green and silky underneath, midrib and side veins conspicuous below, side veins parallel and evenly spaced, young leaves and leaf stalks reddish and velvety, two leafy stipules at base of each leaflet. **Flowers** resembling those of a pea, mauve to purplish, flowering stems and flower buds covered in dark brown hairs, borne on long erect spikes above leaves at tips of branches. **Fruit** a flat woody pod covered with a thick layer of golden-brown hairs, held erect, splitting, valves spiralling when dry. **Wood** with a yellow sapwood and a very heavy, hard and dark reddish brown to dark brown heartwood.

Afrikaans	Omsambeet
Zulu	umSimbithwa
Botanical name	*Millettia grandis*
Family	Pod-bearing Family (Fabaceae)
National tree list no.	227

Name derivation *Millettia* = named after Charles Millet of Canton, China, and *grandis* = large.

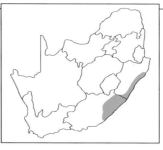

times very effectively used in that the one half of the walking stick is yellow and the other half dark brown. The only animals recorded utilising this tree are baboons that strip and eat the bark. Larvae of the orange-barred playboy (*Deudorix diocles*) and the striped policeman (*Coeliades forestan*) butterflies breed inside the pods and those of the pondo charaxes (*Charaxes pondoensis*) butterfly on the leaves.

The umzimbeet can be planted along pastures and fence lines to act as a windbreak and shelter for animals. As a long-term project it can be planted along the margins of thick bush to be cut when between 10–15 years old. The stumps are easily cut into planks when fresh. It is worthwhile for farmers in the high rainfall areas to plant a stand of umzimbeet. These trees must be pruned annually to form straight trunks. The umzimbeet makes a good garden and park subject and produces the first show of flowers when two to three years old. It is an attractive shade tree which can also be grown as a specimen tree showing off with its grey bark, coppery young leaves, lilac to purple flowers and golden-coloured pods. In high rainfall areas it is very successful as a street tree. It does not have an aggressive root system.

Diagnostic features Bark flaky on older stems; leaves compound with up to 7 pairs of leaflets plus a terminal leaflet, midrib and side veins conspicuous, side veins parallel and evenly spaced; flowers like those of a pea, mauve, on erect inflorescences at tips of branches; pods erect and covered with dense golden-brown hairs; leafy stipels at base of leaflets.

Flowering from November to March.
Fruiting from February to September.

Distribution From KwaZulu-Natal in the north to the Eastern Cape in the south.

Habitat Occurs in evergreen coastal forests and on the margins of evergreen forests.

Economic value An excellent furniture wood much used in the past for benches, chairs and small tables. Still in use today for furniture in a few areas in the Eastern Cape. The hard, heavy, tough wood makes strong walking sticks which are sold to tourists along the Eastern Cape roads. The marked difference in the colour of the sapwood and the heartwood is some-

Other uses The pounded roots can be used as a fish poison, but the fish must be boiled before consumption. Ground seeds soaked in milk are used as a remedy for roundworm, the dose being 1–2 beans.

Cultivation Seed must be sown when fresh. Soak the seeds in hot water and leave to soak overnight, plant the following morning in seedling trays filled with river sand. The seedlings are fast-growing and must be planted out into nursery bags when they reach the 2-leaf stage. Young trees transplant easily. When planted in full sun, they require more water than when planted in the shade of other trees. They have a fast growth rate, 0.8–1 m per year. It can withstand several degrees of frost and therefore makes an ideal tree for colder areas.

WATERBERRY

Description An evergreen tree up to 20 m tall. **Bark** on young four-winged branches green but dark brown, rough and corky on older branches and stems. **Leaves** near ends of branches, opposite, simple, smooth and leathery, blueish green to dark green above and lighter below, young leaves reddish, leaf tip rounded to broadly tapering, margin smooth, crunched leaves smelling like eucalypt oil. **Flowers** in dense heads, individual flowers up to 20 mm in diameter, creamy-white, petals falling early and then exposing stamens which extend beyond the corolla and resemble powder puffs, sweetly scented, containing copious ambunts of nectar. **Fruit** in clusters, up to 20 x 10 mm. **Wood** with no real distinction between sapwood and heartwood, brown with a reddish tone, medium hard and moderately heavy (air-dry 750 kg/m³).

Afrikaans	Waterbessie
Northern Sotho	montlho
Zulu	umDoni
Botanical name	*Syzygium cordatum*
Family	Eucalyptus Family (Myrtaceae)
National tree list no.	555

Name derivation *Syzygium* = Greek word meaning coupled, alluding to the paired leaves and branches, and *cordatum* = heart-shaped.

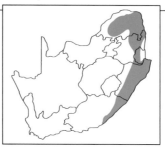

Diagnostic features Evergreen; very young branches with four wings; leaves opposite, base deeply lobed, leaf stalk absent or very short, leaves with eucalypt oil; stamens conspicuous; fruit fleshy, dark purple to blackish when ripe.

Flowering from August to November.
Fruiting from November to March.

Distribution From Kenya in the north to the Eastern Cape in the south.

Habitat Along streams in riverine bush and forest.

Economic value This tree provides much needed shade and shelter for domestic stock and game on the farm. The wood produces a good-quality furniture and can be used as a general purpose timber, especially for beams and window frames. A popular wood in the boat building trade as it is very durable in water. The leaves are browsed by game (kudu, nyala, bushbuck and grey duiker). The ripe fruits are eaten by baboons, monkeys and bushbabies. Fallen fruits are eaten by bushpigs and various game species. The ripe fruits are eaten by tambourine doves, African green pigeons, purple-crested, Knysna, and grey louries. Larvae of the flame-bordered charaxes (*Charaxes protoclea azota*), silver-barred charaxes (*Charaxes druceanus*), apricot playboy (*Deudorix dinochares*), orange-barred playboy (*Deudorix diocles*) and brown playboy (*Deudorix antalus*) butterflies live on the leaves. In Natal the waterberry is an indicator of areas suitable for sugarcane farming. It is also an indicator of a shallow water table. An excellent nectar tree popular with bee farmers. The flowers attract a myriad of insects and they in turn many insect-eating birds.

Plant groves of this tree around water points, springs and on banks of streams or rivers. Water the young plants for a period of three months after planting. The waterberry can withstand extended periods of waterlogging and can be used to stabilise river and stream banks or planted as a shade tree in swampy areas in a garden or park. The waterberry is an asset to any garden with its evergreen glossy leaves, abundant creamish white flowers and blackish fruit. It is one of our fastest growing trees, with a rather aggressive root system. It makes an effective screen plant in a shrubbery and a neat shade tree. Use it as a focal point on the lawn. For those with limited space, it grows well in a container, flowering and fruiting from an early age.

Other uses The ripe fruits are edible, with a thinnish flesh tasting faintly like eucalypt sweets. A good-quality jelly can be cooked from the ripe fruit and certain tribes drink an intoxicating liquor made from the fermented fruit. An extract of the leaves is used as a purgative or treatment for diarrhoea. Pieces of bark or powdered bark is used as a fish poison for catching small fish in small ponds, the bark staining the water a blueish colour for up to three days. Popular as a source of fuel along the KwaZulu-Natal coastal area.

Cultivation Seed should be sown fresh before it dries. Remove the flesh from the fruit and dry in the shade. Sow directly into black nursery bags filled with a mixture of river sand and compost (3:2). If kept moist the seed should germinate within 7–20 days. The germination percentage is 80–100%. Seedlings are hardy and transplant well. The waterberry has a fast growth rate, up to 1 m per year. It is resistant to cold but not frost. In their natural habitat the trees are fire-resistant. A protected species in South Africa.

WEEPING BOER-BEAN

Description A semi-deciduous to evergreen tree up to 25 m tall. **Bark** greyish to reddish brown and rough on older branches and stems. **Leaves** evenly compound, upper leaflets the largest. Young leaves coppery. Leaf stalk sometimes winged. **Flowers** in dense clusters on older branches and old wood, showy sepals forming a tube, petals very small, stamens joined at base. **Fruit** a splitting, dark brown, hard, flat pod, 5–17 x 35–47 mm, splitting on the tree to reveal the brown seeds which remain attached to the rims by sticky, light yellow arils. **Wood** with sapwood yellowish grey and heartwood dark brown to nearly blackish, hard and moderately heavy (air-dry 800 kg/m³).

Afrikaans	Huilboerboon
Northern Sotho	molope
Zulu	umGxamu
Botanical name	*Schotia brachypetala*
Family	Pod-bearing Family (Fabaceae)
National tree list no.	202

Name derivation *Schotia* = named after Richard van der Schot, head gardener of the Schönbrunn Gardens, and *brachypetala* = short petal.

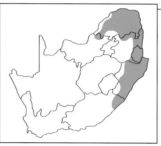

care. The flowers produce abundant nectar, and it is this nectar dripping from the flowers that gives it the common name 'weeping boer-bean'. It is therefore not wise to park a car under a weeping boer-bean in flower. Large numbers of various bird species visit the flowers for the nectar. It also attracts many insects and these in turn attract insect-eating birds to the garden. It makes a neat shade tree after a few years. The root system is not aggressive.

Other uses The bark contains tannin and is used for tanning leather. The roasted seeds are edible if the aril is removed beforehand. A decoction made from the bark is taken for heartburn and diarrhoea. Bark is sometimes powdered and taken for diarrhoea. Leaves are burnt and the smoke is inhaled to stop a bleeding nose. Powdered leaves are applied to tropical ulcers to speed up the healing process. The wood is used for all types of furniture, especially benches and chairs. The wood darkens after a few years if oiled. In certain areas these trees are still cut for floorboards.

Diagnostic features Twigs green; leaves evenly compound with 4–7 pairs of mostly opposite, glossy, dark green leaflets with asymmetrical bases, young leaves copper-coloured; flowers deep red with much reduced petals, stamens joined at base.

Flowering from August to November.
Fruiting from January to May but sometimes later.

Distribution From Zimbabwe and Mozambique in the north to the Eastern Cape in the south.

Habitat Mostly in frost-free areas but not restricted to any type of soil or rock. Often found on river or stream banks and on termite mounds.

Economic value This tree is often utilised by game and is always conspicuous in the veld, making it a must for the game farm. Black rhino eats the bark, and the leaves are eaten by giraffe, kudu, nyala and impala. Vervet monkeys, louries and parrots feast on the flower buds and seeds. Larvae of the foxy charaxes (*Charaxes jasius saturnus*), giant charaxes (*Charaxes castor flavifasciatus*) and the large blue charaxes (*Charaxes bohemani*) feed on the leaves, making it a popular choice for attracting these butterflies to the garden.

A weeping boer-bean in flower is a stunning sight and if planted together with the tree wisteria (*Bolusanthus speciosus*) with its blue-mauve flowers, it gives a beautiful display. It is also a perfect tree for planting along a driveway. It is always neat and requires minimum

Cultivation Easily grown from seed. There are approximately 1 900 seeds in a kilogram. Seed can be stored for up to two years before sowing. Pour boiling water over the seeds and allow them to soak until the next morning when they must be planted in seedling trays filled with river sand. Cover the seeds with a 5 mm layer of sand and keep moist. The first seeds should germinate within 3–6 days. Germination is usually quite erratic and seed should be left for a few weeks before the seedling tray is emptied. The seed which has not germinated after a month or so should be resoaked and sown again. Transplant the seedlings into nursery bags filled with a mixture of river sand, loam and compost (2:1:1) when they reach the 1-leaf stage. As soon as the seedlings are 100 mm tall, they can be taken out into the full sun to harden off. Seedlings and young plants transplant well. The weeping boer-bean can also be propagated by means of truncheons. The truncheon must ideally be 100 mm in diameter and at least 1 m long. It is wise to place some river sand at the bottom of the hole to speed up formation of roots and to prevent the lower tip of the truncheon from rotting. The weeping boer-bean has a fast growth rate, up to 700 mm per year. It can withstand mild frost and long periods of drought.

WHITE BAUHINIA

Description An evergreen tree or scrambler up to 8 m tall, with an open crown. **Bark** on young branches hairy and covered with many small orange glands or scales but grey, smooth and sometimes flaking on older branches and stems. **Leaves** simple, deeply bilobed to ± two-thirds of the way down, with spreading hairs on lower surface, 6–9 prominent veins on lower surface, margin smooth. Leaf stalk 5–10 mm long. **Flowers** 1–3 per inflorescence, petals white and fragile, up to 80 mm long, with crisped margins, midrib hairy on outside, 4 or 5 staminodes, style 20–40 mm long, hairy with glands, sweetly scented. **Fruit** a hard, dark brown woody pod, 60–240 x 17–30 mm, splitting into 2 valves curving upwards. **Wood** without distinction between sapwood and heartwood, light-coloured and finely grained.

Afrikaans	Koffiebeesklou
Botanical name	*Bauhinia petersiana* subsp. *macrantha*
Family	Pod-bearing Family (Fabaceae)
Nationl tree list no.	208.3

Name derivation *Bauhinia* = honouring two 16th century herbalist brothers, Jean and Gaspard Bauhin, and *petersiana* = named after Dr Wilhelm Peters (1815–1883), a German botanist.

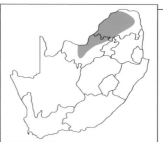

Diagnostic features Leaves deeply bilobed for two-thirds of the way down, lower surface with spreading hairs and 6–9 prominent veins; petals white with crisped margins and up to 80 mm long, midrib hairy on outside; style 20–40 mm long; pod 60–240 x 17–30 m.

Flowering from December to January.
Fruiting from June to September.

Distribution From Tanzania in the north to the Northern Cape in the south.

Habitat Open woodland, wooded grassland and Kalahari shrubveld. Only on sandy soils.

Economic value Leaves and pods are eagerly eaten by domestic stock and game (eland, kudu, gemsbok, impala, steenbok and grey duiker). The flower buds and flowers are taken by grey louries and Meyer's parrots. The thick roots can be baked, pounded and then eaten. Young pods are boiled and eaten as a spinach. The seeds are highly nutritious, the roasted seed having a nutty flavour. When green, the seed is usually roasted in the pods and then removed and eaten. Alternatively it can be removed from the pods and then roasted, peeled and pounded into a pleasant-tasting meal. Many people still burn the seed, grind it and use it as coffee. Hence the common Afrikaans name *koffiebeesklou*.

The analysis of the seed is as follows–

Protein	23 g/100 g
Fibre	12.9 g/100 g
Carbohydrate	40.2 g/100 g
Calcium	237 mg/100 g
Magnesium	220 mg/100 g
Potassium	1 168 mg/100 g
Copper	0.97 mg/100 g
Phosphorus	317 mg/100 g
Thiamine	0.58 mg/100 g
Nicotinic Acid	1.65 mg/100 g

The white bauhinia can be effectively used as a screen plant in a shrubbery in gardens in the dry areas. It makes a superb specimen plant in a flowerbed, the large white flowers giving a magnificent display. A perfect plant for the small garden, with its compact growth, non-aggressive root system and beautiful display of white flowers. This is a good species to grow as a bonsai, the leaves quickly reducing in size.

Other uses A very strong rope can be made from the bark and it is commonly used for binding bundles of firewood and for fastening slats onto beams when building huts. A decoction made from the roots is used as a remedy for diarrhoea. Pounded leaves boiled with salt are applied to wounds.

Cultivation The white bauhinia grows readily from seed. Soak seeds in hot water and leave to soak overnight, plant the next morning in seedling trays filled with river sand. Cover the seeds with a 5 mm thick layer of sand and keep moist. Seeds usually germinate after 7–20 days. Transplant seedlings into nursery bags when they reach the 2-leaf stage and take care not to damage the taproot whilst transplanting. Seedlings and young trees transplant well. The growth rate is fast, up to 800 mm per year. The white bauhinia can withstand long periods of drought and can take cold but no frost.

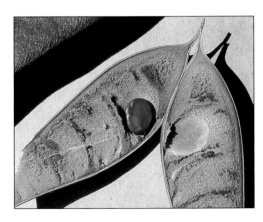

WHITE IRONWOOD

Description An evergreen tree up to 30 m tall with a slightly rounded crown and mostly straight stems. **Bark** smooth and light grey. **Leaves** alternate, compound with three sessile leaflets, leathery and glossy, with scattered oil glands throughout the surface of the leaflets (easily seen when held against the light), emitting a lemon scent when crushed, margins distinctly wavy. Leaf stalk up to 150 mm long. **Flowers** in branched heads at tips of branches, unisexual, small and greenish yellow, with only four petals. **Fruit** 4-lobed and 4–6 mm in diameter, smooth but fleshy and covered in oil glands, blackish when ripe. **Wood** pale yellow to whitish, hard, moderately heavy (air-dry 927 kg/m³), very elastic and with a fine texture.

Afrikaans	Witysterhout
Zulu	uMozane
Botanical name	*Vepris lanceolata*
Family	Citrus Family (Rutaceae)
National tree list no.	261

Name derivation *Vepris* = spiny shrub, and *lanceolata* = refers to the lanceolate leaflets.

up to 200 years. A wood often used in the past for making tables and small pieces of furniture in the Western and Eastern Cape but nowadays seldom used for this purpose. Fruits and seeds eaten by many fruit-eating birds (all the lourie species, Rameron and Delagorgue's pigeons, red-eyed doves, red-winged starlings, crested barbets and black-eyed bulbuls).

This is a useful tree on the farm to provide dense shade for stock in camps but also as protection for smaller game species. A most worthwhile tree to have on a game farm, attracting many fruit-eating birds and masses of insects and which in turn attract many insect-eating birds. It makes a good garden subject which can be pruned into any shape or it can be grown as a screen plant. A must for the bird garden, with its bunches of black berries. It makes a most successful container plant, flowering and fruiting without any problems. It can also be used as a houseplant, but remember to give it enough light and movement of air. It does not have an aggressive root system.

Diagnostic features Evergreen; bark smooth and grey; leaves compound with three sessile leaflets, with oil glands, crushed leaf with citrus smell; unisexual flowers in much branched heads; petals four; fruit blackish and 4-lobed.

Flowering from December to March.
Fruiting from February to July.

Distribution From Ethiopia in the north to the Western Cape in the south. Also on the islands of Mauritius and Réunion.

Habitat Mostly in evergreen forests but also in riverine bush, dune bush and forest. Thrives on sandy soils but sometimes occurs on clay soils.

Economic value The bark is often eaten by porcupines, and as is the case with tamboti, they sometimes ringbark the trees with the resultant death of those trees. Larvae of the greenbanded swallowtail (*Papilio nireus lyaeus*), whitebanded swallowtail (*Papilio echerioides*), mocker swallowtail (*Papilio dardanus cenea*) and citrus swallowtail (*Papilio demodocus*) butterflies feed on the leaves of this tree. The elasticity of the wood is the reason why it is often used for implement handles. Roof beams made from white ironwood are very tough and long lasting, sometimes

Other uses The powdered root is sprinkled on hot coals and the resultant smoke inhaled, or it is taken by mouth in water against colic and influenza. Sometimes used as an emetic.

Cultivation Collect fresh seed from the trees. Seeds on the ground are mostly parasitised by insects. There are ± 50 000 seeds per kilogram. Sow seeds in flat seedling trays filled with river sand and cover lightly with either compost or sand and keep moist. Seeds will germinate erratically over a period of 8–16 weeks. Germination is usually 70–80%. When the seedlings reach the three-leaf stage, transplant them into black nursery bags filled with a mixture of river sand and compost (5:1). Transplant into open ground after one year in the nursery bags. If kept longer, the plant becomes rootbound and will take up to three seasons before regaining its normal growth rate. Young plants transplant very well. The growth rate is fast, 700–900 mm per year. White ironwood tolerates some frost and is quite drought-hardy.

WHITE KAREE

Description A semi-deciduous tree up to 10 m tall with a much branched open crown with pendulous branches and occasional spines on the trunk. **Bark** on young branches light grey-brown and smooth becoming grey-brown, rough and scaly on older branches and stems. **Leaves** compound with three leaflets, leaflets sessile and with a thin texture, smooth, dull green, margins smooth, midrib prominent. Leaf stalk slender and up to 60 mm long. **Flowers** in axillary or terminal, much branched, furry panicles up to 80 mm long, flowers greenish yellow, very small, male and female flowers on different trees. **Fruit** a circular, glabrous, reddish drupe drying black.

Afrikaans	Witkaree
Botanical name	*Rhus pendulina*
Family	Mango Family (Anacardiaceae)
National tree list no.	396

Name derivation *Rhus* = the classical Greek name for *Rhus coriaria*, and *pendulina* = with a hanging habit (of the leaves).

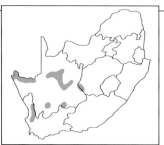

Diagnostic features Bark smooth and pale grey-brown becoming flaky when old, occasional spines on the trunk; dull green pendulous leaves and widely ellipsoid drupes drying black.

Flowering from February to March.
Fruiting from December to May.

Distribution Mostly along the Orange River but also along the Berg and Olifants Rivers in the Western Cape.

Habitat On alluvial soils along rivers and streams sometimes forming impenetrable thickets.

Economic value The wood is durable, borer, and termite-proof and often used for fencing poles and for hut-building. The long, thin branches are debarked and used for making fish traps. The red to blackish spherical fruits are eaten by rock pigeons, starlings, bulbuls and barbets. One of the best trees to attract birds to the garden. This is also the food plant for the pearl charaxes butterfly (*Charaxes varanes*) which occurs in gallery forest and stream bush. The very fast growth rate and long straight branches make this tree ideal for planting on a farm where thin poles are needed. The white karee is becoming increasingly popular among horticulturists and landscapers for planting in parking areas, as street trees, in parks and for general use in shrubberies. Its fast growth rate, hardiness, non-aggressive root system and neat, compact shape make it a favourite choice. It also makes an effective screen plant in a shrubbery. The white karee casts dappled shade. Three or five white karee trees grouped on the lawn make a fabulous focal point with their grey stems and light green leaves.

Other uses The reddish to blackish mature fruits are edible, with a sourish taste which improves when dry. A milk infusion of the leaves is given as an enema to children suffering from stomach upsets.

Cultivation Fresh seeds germinate very easily. Simply sow in seedling trays filled with river sand. Cover seed with a thin layer of fine sand and keep moist. Seeds usually take 8–14 days to germinate, with 80% germination after 10 days. Transplant seedlings into nursery bags when they reach the two-leaf stage. If grown from cuttings, best results are achieved during August. Either hard- or softwood cuttings are successful. Cuttings of between 100 and 200 mm give the best results. Remember to dip the bottom ends of the cuttings into a root-stimulating hormone powder (e.g. Seradix) before planting. Young plants transplant well and do best if watered often. A fast grower, up to 1 m per year is normal. Frost-hardy and will do well on the highveld.

A protected tree in South Africa.

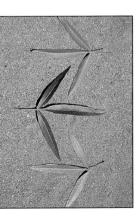

WHITE PEAR

Description An evergreen tree up to 25 m tall with an open spreading crown. **Bark** on young branches smooth and pinkish to purplish but smooth and whitish grey to grey with fine transverse ridges on older branches and stems, usually covered in lichens. **Leaves** simple, alternate, glossy bright to dark green above and duller below, thinly textured, midrib yellowish below, margin smooth and sometimes wavy. Leaf stalk pinkish and up to 20 mm long. **Flowers** in loose heads, white, sweetly scented with a saucer-shaped calyx and free recurved petals. **Fruit** an asymmetrical black, flattened drupe with a red fleshy appendage (pseudaril) and a persistent style. **Wood** with no clear distinction between sapwood and heartwood, light pink to greyish brown, fine, very hard and heavy (air-dry 860 kg/m³).

Afrikaans	Witpeer
Northern Sotho	sephopha-madi
Zulu	umDakane
Botanical name	*Apodytes dimidiata* subsp. *dimidiata*
Family	White Pear Family (Icacinaceae)
National tree list no.	422

Name derivation *Apodytes* = from the Greek for 'to strip off', referring to the uncovered corolla, and *dimidiata* = in two equal parts, referring to the fruit.

Diagnostic features Young bark pinkish to purplish, midrib protruding; leaf stalk pinkish, calyx saucer-shaped; petals recurved; fruit a black flattened drupe with a red fleshy appendage.

Flowering from September to April.
Fruiting from December to June.

Distribution From Ethiopia in the north to the Western Cape in the south.

Habitat From evergreen montane forests to wooded grassland. Plants from open exposed rocky ridges are gnarled and sometimes not higher than 1 m.

Economic value Leaves and bark eaten by black rhino and the ripe fruits eaten from the tree by birds (Rameron pigeons, redwinged starlings, pied barbets and black-eyed bulbuls), spotted ground thrushes and helmeted guineafowl eating the dropped fruit. An excellent wood for making furniture, especially benches and tables. The light-coloured wood tends to darken after a few years of oiling. Also used for flooring, veneering, panelling, engraving for printing and for rifle stocks.

The white pear makes an effective screen plant in the garden with its dense glossy foliage. It can be grown as a hedge and reacts well to pruning. Such a hedge is a breath-taking sight when in full flower. It makes an attractive specimen plant on the lawn, especially when it is in flower or in fruit and it can be successfully grown as a shade tree. It has a non-invasive root system.

Other uses The leaves can be boiled whole and eaten with porridge. An infusion made from the root bark is used as an enema for intestinal parasites.

Cultivation Easily grown from seed sown in late winter or early spring. Sow seeds 3–5 mm deep in seedling trays filled with either seedling mix obtainable from a nursery or garden centre or in a mixture of river sand and compost (1:1). Cover lightly with sand or fine compost and keep moist. Germination is very erratic and it can take up to 6 months for all the seed to germinate. Germination is usually between 60 and 70%. The white pear thrives in well drained compost-rich soil. Growth of the young plants is initially slow but increases later. Protect the young plants for the first year against frost but after this they should be able to survive. The growth rate is ± 700 mm per year.

A protected tree in South Africa.

WHITE STINKWOOD

Description A large deciduous (semi-deciduous in forests) tree up to 40 m tall. **Bark** on young branches hairy but smooth, pale grey, sometimes with horizontal ridges on older branches and stems. **Leaves** alternate, simple and light green when young but dark green when mature, with a drip-tip, margin toothed for upper two-thirds, Leaf stalk up to 35 mm long. **Flowers** appearing at the same time as leaves, yellowish green, male flowers sessile and in dense bundles at base of new branchlets and female flowers single or a few together, on long flower stalks. **Fruit** a small yellowish drupe on 20–25 mm long fruit stalk. **Wood** moderately hard and moderately heavy (air-dry 750 kg/m³), very flexible, pale lemon-yellow with nearly no distinction between sapwood and heartwood.

Afrikaans	Witstinkhout
Northern Sotho	molutu
Zulu	Ndwandwazane
Botanical name	*Celtis africana*
Family	Elm Family (Ulmaceae)
National tree list no.	39

Name derivation *Celtis* = Greek name for the laurel tree, and *africana* = from Africa.

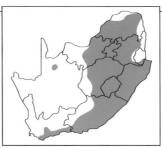

rots, louries, doves and pigeons, especially Rameron pigeons in the more forested areas). Larvae of the African snout (*Libythea labdaca*) and blue-spotted charaxes (*Charaxes cithaeron*) butterflies live on the tree.

This tree is very useful near or in camps on the highveld where stock need protection against the hot summer sun. The white stinkwood is popular as a street and garden tree in spite of its losing its leaves during autumn. The leaves turn an attractive yellow before being shed. Its deciduous habit makes the tree suitable for planting in a shrubbery where it provides shade during summer and allows full sun during the winter months. When without leaves the architecture of the branches and the light grey bark make it a focal point in the garden. The white stinkwood makes an ideal container plant and reacts well to pruning. Remember to water the container at least once a week during hot summer months and once a month during winter. One of the favourites throughout the world for bonsai. The leaves dwarf easily and the plant quickly takes on the appearance of an adult tree.

Diagnostic features Bark smooth and grey; leaves with three main veins from the leaf base, base asymmetrical; male flowers sessile and in bundles, female flowers on long flower stalks, single or a few together.

Flowering from August to October.
Fruiting from October to February.

Distribution From Arabia and Ethiopia in the north to the Western Cape in the south.

Habitat In high rainfall areas in forests and along streams but in the lower rainfall areas in woodland or wooded grassland, on termite mounds or on rock outcrops. Not restricted to a specific type of soil.

Economic value The leaves and young branches are eaten by domestic stock, especially cattle, and by game (kudu, nyala, bushbuck, impala and grey duiker). Animals are more partial to the adult leaves than the younger leaves and will even pick up leaves off the ground. The wood is used for general timber on the farm and for manufacturing furniture. It has excellent bending qualities and is therefore used for making bentwood chairs. This furniture is light but durable. A good wood for shelving as it takes nails and screws well and does not warp. Ripe fruits are eagerly eaten by baboons and monkeys. A very popular tree with fruit-eating birds (bulbuls, mousebirds, barbets, par-

Other uses Young branches and coppice shoots are popular as handles for implements. The wood of white stinkwood carves easily and is durable. This makes it a sought-after wood for carving various household articles, from spoons to dishes. The ripe fruit has a pleasant sweet taste with thin flesh.

Cultivation Fresh seed must be collected on the tree as seeds lying on the ground are invariably infested by insects. Approximately 10 000 seeds weigh 1 kg. Seed collected from frost-hardy trees should be sown if the seedlings are to be planted in areas that experience frost as trees from such areas are genetically adapted to the cold conditions. Sow seed in seedling trays filled with river sand and compost (5:1). Cover the seed with a thin layer of river sand and keep moist. Germination usually takes place within 8–30 days if the trays are kept in a hot but shady area. The germination percentage is usually 50–70%. A fast growing species, usually 2 m per year if planted in deep soil and given enough water. The white stinkwood is drought and frost-resistant. A protected tree in South Africa.

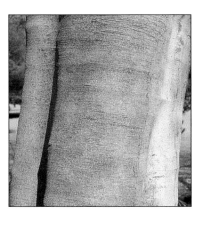

WHITE SYRINGA

Description A deciduous straight-stemmed tree up to 20 m tall. **Bark** grey and fairly smooth to rough on older branches and stems. **Leaves** tending to be bunched at ends of branches, alternate, unevenly compound with a single leaflet at the tip, 200–400 mm long, leaves turning an attractive red colour in autumn. Leaf stalk 50–100 mm long. **Flowers** on long-stemmed, lax heads, individual flowers inconspicuous and cream-coloured. **Fruit** a small light brown four-valved capsule. **Wood** with the sapwood yellowish white and the heartwood light brown with darker markings, medium hard and light (air-dry 640 kg/m^3).

Afrikaans	Witsering
Northern Sotho	modumela
Botanical name	*Kirkia acuminata*
Family	Quassia Family (Simaroubaceae)
National tree list no.	267

Name derivation *Kirkia* = named in honour of Sir John Kirk, explorer and naturalist (1832–1922), and *acuminata* = referring to the tapered or acuminate leaflets.

Diagnostic features Young branches with conspicuous leaf scars; bark grey; leaves compound with 6–15 pairs of thinly textured pointed leaflets; inflorescence of lax branched heads; flowers small; fruit a four-sided capsule.

Flowering from October to November.
Fruiting from January to April and onwards.

Distribution From Tanzania in the north to Mpumalanga in the south.

Habitat Open dry woodland and rocky hillslopes. Always on sandy or alluvial soils.

Economic value The leaves are browsed by game (giraffe, eland, kudu and impala). It provides much needed shade during the hot summer months for domestic stock and game, especially in the lowveld areas. A good furniture and veneer wood, but the silica crystals in the ray cells blunt the teeth on saw blades. It can be used as a live fence, especially to keep smallstock in, by planting truncheons close to each other. The white syringa is regarded as an indicator of sandy soils and areas with shallow calcrete deposits. The wood carves easily and is used for making household utensils. A strong rope can be made from the plaited inner bark but looses much of its strength when dry.

Plant either young trees or truncheons as scattered groups in suitable habitats on the farm. These will provide the necessary shade for livestock and game during summer. It has been successfully used in various towns throughout southern Africa as a street tree – providing shade for pedestrians during summer and allowing sunlight through during winter. It adds an attractive splash of colour to the autumn garden with its burnished orange and crimson-red foliage. For an extra special show the white syringa is best planted in a group on the lawn. It is known to develop a rather aggressive root system with time and one should avoid planting it near buildings and swimming pools.

Other uses The roots of the white syringa can easily be tapped for water. A ± 80 mm in diameter shallow growing root is needed. Cut the root first at the end nearest to the tree and then at the other end. Cut for a length of ± 1 m and tilt the root so that the end nearest to the tree, is now at the bottom. Remove the bark at this end for ± 50 mm. After a short while water will start dripping out of the root. This water is clean and refreshing. Hunters, something to remember! The powdered root is sometimes used as a remedy for toothache.

Cultivation Easily propagated from seed; ± 940 000 seed make up one kilogram. Seed should be sown in flat seedling trays in river sand and covered lightly with sand and kept moist. Seeds usually germinate 8–14 days after sowing. Seedlings can be planted out into black nursery bags when they reach the two-leaf stage. For best results, keep the young trees bagged until they are one year old before transplanting them into open ground. The quickest way to propagate this tree is either from cuttings or truncheons. Cuttings of 100–150 mm long can be made from the previous year's growth. Truncheons of up to 150 mm in diameter can be planted. Be sure to put sand in the bottom of the truncheon hole. This will prevent fungi from growing on the cut end of the truncheon. The white syringa has a fast growth rate, up to 1.5 m per year. It is extremely drought-resistant and can tolerate light frost. In colder areas the young trees must be protected against frost for the first two seasons. A protected tree in South Africa.

WILD APRICOT

Description An evergreen tree up to 13 m tall with an open crown. **Bark** on young branches covered with hairs but pale to dark grey and flaking on older branches and stems. Young branches mostly armed with spines up to 60 mm long. **Leaves** simple, alternate, dark green and glossy above but lighter below, 3-veined from just above base of leaf, tip of leaf blade rounded, base tapering, margin scalloped or sometimes smooth. Leaf stalk up to 8 mm long. **Flowers** greenish yellow, ± 10 mm in diameter, male flowers in axillary clusters of 2–5 and female flowers singly or a few together. **Fruit** oval, fleshy and velvety, bright orange, up to 25 mm long, with persistent sepals. **Wood** dense, white and heavy.

Afrikaans	Wilde-appelkoos
Northern Sotho	morethema
Zulu	umNyazuma
Botanical name	*Dovyalis zeyheri*
Family	Kei-apple Family
	(Flacourtiaceae)
National tree list no.	511

Name derivation *Dovyalis* = based on the Greek word for spear and, *zeyheri* = named after Karl Zeyer (1799–1858), botanical collector.

Diagnostic features Young branches armed with spines up to 60 mm long; leaves glossy above, 3-veined from just above base of leaf, margin scalloped; flowers ± 10 mm in diameter, male flowers in axillary clusters of 2–5, female flowers singly or a few together; fruit oval, velvety, bright orange, sepals persistent.

Flowering from August to December.
Fruiting from November to May.

Distribution From Zimbabwe in the north to the Eastern Cape in the south.

Habitat Sometimes on margins of forests but more often in open woodland and rocky ridges. In areas with clay soils it is associated with termite mounds.

Economic value The fruits are a favourite with fruit-eating birds (hornbills, barbets, louries, mousebirds and starlings). The fruit is edible, with a refreshing acidic taste. A good tasting jelly can be made from the fruit, but add grape juice to sweeten it. Larvae of the African leopard butterfly (*Phalanta phalantha*) feed on the leaves. This tree is a must for the bird garden with many fruit-eating birds (pigeons, louries, mouse-birds, barbets, bulbuls and starlings) spending some time in the tree enjoying the fleshy orange fruit. The over-ripe fruit attract masses of insects and they in turn many insect-eating bird species. The wild apricot can be planted close together to form an impenetrable hedge around homesteads, gardens and croplands to keep out unwanted animals and people. Only the female trees bear fruit and it is best to plant at least three trees to increase the chances of having at least one bearing fruit. It grows well as a container plant, flowering and fruiting without problem. Female plants in fruit on the patio make a stunning sight. Container plants must be watered more often than plants in the garden. It does not have an aggressive root system and can be planted close to pools, paving and buildings.

Other uses The whitish wood is soft and is used for carving household utensils and for making small carvings.

Cultivation Collect ripe fruit and dry them in a shady spot. Remove the seeds and sow them in flat seedling trays filled with river sand. Press the seeds down into the sand until they are flush with the surface of the sand and cover with a layer of fine sand and keep moist. Seeds usually germinate 8–14 days after sowing but germination is erratic in most cases. Seedlings transplant well if watered for a week after planting. The wild apricot thrives in loamy or sandy soil with added compost. It has a moderate growth rate, up to 600 mm per year. Plants will fruit when at least three years old and are usually laden with fruit. It is drought-resistant and can take light frost except the young plants which must be protected for the first two years. It grows well in either full sun or light shade.

WILD DATE PALM

Desription Evergreen palm with an unbranched stem or several stems from the base, up to 12 m tall. **Bark** absent but stem with prominent markings of the shed leaves. **Leaves** borne close together at top of stem, compound, feather-shaped and up to 2.5–4 x 0.3 m, with up to 100 leaflets, lower leaflets forming up to 60 m long spines with dark brown tips, leaflets glossy, dark green. **Flowers** borne in axils of young leaves, male and female plants separate, young inflorescence enclosed in a light brown sheath, flowers on a much branched inflorescence with a thick peduncle, individual flowers yellowish and borne on zig-zag stalks. **Fruit** borne in large drooping bunches, individual fruit oval, up to 25 mm long, with brown skin. **Wood** very fibrous, pale brown with darker flecks and light (airdry 590 kg/m³).

Afrikaans	Wildedadelpalm
Northern Sotho	mopalamo
Zulu	iSundu
Botanical name	*Phoenix reclinata*
Family	Palm Family (Arecaceae)
National tree list no.	22

Name derivation *Phoenix* = Greek name for the date palm, and *reclinata* = Latin for bending down, referring to the leaves.

ripe fruits eaten by baboons, vervet monkeys and birds (grey louries, mousebirds, black-collared barbets, black-eyed bulbuls). The dropped fruits are eaten by bushpigs, nyala and bushbuck. Young stems and inflorescence are cut and tapped for the sap which is left to ferment to form beer/wine. The leaves produce very strong fibres which are used for making mats and hats. Dried inflorescences are used as brooms to sweep areas around dwellings. The larvae of the palm-tree nightfighter (*Zophopetes dysmephila*) butterfly, one of the skippers, feed on the leaves.

Diagnostic features Palm with a single stem and crown of feather-shaped compound leaves; leaflets glossy dark green, forming leaf-like spines at base, separate male and female plants; flowers on branched inflorescence; fruit oval, up to 25 mm long with a thin flesh.

Flowering from August to November.
Fruiting from February to April.

Distribution From Egypt in the north to the Eastern Cape in the south.

Habitat Always occurs near water and therefore found along and in streambeds, sometimes with the roots in flowing water or growing in swamps. Occasionally in grassland where the water table is high.

Economic value The ripe fruits are edible, with a thin sweetish flesh tasting very much like the commercial date. The leaves are eaten by elephant. The

This palm can be very effective if planted as a specimen tree on a lawn, to line the sides of a road or to fill a large opening in a large garden.

Other uses The heart of the crown is sometimes eaten by people. The roots produce an edible gum eaten mainly by children.

Cultivation Fresh, clean seed germinates easily. Sow the seeds in flat seedling trays filled with a mixture of river sand and compost (5:1) and cover the seeds lightly, or they can be pressed into the medium with part of the seed still sticking out, keep moist. The first seedlings should appear after 25–35 days. As soon as the first leaf is 50 mm long it can be transplanted into a bag filled with a mixture of sand and compost (1:1). Plant out into the open after one season in the bag. It can also be propagated from suckers taken off adult plants. The growth rate is relatively fast if the plants receive enough water. They can withstand light frost but young plants must be protected against cold wind and frost for the first two years. The wild date palm prefers full sun but also thrives in light shade. Drought-resistant. Transplants easily.

A protected tree in South Africa.

WILD LABURNUM

Description An evergreen tree up to 10 m tall with an open but roundish crown. Bark on young branches pale brown and hairy but dark brown on older stems and branches. **Leaves** drooping, unevenly compound with 5–15 pairs of leaflets and a terminal leaflet, leaflets light green with tip and base rounded, thinly textured, margins smooth. **Flowers** in 8–30 flowered axillary or terminal sprays up to 250 mm long with pea flowers, petals bright yellow, calyx cup-shaped and teeth shorter than tube. **Fruit** a non-splitting papery light brown pod up to 120 mm long, with a 1–2.5 mm broad wing along upper edge. **Wood** with the sapwood yellowish and a hard and heavy dark brown heartwood.

Afrikaans	Wildegeelkeur
Zulu	umKhiphampethu
Botanical name	*Calpurnia aurea* subsp. *aurea*
Family	Pod-bearing Family (Fabaceae)
National tree list no.	219

Name derivation *Calpurnia* = named after T. Julius Calpurnius, a Latin poet who imitated Virgil, and *aurea* = golden, referring to the flower colour.

are still young and as low as 1 m. It has a neat growth habit, making it perfect for use as a street tree. The wild laburnum gives a splendid display of flowers wherever it is planted in the garden and makes a focal point if planted alone on the lawn. It certainly rivals the laburnum (of Europe) in showiness! A popular species for making bonsai. It makes a good container plant, seldom growing taller than 2 m under these conditions and when in flower it is spectacular. The root system is not aggressive.

Other uses An infusion made from the leaves is used to get rid of maggots in infested sores on cattle. Crushed roots are used in a wash to destroy lice.

Diagnostic features Leaves drooping, unevenly compound with 5–15 pairs of leaflets plus a terminal leaflet, tip and base rounded, thinly textured; flowers in drooping terminal sprays, flowers like those of a pea, yellow, calyx teeth shorter than calyx tube; fruit a papery pod.

Flowering from December to February.
Fruiting from March to June.

Distribution From India and Ethiopia in the north to the Eastern Cape in the south.

Habitat Growing in forest margins, inside evergreen forests and in kloof vegetation.

Economic value Flowers visited by many insect species, especially carpenter bees. Flower buds and young flowers are eaten by dassies. This tree has tremendous horticultural potential. Plants flower when they

Cultivation Seeds germinate readily but must first be immersed in hot water and left overnight to soak before sowing. For the best results seed must be sown during spring. Sow seed in seedling trays filled with a fine seedling mixture obtainable from your local nursery or garden centre. Cover the seeds with a thin layer of the same soil and keep moist. The first seeds usually start to germinate 8–14 days after sowing. Seedlings can be planted out when they reach the 1-leaf stage when they already have long taproots. Take care not to damage the taproot whilst transplanting. The growth rate is fast, up to 1 m per year. The wild laburnum can withstand light frost but seedlings and young plants must be protected for at least the first year. It can survive long periods of drought. Cutting back induces flowering. Growing this as a standard is very rewarding.

One of the first South African plants to be grown in Europe.

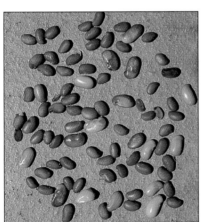

WILD MEDLAR

Description A deciduous tree up to 8 m tall. **Bark** on young branches hairy with conspicuous leaf scars. **Leaves** Leaf blade soft and covered with dense hairs, tips bluntly pointed with net-veining conspicuous on undersurface and veins on upper side somewhat sunken, margin smooth. **Flowers** in clusters in axils of leaves, greenish white to cream-coloured, with hairs inside the flower tube. **Fruit** roundish and up to 40 mm in diameter, with a glossy brown leathery skin. **Wood** with little difference between sapwood and heartwood, fine-textured, pale brown and heavy (air-dry 850–880 kg/m³).

Afrikaans	Grootmispel
Northern Sotho	mmilô
Zulu	umViyo
Botanical name	*Vangueria infausta*
Family	Gardenia Family (Rubiaceae)
National tree list no.	702

Name derivation *Vangueria* = from a Malagasy word, and *infausta* = unlucky, the wood is taboo for making fire.

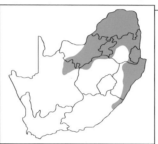

The fruit is eaten raw by humans. The pulp is sometimes soaked in water and then dried to use at a later stage. Seeds can be roasted in the coals and then eaten.

Groups of wild medlar trees can be planted scattered in the veld, near water points and definitely near the homestead along fences. A good subject for the small garden or the farm garden. A must for the bird garden. The flowers attract a myriad of insects, with insect-eating birds making regular visits during this period. Fruit-eating birds feast on the abundant ripe fruit, sometimes leaving only the skin of the fruit for the hungry traveller.

Diagnostic features Bark smooth and light-coloured; leaves simple, hairy and opposite, with interpetiolar stipules; corolla falling early; fruit up to 40 mm in diameter and topped with remains of calyx.

Flowering from September to November.
Fruiting from November to April.

Distribution From Malawi in the north to the Eastern Cape in the south. Also on Madagascar.

Habitat All types of woodland, especially on rocky ridges and hill slopes or in wooded grassland, also near the sea on sand dunes.

Economic value The leaves of the wild medlar are usually not browsed by cattle, but very much so by goats, with the leaves and young branches eaten by elephant, giraffe, kudu and nyala. Red-footed squirrels, bushbabies, vervet monkeys and baboons eat the fruit on the tree, and bushpigs take the dropped fruit on the ground. The fruits are edible, with a fairly pithy sweet-sour pulp. The fresh fruit contains –

Vitamin C	3.7 mg/100 g
Protein	1.4 g/100 g
Carbohydrate	28 g/100 g
Sodium	28 mg/100 g
Nicotinic Acid	0.61mg/100 g

and high levels of calcium and magnesium.

Other uses In the North-West Province farmers distil mampoer from the ripe fruit. The pulp mixed with some sugar and water makes good 'apple sauce' to be enjoyed with meat. The roots and leaves are used to treat malaria and pneumonia. An infusion made from the roots is used in the treatment of coughs and other chest troubles. The pounded leaves are applied to tickbite sores on stock and dogs to speed up healing. A poultice made of the leaves is used to treat swellings on the legs and inflammation of the navel in children. An infusion made from the leaves is used in treating abdominal pains. The root is a popular roundworm remedy.

Cultivation Most of the seed on the ground is parasitised, so collect fruits from the tree and dry in a cool place. Soak seeds overnight and plant the next morning in seedling trays filled with river sand and cover with a thin layer of sand. Germination is usually 80% or more. Transplant the seedlings into nursery bags when they reach the 3-leaf stage. Keep the seedlings in nursery bags for at least one year before transplanting them into the garden. Young plants transplant well but must receive regular watering for the first five weeks after transplanting. Cuttings can be made from the present year's growth, but remember to treat them with a root-stimulating hormone powder (e.g. Seradix). Plant them during early spring in river sand. The growth rate of the wild medlar is usually slow, 400–500 mm per year. It can withstand long periods of drought and frost.

WILD OLIVE

Description An evergreen tree up to 14 m tall. **Bark** grey-brown, rough and flaky on older branches and stems. **Leaves** covered with silvery green scales beneath, venation indistinct, margin smooth and rolled under. Leaf stalk up to 10 mm long. **Flowers** in short and branched axillary inflorescences, individual flowers creamy-white, 6–10 mm long, sweetly scented. **Fruit** a thinly fleshy drupe ± 10 mm long, black when mature. **Wood** with sapwood light brown and heartwood dark reddish brown to dark brown, strong and very hard, fine-grained and heavy (air-dry 1 100 kg/m³).

Afrikaans	Olienhout
Northern Sotho	mohlware
Zulu	umNqumo
Botanical name	*Olea europaea* subsp. *africana*
Family	Olive Family (Oleaceae)
National tree list no.	617

Name derivation *Olea* = Latin for olive, *europaea* = from Europe, and *africana* = from Africa.

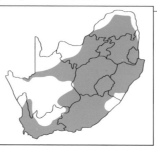

Diagnostic features Evergreen tree; leaves opposite, dark glossy green above and silvery beneath; flowers with four sepals and petals; fruit thinly fleshy; wood heavy and dense.

Flowering from October to February.
Fruiting from March to August.

Distribution Widespread in Africa, Mascarene Islands, Arabia, India to China.

Habitat Grows in almost any type of habitat, especially woodland, stream banks and rocky hillslopes.

Economic value The wild olive is much browsed by stock and game. It is a valuable fodder tree in the drier areas especially the karoo and Griqualand West. The primary browsers in the veld are kudu, grey and blue duiker, with the fruit eaten by vervet monkeys, baboons, bushpigs and warthogs. The termite- and borer-resistant wood makes durable fencing posts lasting for up to a century. As the wild olive is resistant to most of the diseases of the commercial olive, it can be successfully used as a stock for grafting the cultivated olive. A most popular wood for turnery, carvings, cabinet work and furniture. The wood darkens with age. The tree commonly occurs on calcrete soil and acts as an indicator for calcrete. The wild olive is recommended for planting in the garden and around the homestead to attract fruit-eating birds (Rameron pigeons, Cape parrots, Knysna, purple-crested and grey louries, speckled and red-faced mousebirds, bulbuls and various starling species) which relish the fruit. The neat crown, evergreen leaves and the ease with which it takes pruning makes it an ideal choice for a garden and street tree. Plant young trees in large scattered groups in camps. These can act as windbreaks, protection, shade and browsing. The extensive root system makes it a good species for stabilizing erosion dongas. The root system is sometimes aggressive and it is not advisable to plant the wild olive close to walls, patios or swimming pools. A favourite for making bonsai.

Other uses The fruits are edible but some trees have bitter fruit whilst the fruits of others are quite pleasant to eat. The leaves soaked in water can be used as a substitute for tea. An infusion made from the fresh bark is used to relieve colic. An infusion from the leaves is used as an eye lotion, not only for humans but also for cattle. A decoction of the leaves is used as a gargle for a sore throat. Snuff made from dried leaves is used to stop bleeding of the nose. In some areas the juice of the fruit is used in making ink.

Cultivation Fresh seed should be used for the best results. There are ± 8 000 seeds per kilogram. Sow seed in black nursery bags or similar containers filled with river sand. Seeds usually germinate 8–12 days after being sown. Seedlings form a long taproot. Hardwood cuttings can also be used but must be treated with a root-stimulating hormone. Plants should be pruned annually to stimulate growth. It has a fast growth rate of up to 800 mm per year. The wild olive can survive severe drought conditions and is resistant to frost but seedlings must be protected against cold wind for the first two years. It will grow in most soil types, especially alkaline soil. If young trees are kept well watered for the first year, they will respond by growing twice as fast as those not watered.

A protected tree in the Northern Cape, Free State and the North-West Province.

Description A semi-deciduous to evergreen tree up to 20 m tall. **Bark** hairy and yellowish brown on young branches but grey-brown to dark brown and flaky on older branches and stems. **Leaves** simple, lighter and velvety on lower surface, margin smooth or distantly toothed. Leaf stalk up to 25 mm long and velvety. **Flowers** on male trees in 3–7-flowered cymes borne in axils of leaves, yellowish green sepals and petals, densely hairy, with 10 stamens; female flowers solitary in axils of leaves, yellowish to greenish white, ± 10 mm in diameter, male and female flowers on separate trees. **Fruit** a roundish woody capsule up to 20 mm in diameter, with a warty surface, splitting into 5 valves. **Wood** fairly hard with a cream-coloured sapwood and pinkish medium heavy heartwood.

Afrikaans	Wildeperske
Northern Sotho	monepenepe
Zulu	uMunwe
Botanical name	*Kiggelaria africana*
Family	Kei-apple Family
	(Flacourtiaceae)
National tree list no.	494

Name derivation *Kiggelaria* = named after Franz Kiggelaer, Curator of Simon van Beaumont's garden, and *africana* = of Africa.

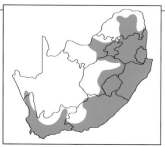

Diagnostic features Bark smooth and grey on branches; leaves with venation prominent on lower surface, with hairy pockets in axils of main veins; separate male and female trees; fruit a warty capsule splitting to reveal black seeds with an oily, reddish orange covering.

Flowering from August to January.
Fruiting from February to July.

Distribution From Kenya in the north to the Western Cape in the south.

Habitat Evergreen forest, on rocky outcrops, wooded grassland and along drainage lines. Plants in forests have large, thinly textured, glabrous leaves and gnarled plants growing in full sun in a dry habitat have thickly textured, small, velvety leaves.

Economic value The oil-rich aril on the seeds attracts many fruit-eating bird species (Rameron pigeons, cinnamon doves, olive woodpeckers, Knysna and purple-crested louries, crowned and trumpeter hornbills, Cape and Heuglin's robins, boubou shrikes, red-winged starlings, Cape thrushes, white-eyes and mousebirds) and this makes it difficult to find ripe seed in open capsules. Larvae of the garden acraea (*Acraea horta*), dusky-veined acraea (*Acraea igola*) and the battling glider (*Cymathoe alcimeda*) butterflies eat the leaves. These larvae, especially those of the garden acraea, are considered a delicacy by Klaas's, Diederik and emerald cuckoo. These larvae sometimes defoliate trees but they quickly recover after the larvae have gone, thereafter producing a crop of new leaves. The leaves contain hydrocyanic acid and are therefore not utilised by stock or game. Wild peach wood was once very popular for furniture and is still used by a few cabinet makers in the Eastern Cape and KwaZulu-Natal. Also used for beams and floor boards.

The wild peach can be planted in camps to provide much needed shade for animals during the hot summer months, or as a windbreak along the margins of lands with crops. It makes an effective shade tree if the lower branches are pruned away to give the tree a clear and straight trunk. Its tolerance of low temperatures and frost makes it ideal for those cold highveld gardens. The root system is not aggressive. The best tree to plant in a bird garden. When in fruit the tree is always alive with birds feasting on the red sticky seeds or on the larvae of the *Acraea* butterflies.

Cultivation Easily grown from either seed or cuttings. Sow fresh seed in trays filled with a mixture of river sand and compost (1:1). Cover with a thin layer of fine sand and keep moist. Fresh seeds usually germinate after 3–12 weeks and give a 70–80% germination. Transplant the seedlings into nursery bags when they reach the two-leaf stage. Plant out into the open ground when the young plants are ± 300 mm tall. If kept in bags for longer, the plants tend to become severely potbound and will take at least one season before they form new branches. The growth rate is high, up to 1.3 m per year. Trees flower for the first time when they are two years old. The wild peach is a frost-hardy species and can tolerate low temperatures and moderate drought conditions.

WILD PEAR

Description A deciduous tree up to 10 m tall with an open roundish crown. **Bark** on young branches smooth and grey with conspicuous corky spots (lenticels) but thickly corky, dark brown to blackish and very rough to fissured on older branches and stems. **Leaves** alternate, simple, almost round, up to 150 mm in diameter, with 5–7 veins from leaf base, venation prominently raised on lower surface of the stiff and leathery leaf blade covered in star-shaped hairs, margin smooth to irregularly toothed, base lobed. Leaf stalk up to 80 mm long. **Flowers** appearing before leaves, crowded in dense clusters at tips of branches, up to 20 mm in diameter, calyx lobes 5–7 mm long covered in star-shaped hairs on outside, petals white to light pink turning brown with age, 7–10 mm long. **Fruit** a hairy, semiround capsule up to 6 mm in diameter, surrounded by the dry petals. **Wood** blueish grey to brown and heavy (air-dry 960 kg/m³).

Afrikaans	Drolpeer
Northern Sotho	mohlabaphala
Zulu	iNhliziyonkhulu
Botanical name	*Dombeya rotundifolia* var. *rotundifolia*
Family	Star-chestnut Family (Sterculiaceae)
National tree list no.	471

Name derivation *Dombeya* = named after J. Dombey (1742–1793), a French botanist, and *rotundifolia* = round leaves.

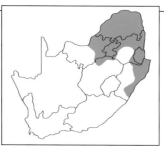

honeybees which visit it for the copious amount of nectar and pollen – making it a favourite with bee farmers. The wood makes very durable furniture, especially small tables and chairs and can also be used as a general purpose timber on the farm. It makes good-quality implement handles. The wood is termite-resistant and is often used for fence posts.

The wild pear is an ideal avenue tree and can be planted along driveways. It does not have an aggressive root system. It makes a good specimen tree in any garden, especially during the flowering period. A most successful street tree and planted as such in various towns and cities. The dry flowers are long lasting and can be used effectively in flower arrangements. A good species to train as a bonsai; after 2–3 years the leaves become quite small and the bark becomes very corky.

Diagnostic features Branches and stems with very rough bark; leaves roundish, with 5–7 veins from leaf base, covered with star-shaped hairs, venation prominent below; fruit a hairy capsule.

Flowering from July to September.
Fruiting from October to December.

Distribution From Ethiopia in the north to KwaZulu-Natal in the south.

Habitat Woodland, wooded grassland and on rocky mountain slopes.

Economic value Trees are sometimes heavily browsed by stock and game (elephant, giraffe, kudu, nyala, sable and steenbok). The sweetly scented flowers are visited by bees and butterflies. A good tree to attract

Other uses The bark fibre produces a very strong rope. A tea is made from the bark and taken to treat nausea and palpitations. An infusion made from the bark is taken by mouth for intestinal ulceration. A strong decoction is taken for relief of haemorrhoids, diarrhoea and intestinal upsets. The root is used as a colic remedy.

Cultivation Easily grown from seed and cuttings. Sow fresh seed during September in a seedling mix obtainable from the local nursery or in a mixture of river sand and compost (1:1). Ensure that you cover the seeds with a thin layer of sand and keep moist. Transplant the seedlings into nursery bags filled with a mixture of river sand and compost (3:1) when they reach the 2-leaf stage. Seedlings and young plants transplant well. The growth rate is very fast, 1–1.5 m per year. The wild pear can tolerate extended periods of drought and frost.

WILD PLUM

Description An evergreen tree up to 20 m tall (up to 35 m in forests) with a dense roundish crown. **Bark** dark grey and smooth showing conspicuous leaf scars on younger branches but dark brown and rough resembling the skin of a crocodile (umGwenya) on older stems. **Leaves** crowded at tips of branches, 200–300 mm long, unevenly compound with 4–8 pairs of opposite leaflets and a terminal leaflet, glossy dark green, midrib slightly off-centre on the leaflet and the base markedly asymmetric, leaves with beautiful red autumn colours but remaining on the tree for up to two years. **Flowers** whitish, in small branched sprays 100–200 mm long at tips of branches, male and female flowers on different trees. **Fruit** oblong and thinly fleshy, 20–25 mm long, red when mature. **Wood** with no clear distinction between sapwood and heartwood, pale reddish to reddish brown, strong and heavy.

Afrikaans	Wildepruim
Northern Sotho	mothêkêlê
Zulu	umGwenya
Botanical name	*Harpephyllum caffrum*
Family	Mango Family (Anacardiaceae)
National tree list no.	361

Name derivation *Harpe* = sickle-shaped, *phyllum* = leaf, and *caffrum* = from Kaffraria (Eastern Cape).

Diagnostic features Evergreen tree with conspicuous leaf scars on young branches; leaves at tips of branchlets, leaves compound, midrib slightly off-centre on the leaflet, base asymmetrical; male and female flowers on different trees; fruit red.

Flowering from November to December.
Fruiting from December to March.

Distribution From Mozambique and Zimbabwe in the north to the Eastern Cape in the south.

Habitat Riverine to evergreen forest and woodland, always near streams.

Economic value A tree much utilised by game. The fruit eaten by baboons, monkeys, bushbabies, bushpigs and bushbuck. The wood can be used for making furniture, especially tables and chairs or for beams and general timber. Larvae of the common hairtail (*Anthene definita*) butterfly live on the flower buds and flowers of this tree. A valuable shade tree for cattle and other domestic stock during the hot summer months. Groups of up to six trees can be planted near water points and camps near homesteads. It is advisable to protect young trees from browsing for the first two seasons. The wild plum is a popular garden tree and an excellent tree to attract fruit-eating birds (African green pigeons, Cape parrots, louries, mousebirds, barbets, bulbuls and starlings) to the garden. Only female trees produce fruit and it is best to plant more than one tree. A useful tree for planting along streets and in parking lots. The root system is not aggressive. This tree tolerates a variety of soil types and grows well in either shade or full sun. This makes it an ideal shade tree to have on the farm or in the garden. The wild plum is easy to train and grow as a bonsai, forming a very thick trunk in no time at all.

Other uses The ripe fruits are edible. Some trees have sweet tasting fruit whilst others bear sour tasting ones. The fruit contains citric and malic acid. A good-quality jelly and/or jam can be made from the fruit. A drink similar in taste to lemonade can be made by adding water and sugar to peeled fruit. A decoction of the bark is used as an emetic and blood purifier.

Cultivation Grows easily from seed. Approximately 600 seed per kilogram. Remove the flesh around the seed by soaking it in water for a day or two and scrub clean with a brush. Sow the seed in seedling trays filled with river sand. The seed must not be planted deeper than 10 mm. Germination is erratic at the best of times, the first seeds germinating 8–12 days after sowing. Transplant seedlings into black nursery bags when they reach the 2-leaf stage. The wild plum can also be grown from truncheons. After cutting truncheons, leave them in the shade for two days until all exudate has dried. Place some coarse sand at the bottom of the hole before planting the truncheon to promote root formation and combat fungal diseases. The wild plum can withstand light frost and short periods of drought The growth rate is fast, 1–1.5 m per year.

WILD PRIDE-OF-INDIA

Description An evergreen tree up to 10 m tall with an open rounded canopy. **Bark** on the young rectangular branches pale grey and smooth but darker grey and rougher cracking into small blocks on older branches and stems. **Leaves** opposite, simple, glossy dark green, leathery, midrib ending in a raised gland situated at tip of blade which is prominent on under-surface, margins conspicuously wavy, leaf stalk up to 3 mm long, new leaves coppery red. **Flowers** in dense sprays at tips of branches, white, with a bell-shaped calyx and crinkly petals, stamens attached to mouth of calyx tube. **Fruit** a reddish brown roundish capsule, 3–5 mm in diameter, partially enveloped by remains of calyx. **Wood** hard, moderately heavy (air dry 800 kg/m³), light brown, with a fine texture.

Diagnostic features Evergreen; branchlets rectangular, bark grey; leaves opposite, dark glossy green, with strong wavy margins, midrib ending in a gland at tip of leaf; petals white and crinkly, stamens attached to mouth of calyx tube; fruit partially enveloped by remains of calyx.

Flowering from October to May.
Fruiting from April to July.

Distribution From Zimbabwe in the north to KwaZulu-Natal in the south.

Habitat Grows in various woodland types, thickets, scrub forest and sometimes in evergreen forest margins.

Afrikaans	Transvaalliguster
Zulu	umDlampangele
Botanical name	*Galpinia transvaalica*
Family	Pride-of-India Family (Lythraceae)
National tree list no.	523

Name derivation *Galpinia* = named after E.E. Galpin, banker in Barberton at the turn of the century, and *transvaalica* = from the Transvaal.

Economic value The leaves are browsed by game (elephant, giraffe, kudu and nyala) and cattle. Plants in the lowveld are sometimes completely defoliated by kudu during the winter months. The wild pride-of-India is an important fodder plant on cattle and game farms. The bunches of white flowers attract many insect species, especially flies and butterflies, and they again many insect-eating birds.

Plant wild pride-of-India trees along fences or in groups of up to 20 plants in a suitable habitat in the veld. It is a worthwhile garden subject with attractive bunches of white flowers and glossy dark green leaves. Trees planted in the colder areas display yellow and red autumn colours. This is regarded as the indigenous counterpart of the privet and can therefore be planted successfully as a hedge. Plants respond well to pruning. The non-aggressive root system makes it ideal to plant close to walls and paved ares. The wild pride-of-India is successfully used as a potplant and is an ideal subject for a container on a patio. It is easy to train as a bonsai, resembling an adult plant after only three years.

Cultivation Sow the fine seeds in trays filled with river sand, cover with a thin layer of fine sand and keep moist. Seedlings usually appear after 7–10 days. Transplant seedlings into nursery bags when they reach the 2-leaf stage. Seedlings are fast growing but very frost-sensitive at this stage. The growth rate is fast, up to 1 m per year. Adult plants are frost-sensitive but they can survive long periods of drought.

WILD SILVER OAK

Description An evergreen tree which can grow up to 10 m tall in the garden but reaches 30 m in forests, which had a much branched and somewhat untidy crown. **Bark** on young branches covered with whitish woolly hairs, older stems and branches pale brown with deep longitudinal grooves. **Leaves** simple and alternate, thinly leathery, dark glossy green above but whitish and woolly beneath with prominent venation, margin of leaf blade with irregular teeth, base and tip tapered. Leaf stalk up to 20 mm long. **Flowers** in large clusters at tips of branches, male and female flowers on different trees, individual flowers creamy white and sweetly scented. **Fruit** a nutlet with a tuft of yellowish to brownish bristle hairs. **Wood** with a thin and yellowish white sapwood and yellowish brown heartwood, hard, durable and heavy (air-dry 863 kg/m³).

Afrikaans	Bosvaalbos
Northern Sotho	mphahla
Zulu	umPhahla
Botanical name	*Brachylaena discolor*
	subsp. *transvaalensis*
Family	Daisy Family (Asteraceae)
National tree list no.	731

Name derivation *Brachylaena* from *brachus* = short and *klaina* = cloak, referring to the florets which are longer than the bracts surrounding the flower head, and *discolor* = to change colour, referring to the bicoloured leaves and *transvaalensis* = from Transvaal.

Diagnostic features Bark on young stems covered with whitish woolly hairs; leaves glossy dark green above, whitish below, venation prominent on lower surface; male and female flowers on different trees, flower head with many bracts; fruit with a tuft of hairs.

Flowering from July to October.
Fruiting from August to December.

Distribution From Mozambique in the north to the Eastern Cape in the south.

Habitat Grows in coastal bush, wooded ravines, grassland and margins of evergreen forests.

Economic value The leaves are intensely bitter but the young leaves are browsed by game (nyala, bushbuck, red and blue duiker). When in flower, the whole tree is covered in flowers producing large amounts of nectar and thus a good honey tree popular with bee farmers. The wood is very durable in water and is used for building boats, especially along the Mozambique coast. The long, straight branches are used for roof construction in the building of huts. The fast growth rate and the fact that it can withstand strong winds and salt spray make it ideal for stabilizing sand dunes along the coast. The wood makes durable fence posts and was commonly used for this purpose until recently. The wood is very pliable and therefore used for hammer, axe and pick handles.

This tree makes an interesting specimen tree if planted singly or in small groups on a lawn. In this case the lower branches must be removed from an early age otherwise the tree will have a bushy appearance. A must for every park. It can also be planted in a shrubbery to provide colour during winter, the bicoloured leaves being very attractive when they move about in the wind. If planted close together, they make an excellent hedge which will become dense after a few years of pruning. It can also be used as an effective screen. The root system is not aggressive. The wild silver oak makes a rewarding container plant which can be kept either in full sun or light shade.

Other uses An infusion made from the roots is used as an enema to stop bleeding of the stomach. Diabetes and roundworm infection are treated with an infusion made from the leaves. The ash of burnt leaves can be used as an alkali for making soap.

Cultivation Sow seed in trays filled with pure river sand and cover with glass. Seedlings usually appear after 4–6 weeks but the germination is usually erratic. Transplant the seedlings into nursery bags when they reach the 2-leaf stage and keep in the bags for not longer than a season before planting them out into the open ground. It can also be grown from hardwood cuttings taken in early spring. The cuttings should ideally be 100–150 mm long and as thick as a pencil. Dip the lower part of the cutting in root-stimulating hormone powder for hardwood cuttings before planting. Young plants transplant well. The growth rate is fast, up to 1.5 m per year. The wild silver oak can withstand a surprising amount of frost and drought. Plants grow well in deep shade and full sun. They need a moderate amount of water for the first two years after which they will survive on their own. They grow best in sandy to loamy soils with a fair amount of compost.

WING BEAN

Description A deciduous tree up to 15 m tall with a dense roundish crown. **Bark** on young branches smooth and thickly covered with hairs but grey-brown and rough, flaking in large irregular pieces on older branches and stems; a blood-red sticky sap exuding from wounds. **Leaves** crowded near tips of branches, up to 370 mm long, compound with 6–17 alternate to sub-opposite oblong leaflets and one leaflet at the tip, young leaves covered with fine golden hairs, tips and bases of leaflets rounded, margin smooth and wavy. **Flowers** appearing before or with the new leaves, white to greenish white, shaped like those of a pea, in branched sprays crowded at ends of branchlets, sepals and flower stalks covered with dense hairs. **Fruit** a flattened pod up to 150 x 25 mm, tapering to both ends with conspicuous veined swellings over seeds and a broad wing all around the margin. **Wood** with no prominent heartwood, hard and dark yellowish brown.

Afrikaans	Vlerkboon
Botanical name	*Xeroderris stuhlmannii*
Family	Pod-bearing Family (Fabaceae)
National tree list no.	240

Name derivation *Xeroderris* = Greek for dry and the genus *Derris*, and *stuhlmannii* = named after Frans Ludwig Stuhlmann, a German senior official and plant collector.

Diagnostic features Flaky bark; compound leaves with roundish leaflets; sepals and flower stalks covered with dense hairs; fruit a flat tapered pod with veined swellings over seeds and a broad wing all around margin.

Flowering from September to December.
Fruiting from November to August.

Distribution From Tanzania in the north to the Northern Province in the south.

Habitat Grows in dry woodland in well drained soil.

Economic value The fruits and leaves make an excellent fodder for stock and game (elephant, giraffe, eland, kudu and grey duiker). The seeds are dried and ground into a meal which is added to maize meal to make porridge. The wood is cut into planks for general-purpose timber and for shelving. In the countries north of the Zambezi River it is used for making dugout canoes. In earlier years most of the tall wing bean trees in Zimbabwe and Zambia were cut down for railway sleepers. The red sap is tapped and used in water for tanning leather.

This is a splendid specimen tree to plant on a lawn. In larger gardens and on the farm it can be planted in groups of five or more. The dense foliage makes a beautiful show in summer and the rough texture of the bark is also attractive in winter when the plants are without leaves. It makes a good shade tree during the hot summer months when the tree has a dense canopy. Its frost-sensitivity and rather aggressive root system unfortunately make it unsuitable for the small garden and the cold, frost-areas of the country.

Other uses An infusion made from the roots is used to treat stomach disorders and chest complaints.

Cultivation This tree can easily be grown from seed. Seeds are usually not parasitised. Immerse the seeds in hot water, leave to soak overnight and plant the next morning in seedling trays filled with river sand. Cover the seeds very lightly with sand and keep moist. The seeds usually germinate after 3–8 days. Transplant the seedlings when they reach the 1-leaf stage but take care not to damage the taproot whilst transplanting. Keep the seedlings in the nursery bags for a year before planting them out into the open. The growth rate is medium to slow, up to 300 mm per year. The plants are frost-sensitive and therefore only for gardens in frost-free areas.

A protected tree in South Africa.

WONDERBOOM FIG

Description Spreading evergreen tree up to 20 m tall but mostly up to 10 m with a slightly open crown. All parts exuding a milky latex. **Bark** smooth and grey on young branches but dark grey and rough on older stems. **Stipules** very large and covering the growth tip. **Leaves** simple, usually glaucous green and thickly leathery and folded, the net-veining clearly visible on both surfaces but prominent on lower surface, tip broadly tapering, base slightly lobed to heart-shaped, margins smooth. Leaf stalk 18–25 mm long. **Figs** many along branchlets in leaf axils, 5–8 mm in diameter, white turning yellowish pink when ripe, three bracts covering mouth of opening, stalkless or very shortly stalked. **Wood** greyish white, light (air-dry 590 kg/m³), with no heartwood.

Afrikaans	Wonderboomvy
Northern Sotho	mohlatsa
Zulu	isiSantu
Botanical name	*Ficus cordata* subsp. *salicifolia*
Family	Fig Family (Moraceae)
National tree list no.	60

Name derivation *Ficus* = the classical name for the cultivated fig, *cordata* = cordate, referring to the leaf, and *salicifolia* = with the leaves of a willow.

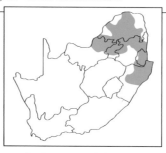

Diagnostic features All parts with milky latex, bark grey, very large stipules covering growth tip; leaves glaucous, thickly leathery; figs in axils of leaves, 5–8 mm in diameter.

Fruiting from August to May.

Distribution From the Sudan in the north to KwaZulu-Natal in the south.

Habitat Rocky areas on hills and mountain slopes or on rocky outcrops, in kloofs along watercourses and various types of woodland.

Economic value Domestic stock seldom utilise this tree for browsing but it is a hardy shade tree which can withstand severe drought conditions. The ripe fruits are eaten by many fruit-eating birds such as Rameron pigeons, African green pigeons, Meyer's parrots, brown-headed parrots, Knysna louries, purple-crested louries, grey louries, barbets, orioles and bulbuls. The dropped fruits are eaten by kudu, nyala, impala, grey duiker, warthogs, bushpigs and bushbabies. Larvae of the common figtree butterfly (*Myrina silenus ficedula*) live on the leaves.

The Wonderboom fig can be planted in cattle camps and next to crop lands to provide shade to man and animal during the hot summer months. Wherever this tree is planted it attracts a myriad of insects, as well as insect and fruit-eating birds. The aggressive root system limits the use of this tree near paving and buildings. A popular species for making bonsai.

Other uses The ripe fruits are edible but nearly always infested with insects. They can be dried and then ground at a later stage to mix with food. It tests positively for flavinoids and sterols. The wood of this tree is suitable for making fire-by-friction and it is usually used for the base block and carried on the person.

Cultivation Cultivated from seed or truncheons. The seed must be fresh. It is extremely small and should first be mixed with fine river sand before sowing to ensure even distribution. Seedling trays can be filled with a mixture of river sand and compost (3:1). Cover the seed with a thin layer of fine sand or leave uncovered and keep moist. Seeds germinate within 15–20 days but germination is at the best of times erratic. Transplant the seedlings into black nursery bags when they reach the 2-leaf stage. Cuttings taken from either the softwood or hardwood, root easily if treated with a root-stimulating hormone and planted in river sand. Truncheons must be left in the shade for a few days prior to planting. Branches with a diameter of 50–120 mm in diameter and 1 m long are the best to use. The Wonderboom fig is frost-tender but if planted in a frost-free area, it is a fast growing species, up to 800 mm per year. It can survive long periods of drought.

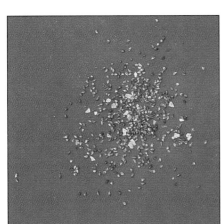

YELLOW TREE BAUHINIA

Description A small tree up to 8 m tall with long straight branches. **Bark** grey and smooth or slightly hairy on young branches becoming brown and smooth on the older stems. **Leaves** simple, 2-lobed, deeply divided one-third of the way down or less, resembling butterfly wings and joined at base, lobes rounded at tips, either hairy or smooth, 30–80 mm long. Leaf stalk 10–30 mm long. **Flowers** drooping, solitary or sometimes in groups of up to five, bell-shaped, 50–70 mm long, petals lemon- to sulphur-yellow with a maroon blotch on one or more petals at base and turning a veined reddish brown with age. **Pods** thinly woody, splitting on the tree, narrow and velvety, up to 110 mm long.

Afrikaans	Bosbeesklou
Zulu	isiThibathibana
Botanical name	*Bauhinia tomentosa*
Family	Pod-bearing Family (Fabaceae)
National tree list no.	208.1

Name derivation *Bauhinia* = named after two brothers, Jean and Gaspard Bauhin, 16th century herbalists, and *tomentosa* = tomentose, with dense interwoven hairs.

ture flowers. CMR-beetles can sometimes destroy all the flowers on a tree in a single morning. Larvae of the orange barred playboy butterfly (*Virachola diocles*) pupate in the pods of this tree.

The yellow tree bauhinia can be effectively used as a hedge or a screen plant between camps along fences or between blocks of various crops, for example in tomato lands. An ideal plant for the small garden. The root system is not aggressive at all and it can be planted close to a swimming pool or paving. Can be used together with other large shrubs in a shrubbery. One of the best indigenous trees to grow in a container on the patio. It can be grown in the shade or full sun.

Diagnostic features Leaves 2-lobed and deeply divided one-third of the way down or less, lobes rounded at base; flowers yellow with a purple blotch at base of one or more petals; pod thin.

Flowering from November to April.
Fruiting from February to July.

Distribution From Ethiopia in the north to KwaZulu-Natal in the south. Also in Sri-Lanka and India.

Habitat Forest edges, woodland, scrub on rocky slopes and common in coastal dune bush.

Economic value An excellent tree to have on the farm as it produces long, straight branches which can be used for various purposes. They are also used as rafters for huts and in making baskets. Not an important browsing tree for cattle as it contains prussic acid in the flowers and even more in the pods. Goats tend to nibble the leaves but do not consume much. Leaves are browsed by game (black rhino, kudu and grey duiker). Grey louries enjoy the flower buds and ma-

Other uses A decoction of the root bark is used as a vermifuge and an infusion made from the stem bark is used as an astringent gargle. Flowers are used as a remedy for dysentery and diarrhoea.

Cultivation Easily cultivated from seed. It is always better to immerse seed in hot water and then leave it to soak overnight. Plant the soaked, swollen seeds directly into black nursery bags filled with a mixture of river sand and compost (5:1). If sown in flat seedling trays, the seedlings must be planted out into bags at an early stage as they soon develop a very long taproot. Germination is usually within 7–15 days. The young plants grow fast and transplant with no problems. A fast grower, up to 900 mm per year, and will flower in its second year. The tree is usually very floriferous, bearing flowers during most months of the year. Flowering can be stimulated by pruning the plants once a year during the winter. It can withstand light frost and is somewhat drought-hardy. If you live in a dry area, it is advisable to obtain seed from plants growing in dry areas, for example Sekukuneland.

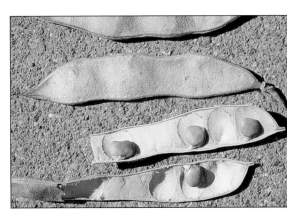

ZANZIBAR FIG

Description An evergreen tree up to 20 m tall with an open roundish crown, sometimes growing as a strangler. A non-toxic white latex exudes from all parts of the tree. *Stipules* forming a protective cap over the growth tip. **Bark** on young stems light grey with prominent stipular scars but grey and smooth on older branches and folded stems. **Leaves** alternate, simple, sides almost parallel, venation prominent, midrib sunken above and prominent below, blade up to 170 x 100 mm, tip rounded to bluntly pointed, margin smooth, base rounded. Leaf stalk 10–60 mm long. **Figs** borne in groups of 2 or 3 on stout, wartlike branchlets on trunk and major branches, large, up to 50 mm in diameter, smooth, on conspicuous stalks 10–25 mm long, yellowish green to purplish when ripe. **Wood** soft, pale brown and light (air-dry 590 kg/m³).

Diagnostic features Evergreen, sometimes a strangler; sides of leaves nearly parallel, blade 170 x 100 mm, leaf stalk 10–60 mm long; figs in groups of 2 or 3 on wartlike branches, up to 50 mm in diameter, purplish when ripe.

Flowering/fruiting from October to February.

Distribution From Tanzania in the north to KwaZulu-Natal in the south.

Habitat Grows in woodland on well-drained soil.

Economic value The leaves and young branches are eaten by elephant, giraffe, kudu and nyala. The ripe fruits are popular with baboons, vervet monkeys, squirrels and various fruit-eating birds (African green pigeons, brown-headed parrots, grey louries, red-faced mousebirds, barbets and black-eyed bulbuls), insect-eating birds being attracted by the myriad of insects in and around the decaying fruit. The wood is light but can be used as a general timber on the farm.

It can be planted as a shade tree on farms in the frost-free areas or in parks. One of the best shade trees in frost-free areas. A must for the bigger garden to attract birds. A decorative plant, especially when in fruit. The root system is very aggressive, making this a plant for large open areas only. Young plants make very attractive potplants, doing well in front of a window where they receive enough light. Popular for bonsai.

Other uses The ripe figs are edible but have a thick, pink flesh with an unpleasant bitter to sourish taste. A good tasting jam can be made from the fruit.

Cultivation Easily grown from seed or cuttings. The seed is very fine and it is advisable to mix the seed with fine river sand to ensure even distribution when sowing. Sow in seedling mix or in a mixture of river sand and compost in a ratio of 1:1. Cover the seeds with a thin layer of the mix and keep moist. Seeds usually germinate after 15–30 days. Transplant them when they reach the 3-leaf stage. Seedlings and young plants transplant easily. Cuttings must be at least 100 mm long, with all the leaves removed except the upper pair. Dip the lower end of the cuttings into a root-stimulating hormone powder before planting them in pure river sand. They strike very easily. It can also be propagated by means of truncheons. Cut a branch of at least 100 mm thick and 2–3 m long. Place some sand at the bottom of the hole, to speed up root growth and control fungus growth. A fast growing species, 1–1.2 m per year. A frost-sensitive species but able to survive long periods of drought.

Afrikaans	Zanzibarvy
Northern Sotho	mohlapu
Botanical name	*Ficus sansibarica* subsp. *sansibarica*
Family	Fig Family (Moraceae)
National tree list no.	47

Name derivation *Ficus* = the classical name for the cultivated fig, and *sansibarica* = from Zanzibar.

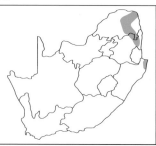

UTILISATION BY ANIMALS

Only direct utilisation, and in many instances only the most common, is mentioned here. In the case of butterflies, note that it is exclusively the larvae that utilise the foliage. More detailed information, such as the part of the tree utilized by the animal, can be obtained under the relevant tree description.

TREE	MAMMALS	BIRDS	INSECTS
African Holly *Ilex mitis*		crested barbets, pied barbets, black-eyed bulbuls, cinnamon doves, Knysna louries, purple-crested louries, Rameron pigeons, plum-coloured starlings, red-winged starlings	
African Mangosteen *Garcinia livingstonei*	cattle, elephant, giraffe, kudu, bushbuck, nyala, grey duiker, baboons, vervet monkeys	crested guineafowl, barbets, louries, mousebirds	
African Teak *Pterocarpus angolensis*	elephant, kudu, baboons, vervet monkeys, yellow-footed squirrels		honeybees, bushveld charaxes butterflies
African Wattle *Peltophorum africanum*	cattle, goats, elephant, black rhino, giraffe, kudu, impala, grey duiker		honeybees, Van Son's charaxes, Satyr charaxes, Braine's charaxes butterflies
Ana Tree *Faidherbia albida*	domestic stock, elephant, giraffe, kudu, nyala, impala		brown playboy butterflies
Apple-Leaf *Lonchocarpus capassa*	cattle, giraffe, eland, kudu, nyala, Lichtenstein's hartebeest, impala, yellow-spotted rock dassie	barbets, owls, rollers	honeybees, large blue charaxes butterflies
Baobab *Adansonia digitata*	cattle, elephant, kudu, nyala, impala		
Bead-Bean Tree *Maerua angolensis*	cattle, elephant, giraffe, kudu, nyala, bushbuck, grey duiker, klipspringer		zebra white, scarlet tip, small orange tip, veined tip, diverse rainforest white, forest white butterflies
Black Monkey-thorn *Acacia burkei*	cattle, black rhino, giraffe, kudu, nyala, impala, steenbok, grey duiker		
Black Thorn *Acacia mellifera* subsp. *detinens*	cattle, black rhino, giraffe, eland, kudu, blue wildebeest, gemsbok, impala, springbok, grey duiker, steenbok		honeybees
Bladder-nut *Diospyros whyteana*	cattle, kudu, nyala, klipspringer, Sharpe's grysbok	Rameron pigeons, African green pigeons, louries, barbets, bulbuls	
Brandybush *Grewia flava*	domestic stock, giraffe, kudu, sable, nyala, grey duiker, steenbok	grey louries, helmeted guineafowl, black korhaan, francolin species	white-cloaked skipper, spotted velvet skipper butterflies

TREE	MAMMALS	BIRDS	INSECTS
Broom Cluster Fig *Ficus sur*	cattle, elephant, kudu, nyala, blue duiker, baboons, bushpigs, fruit-eating bats, vervet and samango monkeys	African green pigeons, Cape parrots, Meyer's parrots, brown-headed parrots, Knysna louries, grey louries, purple-crested louries	fig tree blue, lesser fig tree blue, African map butterflies
Brown Ivory *Berchemia discolor*	elephant, giraffe, kudu, bush-buck, impala, Damara dik-dik, baboons, vervet monkeys	louries, pigeons, starlings, barbets, hornbills	
Buffalo Thorn *Ziziphus mucronata* subsp. *mucronata*	cattle, giraffe, eland, kudu, sable, black wildebeest, nyala, impala, klipspringer, springbok, steenbok, Damara dik-dik, warthogs, Sharpe's grysbok	guineafowl, francolins, Meyer's parrots, purple-crested louries, grey louries, Burchell's coucals	black pie, common dotted blue, Hintza pie, white pie butterflies, honeybees
Bushman's Tea *Catha edulis*			foxy charaxes butterflies
Camel's Foot *Piliostigma thonningii*	cattle, elephant, kudu, baboons		bushveld charaxes butterflies
Camel Thorn *Acacia erioloba*	cattle, elephant, giraffe, eland, kudu, gemsbok, grey duiker	Kori bustards	topaz blue butterflies
Camphor Bush *Tarchonanthus camphoratus*	domestick stock, giraffe, eland, kudu, gemsbok, sable, black wildebeest, nyala, impala, springbok, grey duiker ˇ		
Cape Ash *Ekebergia capensis*	cattle, kudu, nyala, bushbuck, baboons, vervet and samango monkeys, bushpigs	Knysna louries, purple-crested louries, barbets, hornbills, bulbuls, mousebirds	white- barred charaxes butterflies
Cape Beech *Rapanea melanophloeos*	baboons, samango monkeys, vervet monkeys, bushpigs	crested guineafowl, African green pigeons, Rameron pigeons, Knysna louries, purple-crested louries, barbets	
Cape Chestnut *Calodendrum capense*	samango monkeys, vervet monkeys	Cape parrots, Rameron pigeons, cinnamon doves	citrus swallowtail, green banded swallowtail, emperor swallowtail butterflies
Cape Honeysuckle *Tecomaria capensis*	domestic stock, kudu, nyala, bushbuck, klipspringer, red duiker, grey duiker	sunbirds, starlings, orioles	common pea blue, Barker's smokey blue butterflies
Cheesewood *Pittosporum viridiflorum*	cattle, goats, kudu, nyala, bushbuck, klipspringer, grey duiker	red-eyed doves, turtle doves, Rameron pigeons, grey louries, pied barbets, crested barbets, black-collared barbets, bulbuls, redwing-ed starlings, Cape glossy starlings, crested francolins, guineafowl	
Common Cabbage Tree *Cussonia spicata*	domestic stock, black rhino, kudu, bushpigs, baboons, elephant	louries, bulbuls, starlings, barbets, mousebirds	
Common Coral Tree *Erythrina lysistemon*	elephant, black rhino, kudu, nyala, klipspringer, baboons, vervet monkeys, bushpigs, porcupines	sunbird species, brown-headed parrots, grey louries, barbets, woodpeckers, pearl-spotted owls	giant charaxes butterflies

TREE	MAMMALS	BIRDS	INSECTS
Common Hook Thorn *Acacia caffra*	domestic stock, black rhino, giraffe, kudu, impala, reedbuck, grey duiker,		Van Son's playboy, Amakosa rocksitter butterflies
Common Rothmannia *Rothmannia capensis*	baboons, vervet monkeys, samango monkeys, bushbuck, grey duiker, bushpigs		
Common Wild Fig *Ficus thonningii*	domestic stock, elephant, kudu, giraffe, nyala, bushbuck, impala, Damara dik-dik, baboons, vervet monkeys, samango monkeys, por-cupines, civets, slender mongoose, rock- and tree dassies, bushpigs, warthog, grey duiker, fruit-eating bats	louries, parrots, pigeons, starlings, barbets, bulbuls	lesser fig tree blue, common fig tree blue butterflies
Cork Bush *Mundulea sericea*	domestic stock, elephant, giraffe, eland, impala	greater double-collared sunbirds, Marico sunbirds, shortbilled sunbirds	Natal bar, dusky blue, common pea blue butterflies
Cross-berry *Grewia occidentalis* var. *occidentalis*	cattle, goats, black rhino, giraffe, kudu, nyala, grey duiker	Knysna louries, speckled bulbuls, mousebirds, black-eyed bulbuls, Cape bulbuls, barbets	rufous-winged elfin, buff-tipped skipper butterflies
Dogwood *Rhamnus prinoides*		starlings, bulbuls, barbets, francolins	honeybees, forest-king charaxes butterflies
Dune Soap-berry *Deinbollia oblongifolia*	kudu, nyala, bushbuck, impala, grey duiker, red duiker, bushpigs, baboons, samango monkeys, vervet monkeys	black-eyed bulbuls, speckled mousebirds, red-faced mousebirds, glossy starlings, Cape white-eyes, masked weavers	violet-spotted charaxes, forest queen, gold-banded forester, purple-brown hairstreak, coastal hairstreak, black-and-orange playboy, orange playboy butterflies
Dwarf Coral Tree *Erythrina humeana*	grey duiker, klipspringer	sunbirds, black-eyed bulbuls, Cape white-eyes, brown-headed parrots	
East African Mahogany *Khaya anthotheca*			whitebarred charaxes butterflies
False Marula *Lannea schweinfurthii* var. *stuhlmannii*	cattle, elephants, giraffe, kudu, nyala, bushbuck, grey duiker, kudu, bushpigs, warthogs, baboons, vervet monkeys	grey hornbills, grey louries, pied barbets, black collared barbets, crested barbets, Meyer's parrots, brown-headed parrots, red-faced mousebirds, Swainson's francolins, crested francolins, guineafowl	
False Olive *Buddleja saligna*			various butterflies and bees
Fever Tree *Acacia xanthophloea*	elephant, giraffe, vervet monkeys		
Forest Elder *Nuxia floribunda*	domestic stock, kudu, bushbuck, nyala, klipspringer, red duiker, grey duiker		

TREE	MAMMALS	BIRDS	INSECTS
Forest Fever-berry *Croton sylvaticus*	bushbuck, blue duiker, bushpigs	African green pigeons, cinnamon doves, tambourine doves, red-eyed doves, trumpeter hornbills, forest weavers	green-veined charaxes butterflies
Forest Fever Tree *Anthocleista grandiflora*	cattle, elephants, bushpigs, vervet monkeys, samango monkeys		
Giant Raisin *Grewia hexamita*	domestic stock, elephant, black rhino, buffalo, giraffe, eland, kudu, Lichtenstein's hartebeest, impala, bushbuck, grey duiker, steenbok	helmeted guineafowl, crowned guineafowl, various francolin species	
Jackal-berry *Diospyros mespiliformis*	elephant, giraffe, black rhino, buffalo, eland, kudu, klipspringer, warthogs, baboons, vervet monkeys, yellow-spotted rock dassies, vervet monkeys	pigeons, parrots, hornbills, louries, bulbuls	
Jacket-plum *Pappea capensis*	domestic stock, elephant, giraffe, kudu, nyala, bushbuck, impala, grey duiker	mousebirds, starlings, barbets	pearlspotted charaxes, common hairtail, brown playboy butterflies
Karee *Rhus lancea*	domestic stock, kudu, roan, sable	bulbuls, guineafowl, francolins	
Karoo Rhigozum *Rhigozum obovatum*	domestic stock, kudu, steenbok, springbok, grey duiker		
Kei-apple *Dovyalis caffra*	domestick stock, goats, kudu, nyala, bushbuck, grey duiker, vervet monkeys, baboons	purple-crested louries, Knysna louries, grey louries, black-eyed bulbuls	African leopard butterflies
Knob Thorn *Acacia nigrescens*	cattle, elephant, giraffe, kudu, impala, grey duiker, steenbok,	brown-headed parrots	dusky charaxes butterflies
Kooboo-berry *Cassine aethiopica*	domestic stock, black rhino, kudu, blue wildebeest, nyala, impala, grey duiker, red duiker, bushpigs, warthogs, baboons, samango and vervet monkeys	purple-crested louries, Cape parrots, African green pigeons, black-eyed bulbuls, Swainson's francolins	
Large Fever-berry *Croton megalobotrys*	elephant, black rhino, kudu, nyala, impala, bushbuck, yellow-footed squirrels		green-veined charaxes butterflies
Large-leaved Coral Tree *Erythrina latissima*	elephant	sunbirds, grey louries, brown-headed parrots	
Large-leaved Dragon Tree *Dracaena aletriformis*		Rameron pigeons, African green pigeons, Knysna louries, purple-crested louries, black-eyed bulbuls	bush nightfighter butterflies
Large-leaved False Thorn *Albizia versicolor*	elephant, kudu	brown-headed parrots	

TREE	MAMMALS	BIRDS	INSECTS
Large-leaved Rock Fig *Ficus abutilifolia*	kudu, nyala, bushbuck, klipspringer, grey duikers, vervet monkeys, baboons	Rameron pigeons, African green pigeons, brown-headed parrots, Rüppell's parrots, purple-crested louries, grey louries, barbets, bulbuls, starlings	
Large Num-num *Carissa macrocarpa*	baboons, vervet monkeys	Knysna louries, starlings, bulbuls	various butterflies and other insects
Large Sourplum *Ximenia caffra*	giraffe, eland, kudu, impala, bushbuck, klipspringer, grey duiker, steenbok, warthogs	barbets, bulbuls, starlings	Natal bar, silvery bar, Bowker's sapphire, saffron sapphire, brown playboy, bush scarlet butterflies
Lavender Tree *Heteropyxis natalensis*	black rhino, kudu, grey duiker		various insects
Leadwood *Combretum imberbe*	elephant, giraffe, kudu, red lechwe, impala, grey duiker		various insects
Lemon Thorn *Cassinopsis ilicifolia*	goats, cattle, kudu, klipspringer, grey and blue duiker	bulbuls, starlings, barbets, pigeons, guineafowl, francolins	
Marula *Sclerocarya birrea* subsp. *caffra*	cattle, elephant, giraffe, eland, kudu, waterbuck, warthogs	Meyer's parrots	
Mitzeeri *Bridelia micrantha*	black rhino, nyala, bushbuck, grey duiker	African green pigeons, Cape glossy starlings, purple-crested louries, grey louries, pied barbets, black-collared barbets, crested barbets, mousebirds, bulbuls	giant charaxes, Morant's orange butterflies
Mobola Plum *Parinari curatellifolia*	elephant, kudu, impala, bushbuck, grey duiker, steenbok, bushpigs, baboons, vervet monkeys, porcupines		striped policeman butterflies, honeybees
Monkey Thorn *Acacia galpinii*	giraffe, kudu		
Mopane *Colophospermum mopane*	domestic stock, elephant, giraffe, buffalo, eland, kudu, Lichtenstein's hartebeest, nyala, impala, grey duiker, steenbok		foxy charaxes butterflies, mopane worms
Mountain Hard Pear *Olinia emarginata*		Rameron pigeons, African green pigeons, Knysna louries, purple-crested louries, bush blackcaps, bulbuls, crested barbets	
Mountain Karee *Rhus leptodictya*	domestic stock, giraffe, eland, kudu, impala, grey duiker, steenbok	barbets, bulbuls, guineafowl, francolins	
Mountain Mahogany *Entandrophragma caudatum*	elephants, kudu, grey duiker		

TREE	MAMMALS	BIRDS	INSECTS
Mountain Syringa *Kirkia wilmsii*	domestic stock, kudu, grey duiker, klipspringer, impala		
Natal Camwood *Baphia racemosa*	grey duiker	parrots	blue-spotted charaxes, brown playboy, orange-barred playboy butterflies
Natal Mahogany *Trichilia emetica*	giraffe, kudu, nyala, baboons, vervet monkeys	starlings, grey louries, purple-crested louries, hornbills, barbets, sunbirds	whitebarred charaxes butterflies
Natal Wild Banana *Strelitzia nicolai*	blue duiker, samango monkeys, vervet monkeys	grey sunbirds, olive sunbirds, Indian mynahs, barbets, starlings	strelitzia nightfighter butterflies
Outeniqua Yellowwood *Podocarpus falcatus*	bats, bushpigs	Cape parrots, purple-crested louries, Knysna louries, Ross's louries, Rameron pigeons, African green pigeons, Delagorgue's pigeons	
Paperbark False-thorn *Albizia tanganyicensis* subsp. *tanganyicensis*	elephant, kudu, impala	brown-headed parrots	satyr charaxes butterflies
Peawood *Craibia zimmermannii*			blue-spotted charaxes butterflies
Pod Mahogany *Afzelia quanzensis*	elephants, eland, duikers, rodents	hornbills	flame-bordered charaxes, foxy charaxes, giant charaxes, large blue, charaxes, blue-spotted charaxes, violet-spotted charaxes, scarce forest charaxes, golden piper butterflies
Pride of De Kaap *Bauhinia galpinii*	black rhino, kudu, bushbuck, grey duiker	grey louries, purple-crested louries	brown playboy, orange barred playboy, foxy charaxes, protea charaxes, bushveld charaxes butterflies
Puzzle Bush *Ehretia rigida*	domestic stock, kudu, nyala, bushbuck, impala, grey duiker	crested francolins, helmeted guineafowl, crested guineafowl, brown-headed parrots, Meyer's parrots, grey louries, ellowbilled hornbills, crested barbets, black-eyed bulbuls, starlings	
Quinine Tree *Rauvolfia caffra*	nyala, vervet monkeys, bushbabies	hornbills, barbets, pigeons, bulbuls	various butterflies and other insects
Red Beech *Protorhus longifolia*	black rhino, bushpigs, red duiker, samango and vervet monkeys	pigeons, parrots, louries, mousebirds, barbets, bulbuls, starlings	
Red Bushwillow *Combretum apiculatum* subsp. *apiculatum*	domestic stock, elephant, giraffe, eland, kudu, bushbuck, impala, klipspringer, steenbok	brown-headed parrots	striped policeman butterflies

TREE	MAMMALS	BIRDS	INSECTS
Red Currant *Rhus chirindensis*	black rhino, kudu, nyala, bushbuck, red duiker, vervet monkeys, samango monkeys	African green pigeons, Knysna louries, purple-crested louries, black-eyed bulbuls, pied barbets, crested barbets, Cape white-eyes, Cape parrots	
Red Ivory *Berchemia zeyheri*	giraffe, eland, kudu, nyala, blue wildebeest, bushbuck, impala, porcupine, baboons, vervet monkeys	Rameron pigeons, African green pigeons, Meyer's parrots, grey louries, purple-crested louries, mousebirds, crested barbets, black-collared barbets, pied barbets, black-eyed bulbuls, redwinged starlings	
Red-leaved Rock Fig *Ficus ingens* var. *ingens*	kudu, nyala, grey duiker, suni, baboons, bushbabies, bushpigs, warthogs, squirrels, dassies, vervet monkeys	Rameron pigeons, African green pigeons, Cape parrots, brown-headed parrots, Meyer's parrots, Knysna louries, purple-crested louries, grey louries, bulbuls, starlings, barbets	
River Bushwillow *Combretum erythrophyllum*	elephant, giraffe, nyala, bushbuck, giraffe	pied barbets, herons, cormorants	
Round-leaved Kiaat *Pterocarpus rotundifolius* subsp. *rotundifolius*	domestick stock, elephant, giraffe, kudu, impala		bushveld charaxes butterflies, honeybees
Russet Bushwillow *Combretum hereroense*	cattle, elephant, giraffe, kudu, nyala, impala, steenbok	Meyer's parrots	various butterflies and wasps
Safsaf Willow *Salix mucronata*	domestic stock, hippo, kudu, nyala, bushbuck, grey duiker,	herons, darters, cormorants,	African leopard butterflies
Sagewood *Buddleja salviifolia*	eland, kudu, bushbuck, impala, grey duiker		African leopard butterflies, honeybees and various other insect species
Sausage Tree *Kigelia africana*	domestic stock, elephant, kudu, nyala, impala, grey duiker, bushpigs		
Scented Thorn *Acacia nilotica* subsp. *kraussiana*	cattle, black rhino, giraffe, eland, kudu, gemsbok, nyala, impala, grey duiker		
September Bush *Polygala myrtifolia*		laughing doves	carpenter bees
Shepherd's Tree *Boscia albitrunca* var. *albitrunca*	cattle, giraffe, gemsbok, kudu, nyala, impala, steenbok, Damara dik-dik	doves, parrots, mousebirds, hornbills, barbets, bulbuls, starlings	zebra white, brownveined white, queen purple tip, speckled sulphur tip, banded gold tip, lemon traveller tip butterflies
Sickle Bush *Dichrostachys cinerea*	cattle, giraffe, buffalo, kudu, Lichtenstein's hartebeest, nyala, impala, klipspringer, red duiker, grey duiker, Damara dik-dik		satyr charaxes butterflies and various other insects

TREE	MAMMALS	BIRDS	INSECTS
Simple-spined Num-num *Carissa edulis*	eland, kudu, nyala, bushbuck, impala, grey duiker, baboons, vervet monkeys, bushpigs	francolins, louries, hornbills, barbets, bulbuls	
Sjambok Pod *Cassia abbreviata* subsp. *beareana*	elephant, giraffe, kudu, nyala	brown-headed parrots, Meyer's parrots, grey louriés, barbets, various hornbill species	
Small Knobwood *Zanthoxylum capense*	kudu, klipspringer, grey duiker, vervet monkeys, baboons	various bird species	citrus swallowtail, white-banded swallowtail, emperor swallowtail butterflies
Sneezewood *Ptaeroxylon obliquum*	giraffe, nyala, kudu, impala, grey duiker		citrus swallowtail butterflies
Spekboom *Portulacaria afra*	domestic stock, elephant, kudu, nyala, bushbuck, impala, klipspringer, grey duiker		honeybees
Sumach-bean *Elephantorrhiza burkei*			honeybees and many other insect species
Sweet Thorn *Acacia karroo*	domestic stock, black rhino, giraffe, eland, kudu, nyala, sable, gemsbok, impala, springbok		club-tailed charaxes, silver spotted grey, black-striped hairtail, common hairtail, ota-cilia hairtail, talbot's hairtail, black heart, topaz-spotted blue, thorn-tree blue, Natal spotted blue, velvet spotted blue butterflies
Sycamore Fig *Ficus sycomorus*	elephant, giraffe, kudu, nyala, bushbuck, impala, grey duiker, bushpigs, warthogs, baboons, bushbabies, fruit-eating bats, vervet monkeys	pigeons, doves, parrots, louries, mousebirds, hornbills, barbets, bulbuls, starlings	many insects
Tamboti *Spirostachys africana*	porcupines, elephant, black rhino, giraffe, eland, kudu, nyala, bushbuck, impala, Damara dik-dik, grey duiker	guineafowl, francolins, various dove species	
Tassel Berry *Antidesma venosum*	elephant, kudu, nyala, bushbuck, impala, baboons, vervet monkeys	guineafowl, francolins, greenspotted doves, tambourine doves, African green pigeons, louries, hornbills, barbets, bulbuls, mousebirds	
Transvaal Bluebush *Diospyros lycioides* subsp. *guerkei*	nyala, bushbuck, impala, Sharpe's grysbok, grey duiker, dassies	purple-crested louries, grey louries, speckled mousebirds, red-faced mousebirds, black-collared barbets, pied barbets, crested barbets, black-eyed bulbuls, redwinged starlings	Mooi River opal butterflies
Transvaal Gardenia *Gardenia volkensii* subsp. *spatulifolia*	domestic stock, elephant, giraffe, eland, kudu, impala, nyala, vervet monkeys, dassies		

TREE	MAMMALS	BIRDS	INSECTS
Transvaal Red-milkwood *Mimusops zeyheri*	elephant, eland, kudu, nyala, grey duiker, bushpigs, baboons, samango monkeys, vervet monkeys	Rameron pigeons, African green pigeons, purple-crested louries, grey louries, red-collared barbets, crested barbets, bulbuls	pied false acraea butterflies
Tree Fuchsia *Halleria lucida*	domestic stock, eland, kudu, nyala, bushbuck, grey duiker	sunbirds, Rameron pigeons, Knysna louries, purple-crested louries, Cape parrots, Kurrichane thrushes, bulbuls, robins, white-eyes	honeybees
Tree Wisteria *Bolusanthus speciosus*	kudu, grey duiker, giraffe, gemsbok, vervet monkeys		
Umbrella Thorn *Acacia tortilis* subsp. *heteracantha*	domestic stock, elephant, giraffe, eland, waterbuck, kudu, gemsbok, nyala, springbok, bushbuck, impala, grey duiker, baboons, vervet monkeys	Meyer's parrots, brown-headed parrots	
Umzimbeet *Millettia grandis*	baboons		orange-barred playboy, striped policeman, pondo charaxes butterflies
Waterberry *Syzygium cordatum*	kudu, nyala, bushbuck, grey duiker, baboons, bushbabies, bushpigs, vervet monkeys, samango monkeys	tambourine doves, African green pigeons, purple-crested louries, Knysna louries, grey louries	flame-bordered charaxes, silver-barred charaxes, apricot playboy, orange-barred playboy, brown playboy butterflies, honeybees
Weeping Boer-bean *Schotia brachypetala*	black rhino, giraffe, kudu, nyala, impala, vervet monkeys	louries, parrots	foxy charaxes, giant charaxes, large blue charaxes butterflies
White Bauhinia *Bauhinia petersiana* subsp. *macrantha*	domestic stock, eland, kudu, gemsbok, impala, steenbok, grey duiker	grey louries, Meyer's parrots	
White Ironwood *Vepris lanceolata*	porcupines	louries, Rameron and Delagorgue's pigeons, red-eyed doves, red-winged starlings, crested barbets, black-eyed bulbuls	greenbanded swallowtail, whitebanded swallowtail, mocker swallowtail, citrus swallowtail butterflies
White Karee *Rhus pendulina*		rock pigeons, starlings, bulbuls, barbets	pearl charaxes butterflies
White Pear *Apodytes dimidiata* subsp. *dimidiata*	black rhino	Rameron pigeons, redwinged starlings, pied barbets, black-eyed, bulbuls, spotted ground thrushes, helmeted guineafowl	
White Stinkwood *Celtis africana*	cattle, kudu, nyala, bushbuck, impala, grey duiker, vervet monkeys, baboons	bulbuls, mousebirds, barbets, parrots, louries, doves, Rameron pigeons	African snout , blue-spotted charaxes butterflies
White Syringa *Kirkia acuminata*	giraffe, eland, kudu, impala		
Wild Apricot *Dovyalis zeyheri*		hornbills, barbets, louries, mousebirds, starlings, pigeons, barbets, bulbuls	African leopard butterflies

TREE	MAMMALS	BIRDS	INSECTS
Wild Date Palm *Phoenix reclinata*	elephant, baboons, vervet monkeys, bushpigs, nyala, bushbuck	grey louries, mousebirds, black-collared barbets, black-eyed bulbuls	palm-tree nightfighter, skipper butterflies
Wild Laburnum *Calpurnia aurea* subsp. *aurea*	dassies		carpenter bees
Wild Medlar *Vangueria infausta*	goats, elephant, giraffe, kudu, nyala, red-footed squirrels, bushbabies, vervet monkeys, baboons, bushpigs	various fruit-eating birds	various insects species
Wild Olive *Olea europaea* subsp. *africana*	domestic stock, kudu, grey duiker, blue duiker, vervet monkeys, baboons, bushpigs, warthogs	Rameron pigeons, Cape parrots, Knysna louries, purple-crested louries, grey louries, speckled mousebirds, red-faced mouse-birds, bulbuls, starlings	
Wild Peach *Kiggelaria africana*		Rameron pigeons, cinnamon doves, olive woodpeckers, Knysna louries, purple-crested louries, crowned hornbills, trumpeter hornbills, Cape robins, Heuglin's robins, boubou shrikes, red-winged starlings, Cape thrushes, white-eyes, mousebirds, cuckoos	garden acraea, dusky-veined acraea, battling glider butterflies
Wild Pear *Dombeya rotundifolia* var. *rotundifolia*	domestic stock, elephant, giraffe, kudu, nyala, sable, steenbok		various butterflies, honeybees
Wild Plum *Harpephyllum caffrum*	baboons, bushbabies, bushpigs, bushbuck, vervet and samango monkeys	African green pigeons, Cape parrots, louries, mousebirds, barbets, bulbuls, starlings	common hairtail butterflies
Wild Pride-of-India *Galpinia transvaalica*	cattle, elephant, giraffe, kudu, nyala, grey duiker		flies and butterflies
Wild Silver Oak *Brachylaena discolor* subs. *transvaalensis*	nyala, bushbuck, red duiker, blue duiker		honeybees
Wing Bean *Xeroderris stuhlmannii*	domestic stock, elephant, giraffe, eland, kudu, grey duiker		
Wonderboom Fig *Ficus cordata* subsp. *salicifolia*	kudu, nyala, impala, grey duiker, warthogs, bushpigs, bushbabies	Rameron pigeons, African green pigeons, Meyer's parrots, brown-headed parrots, Knysna louries, purple-crested louries, grey louries, barbets, orioles, bulbuls	common fig tree butterflies
Yellow Tree Bauhinia *Bauhinia tomentosa*	black rhino, kudu, grey duiker	grey louries	CMR-beetles, orange-barred playboy butterflies
Zanzibar Fig *Ficus sansibarica* subsp. *sansibarica*	elephant, giraffe, kudu, nyala, baboons, vervet monkeys, squirrels	African green pigeons, brown-headed parrots, grey louries, red-faced mousebirds, barbets, black-eyed bulbuls	many insects

REFERENCES

ACOCKS, J.P.H. 1988. *Veld types of South Africa. Memoirs of the Botanical Survey of South Africa* No. 57.

ARNOLD, T.H. & DE WET, B.C. (eds) 1993. *Plants of southern Africa: names and distribution. Memoirs of the Botanical Survey of South Africa* No. 62.

BERG, C.C. 1988. New taxa and combinations in *Ficus* (Moraceae) of Africa. *Kew Bulletin* 43,1: 77–97.

CARR, J.D. 1976. *The South African Acacias*. Conservation Press, Johannesburg.

CARR, J.D. 1988. *Combretaceae in southern Africa*. Tree Society of Southern Africa, Johannesburg.

COATES PALGRAVE, K. 1956. *Trees of central Africa*. National Publications Trust.

COATES PALGRAVE, K. 1983. *Trees of southern Africa*. Struik, Cape Town.

CODD, L.E. 1963. Apocynaceae. *Flora of southern Africa* 26: 244–296.

CODD, L.E. 1976. Canellaceae. *Flora of southern Africa* 22: 39–41.

DAVIDSON, L. & JEPPE, B. 1981. *Acacias*. Centaur, Johannesburg.

DE WINTER, B. 1963. Ebenaceae. *Flora of southern Africa* 26: 54–99.

DE WINTER, B. 1963. *et al. Sixty-six trees of the Transvaal*. Voortrekker Pers Beperk, Pretoria.

DRUMMOND, R.B. 1966. Rhamnaceae. *Flora Zambesiaca* 2,2: 419–439.

DRUMMOND, R.B. 1981. *Common trees of the central watershed woodlands of Zimbabwe*. Department of Natural Resources, Causeway.

EXELL, A.W. 1978. Combretaceae. *Flora Zambesiaca* 4: 100–183.

FOX, F.W. & NORWOOD YOUNG, M.E. 1982. *Food from the veld*. Delta Books, Johannesburg.

GALPIN, E.E. 1925. *The native timber trees of the Springbok Flats. Botanical Survey of South Africa. Memoir* No. 7.

GELFAND, M. 1983. *et al. The traditional medical practitioner in Zimbabwe*. Mambo Press.

HARTMANN, H.T. & KESTER, D.E. 1983. *Plant propagation, principles and practices*. Prentice-Hall, Inc. New Jersey.

HENNESSY, E.F. 1991. *Erythrina* (Fabaceae) in southern Africa. *Bothalia* 21,1: 1–25.

IMMELMAN, K.L. 1986. Simaroubaceae. *Flora of southern Africa* 18,3: 1–3.

JOFFE, P. 1993. *The gardener's guide to South African plants*. Tafelberg, Cape Town.

JOHNSON, D. & S. 1993. *Gardening with indigenous trees and shrubs*. Southern Books, Halfway House.

KELLERMAN, T.S., COETZER, J.A.W. & NAUDé, T.W. 1988. *Plant poisonings and mycotoxicoses of live-stock in southern Africa*. Oxford University Press, Cape Town.

KILLICK, D.J.B. 1970. *Maerua. Flora of southern Africa* 13: 159–171.

KUPICHA, F.K. 1983. Sapotaceae. *Flora Zambesiaca* 7,1: 210–247.

KUPICHA, F.K. 1983. Oleaceae. *Flora Zambesiaca* 7,1: 300–327.

LANGENEGGER, J.E. 1976. *Dovyalis. Flora of southern Africa* 22: 84–90.

LEISTNER, O.A. 1966. Podocarpaceae. *Flora of southern Africa* 1: 34–41.

MABOGO, D.E.N. 1990. *The ethnobotany of the Vhavenda.* Unpublished M.Sc. thesis, University of Pretoria.

MEEUSE, A.D.J. 1963. Sapotaceae. *Flora of southern Africa* 26: 31–53.

MENDES, E.J. 1963. Icacinaceae. *Flora Zambesiaca* 2,1: 340–351.

PALMER, E. & PITMAN, N. 1972. *Trees of southern Africa*, 3 vols. Balkema, Cape Town.

PARDY, A.A. 1951–1956. *Notes on indigenous trees and shrubs of Southern Rhodesia.* Govt. Stationery Office, Salisbury.

QUIN, P.J. 1959. *Foods and feeding habits of the Pedi.* Witwatersrand University Press, Johannesburg.

ROSS, J.H. 1979. A conspectus of the African *Acacia* species. *Memoirs of the Botanical Survey of South Africa* No. 44.

ROWAN, M.K. 1983. *The doves, parrots, louries and cuckoos of southern Africa.* David Phillip, Cape Town.

VAN GREUNING, J.V. 1990. A synopsis of the genus *Ficus* (Moraceae) in South Africa. *South African Journal of Botany* 56,6: 599–630.

VAN WYK, P. 1984. *Trees of the Kruger National Park*, 2 vols. Purnell, Cape Town.

VERDOORN, I.C. 1963. Oleaceae. *Flora of southern Africa* 26: 100–128.

VERDOORN, I.C. & HERMAN, P.P.J. 1986. Revision of the genus *Dombeya* (Sterculiaceae) in southern Africa. *Bothalia* 16,1: 1–9.

VON BREITENBACH, F. 1986. *National list of Indigenous Trees.* Dendrological Foundation, Pretoria.

WATT, J.M. & BREYER-BRANDWIJK, M.G. 1962. *The medicinal and poisonous plants of southern and eastern Africa.* Livingstone Ltd., London.

WEHMEYER, A.S. 1967. Edible wild fruits of the Transvaal. *Food Industry in South Africa* 19 (12): 49–53.

WHITE, F. & ANGUS, A. 1962. *Forest flora of Northern Rhodesia.* Oxford University Press, London.

WHITE, F. 1978. Myrtaceae. *Flora Zambesiaca* 4: 183–212.

WHITE, F. 1983. Ebenaceae. *Flora Zambesiaca* 7,1: 248–300.

WHITE, F. & STYLES, B.T. 1963. Meliaceae. *Flora Zambesiaca* 2,1: 285–319.

WHITE, F. 1986. Ptaeroxylaceae & Meliaceae. *Flora of southern Africa* 18,3: 35–61.

WILD, H. 1960. Capparaceae. *Flora Zambesiaca* 1,1: 194–245.

WILD, H. 1963. Tiliaceae. *Flora Zambesiaca* 2,1: 33–91.

WILD, H. 1984. Tiliaceae. *Flora of southern Africa*. 21,1: 1–42.

WILD, H. & PHIPPS, J.B. 1963. Simaroubaceae. *Flora Zambesiaca* 2,1: 210–220.

INDEX TO NAMES